Rigging
Anchors

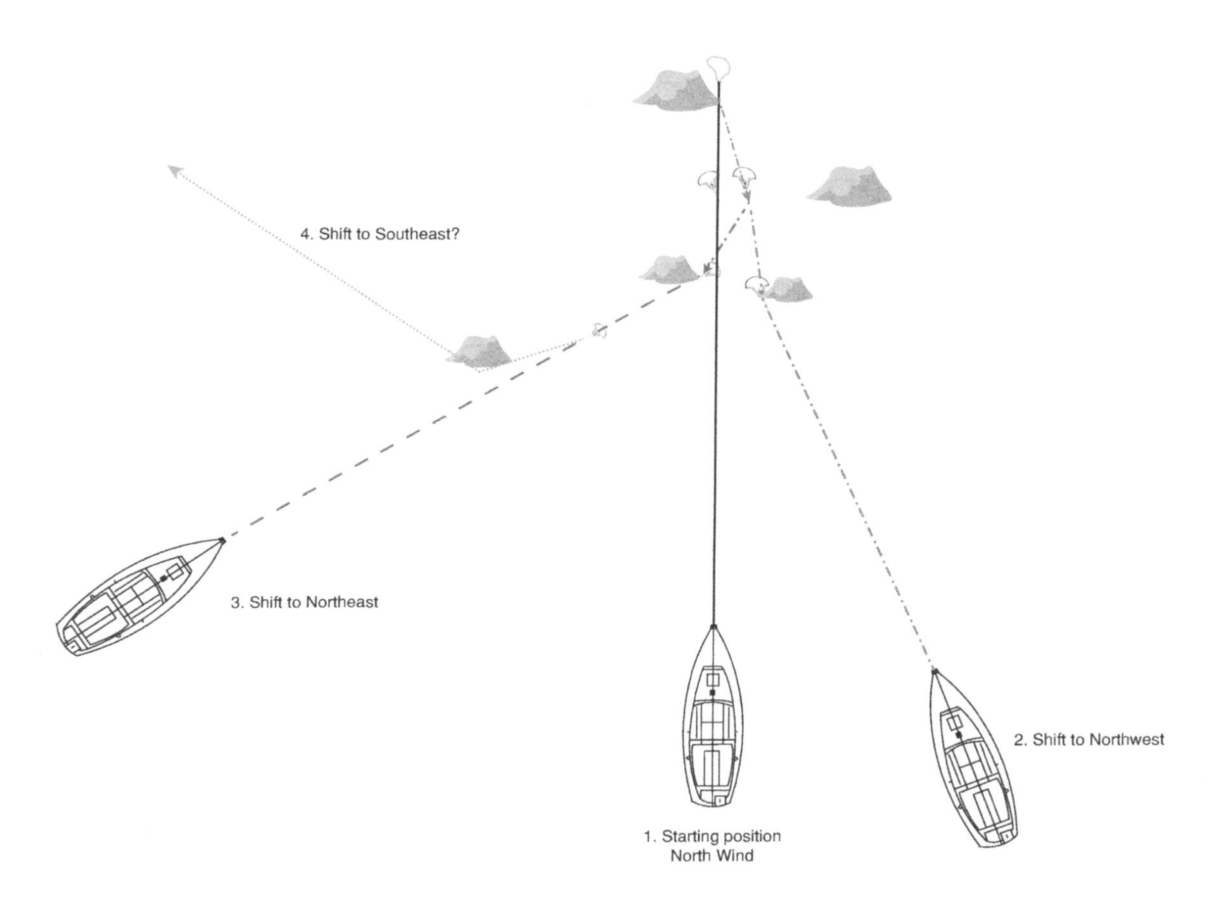

by

Drew Frye

SEAWORTHY PUBLICATIONS, INC. • MELBOURNE, FLORIDA

Rigging Modern Anchors

by
Drew Frye

Published in the USA by:
Seaworthy Publications, Inc.
6300 N Wickham Rd.
#130-416
Melbourne, FL 32940
Phone 321-610-3634
email orders@seaworthy.com
www.seaworthy.com - Your Bahamas and Caribbean Cruising Advisory

Library of Congress Cataloging-in-Publication Data

Names: Frye, Drew, 1961- author.
Title: Rigging modern anchors / Drew Frye.
Description: Melbourne, Florida : Seaworthy Publications, Inc., [2018] |
Includes bibliographical references and index.
Identifiers: LCCN 2018022689 (print) | LCCN 2018037561 (ebook) | ISBN 9781948494083 (E-book) | ISBN 1948494086 (E-book) | ISBN 9781948494076 (pbk. : alk. paper) | ISBN 1948494078 (pbk. : alk. paper)
Subjects: LCSH: Anchors. | Anchorage.
Classification: LCC VM791 (ebook) | LCC VM791 .F78 2018 (print) | DDC 623.8/62--dc23
LC record available at https://lccn.loc.gov/2018022689

Table of Contents

Acknowledgments

2017

My first passion, before sailing, was technical rock climbing and ice climbing. The penalty for a failed climbing anchor is nearly always serious injury or death, rather than an inconvenient financial loss, eventually covered by insurance. That's not to say poor anchoring is not dangerous to the crew—it can be—but it was climbing that fixed it in my head that an anchor must be utterly dependable, and that if we take the time to understand the physics and execute the rigging correctly, it can be. If the anchor cannot meet this standard, then we must embrace it for the shite that it is. "Psychological" anchors—the sort that make us feel good but which are not secure—are dangerous and cannot be accepted.

Any worthwhile project is a collaboration. Laura, my wife, provided logistical, emotional, and editing support. Fellow freelance writer, Jonathan Neeves, has been a constant sounding board, swapping emails with me over the years, debating anchoring topics from nonconventional perspectives. Longtime climbing partner, Dave Rockwell, introduced me to climbing anchors and the idea that writing mattered. Fortress Anchors and Mantus Anchors provided technical review. Numerous local and globe-wandering sailors have tried my ideas, provided comments, and directed me towards deeper exploration by means of insightful questions. I wouldn't want to write a book alone.

Preface to First Edition

Sailing is a very tradition-oriented activity, nowhere more so than with anchoring lore. Whether a modern text or one from 1910, the same old advice is repeated over and over, often usable, but seldom optimized for today's new anchors. Cruiser anecdotes proclaim what works, but like most eyewitness evidence, they contain less real information than first appearances suggest. They don't know why the anchor actually held or what happened underwater during the storm. Perhaps the anchor caught on a lucky rock or tuft of grass. Another time the anchor dragged, likely because of an error the cruiser didn't understand, but the incident was blamed on the anchor or rigging method. And so conventional wisdom is handed down, writers staying the course rather than thinking deeply about what may have changed over the years.

My anchoring philosophy is certainly influenced by many years of cruising my home waters, the Chesapeake Bay. The bottom varies from bottomless ooze that won't hold an anchor, to shells, weeds, and some good sand, punctuated by sedimentary hardpan a nail won't penetrate. As a novice sailor I read of two-anchor schemes, used most of them over many years of cruising, and eventually began systematic testing with a variety of anchors and rigs. Beach observation and lots of diving helped characterize behaviors, and load cell testing quantified forces. Little by little, it became clear to me that many authors had neither systematically tested nor closely observed the rigs they were writing about, and were either parroting what they had read or writing what they personally believed, without rigorous confirmation. For example, most in-line tandem rigs failed consistently in both beach and field testing, in spite of my sincere hope that they would work. I loved their simplicity. But repeated testing revealed they could never have worked as reported.

So I rolled up my sleeves, pulled out load cells, ropes, chains, and anchors of many different types and sizes, and proceeded to put real numbers to different anchor types, bottom types, and rigging methods. Instead of boring you with anchoring lore from the past century, we'll explore measured results, recorded both in controlled conditions and while cruising. I snorkeled for hours, watching intentionally undersized anchors shift and drag through surges and wind shifts, making certain I understood what was going on beneath the brown water. Sometimes I found myself probing shoulder-deep in the ooze, the only way to confirm what was actually going on underground, deep within the smelly sediments. Kind of disgusting, but it all washed off.

I'm not asking you to go out and buy the latest new generation anchor. While it's true that modern designs have brought measurable improvements, the rigging methods I describe here will get more out of any anchor, and in spite of the title, these methods often apply just as well to traditional designs. Testing over rock-strewn bottoms, a 65-year-old Northill was consistently the top performer, proof that the roots of "modern anchors" go deep.

This book is not about hurricane rigging—it is about squalls and nor'easters. For hurricanes you must envision waves rolling over breakwaters and spits when storm surge buries them deep. The anchorage will be 10 feet deeper because of extreme tides. Docks come apart, boats break free and drift, and the water and air are filled with flying debris. The wind force may be four times greater than anything we'll discuss, and it will last. The same principles apply, but multiplied by four, and location and bottom become crucial. Leaving is best.

Although I have tried to provide balance, I've focused on what works for a coastal sailor, unavoidably with a US East Coast slant. I don't mind that, since chapters on coral sand, narrow rocky coves with shore ties, and Mediterranean moors mean nothing to most of us. We live with sand, oyster shells, and bottomless mud. We don't cross oceans, don't want to, and we are legion. I don't believe most sailors need a one-size-fits-all solution, any more than they need a blue water boat; it wouldn't be the best boat for the waters we cruise.

The test bed for much of the load testing was my PDQ 32 catamaran, *Shoal Survivor.* It weighs about 10,000 pounds loaded, has a 16-foot beam, and is comparable in windage and anchoring loads to a 40-foot monohull. I also tested on a Cal 27 monohull and a Corsair F-24 trimaran. Findings were converted to a range of boat types, sizes, and conditions so that you can translate my experience to your boat and cruising grounds.

Science is hard. The journey to the bottom of this rabbit hole was messy and convoluted, but ultimately, well worth it.

Chapter 1: The Basics

IN SPORTS AND IN LIFE, solid fundamentals work best 95% of the time. The same is true with anchoring. Chapters 2-5 examine the forces and basic rigging in great detail, combining experimental data, theory, and experience. Chapters 6-13 dig into advanced anchoring techniques that help with difficult bottoms and storm conditions. But good anchoring starts with the efficient application of a single working anchor. The following basic anchoring technique will insure you get the most from that single anchor. Always start with the basics.

One Anchor

A single, conservatively sized anchor is the right answer 95% of the time. If you're dragging in moderate storms over average bottoms, review basic practices and perhaps get a larger anchor or a different anchor. While a second anchor can be beneficial in specific circumstances, there are complications in setting, raising, swinging with wind and tide shifts, and tangles. Anchors are designed to be used singly and to rotate as the wind shifts.

Anchor Selection

Follow vendor recommendations, assuming severe thunderstorms are always a possibility. In practice, a modern anchor that is about as many pounds as the boat is long up to 45 feet, after which size increases to 1.5 times length or even double. See Appendix VI for additional sizing recommendations. Over very poor bottoms and in the strongest conditions, you may need to deploy a second anchor, as discussed in Chapters 10 and 12. But this should be a very rare practice; a conservatively sized primary anchor should be sufficient 95% of the time.

ABYC recommendations (Chapter 2, Table 1) provide a very conservative estimate of the working load on the anchor and ground tackle; use the storm figure for your main anchor. I measured rode tension with all-chain rode and a good anchor in firm sand (Chapter 2, Table 2), and confirmed those loads represent a realistic worst-case scenario. However, if you look at the actual holding capacity of common anchors in soft mud (Table 10 in Chapter 5), a ridiculously large anchor is required. But all is not lost. Chapter 2 explains how a proper snubber reduces the load by 30-70%. Chapter 4 explains how mud anchors generally perform 30-70% better than predicted by standard test methods as a result of slow setting and soil consolidation over time. Chain catenary also reduces impact loads in light to moderate conditions or in deep water (Chapters 2 and 4). Combined, these factors result in a far more reasonable size estimate, more in line with vendor recommendations (Appendix VI).

As a general rule, a modern scoop-style anchor is your best working anchor. Solid choices include Manson Supreme, Mantus, Rocna, Spade, Super Sarca, and Ultra. Claw-type (Bruce, Lewmar Claw,

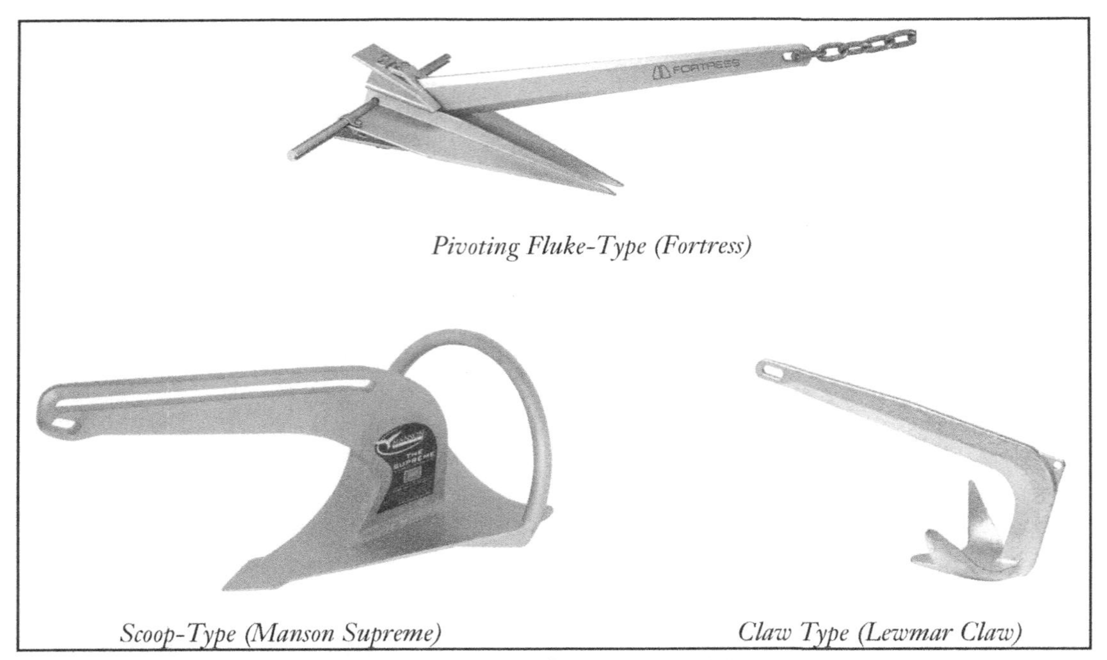

Pivoting Fluke-Type (Fortress)

Scoop-Type (Manson Supreme)

Claw Type (Lewmar Claw)

Example photos of pivoting fluke, scoop, and claw anchors.

and Manson Ray) and plow-type (Delta and CQR) anchors also work, but must be upsized to provide the same holding capacity, particularly in soft mud. Pivoting fluke anchors (Fortress and Danforth) are most often used as kedge and secondary anchors for sand and soft mud. They can also be the very best primary anchors in very soft mud, holding when nothing else will. Set them very deep since that is what makes them stable in a wind shift. (See Chapters 4 and 7.) In firm bottoms and sand, where they cannot set as deeply, they may be less reliable in wind shifts and may not reset reliably.

Practice using your secondary and tertiary anchors as your primary anchor. There is no better way to understand the setting characteristics of an anchor than to use it many times in a variety of conditions. A recipe for disaster is saving a storm anchor for tough conditions and then not knowing how to best use it, what its behavior is telling you, and what is reasonable to expect. Dive on your practice sets and observe what is going on, both after setting and after a wind shift in a strong breeze. A craftsman learns to use all of his tools.

Anchor Rode

Strength. Follow the ABYC Deck Gear Strength Recommendations presented in Chapter 2, Table 1, storm row. These are conservative recommendations, and that's proper for a critical system that cannot fail. I like grade 43 chain; I would rather carry a longer chain than a heavier chain, a tradeoff which is closely examined in Chapter 2. Match the shackle strength to the chain; high strength chain requires higher strength, load-rated shackles (see Appendix V). Safety wire the shackles—it's rare, but they have been known to come loose. Remember that the bow portion of the anchor shackle goes through the shackle eye on the anchor; placing the pin through the eye weakens the shackle as much as 50% when the pull is off center. Two shackles may be required; a larger one to fit the anchor, and a smaller high-strength shackle that fits the chain. Note that Table 1 gives working load values, not breaking strength.

Rope Versus Chain

If you frequently anchor in areas of rock or coral, all chain is the standard advice. Rope can quickly chafe through if wrapped around something sharp. On the other hand, some very well-travelled cruisers have been perfectly happy using a chain leader long enough (typically 60-100 feet) to keep the rope off of the bottom. The balance of the rode is nylon, which reduces anchoring forces through its considerable elasticity. Combination rodes are discussed in Chapter 2 and Chapter 13.

Galvanized Versus Stainless Steel

Stainless steel ground tackle has become something of a pariah in some circles, the result of a few unexpected failures of chain or swivels. Galvanized chain and shackles have proven very reliable. At some point they become visibly rusty, giving a clear indication they are due for replacement. Stainless, on the other hand, is used for many critical high load applications, including standing rigging. It lasts seemingly forever, free from visible corrosion. Stainless chain is less prone to mounding in the chain locker. However, if of poor quality, worked hardened, and perhaps occasionally overloaded, it can develop stress fractures and fail without visible warning. Thus, even though stainless will remain unblemished for decades, the safe working life for the regular cruiser is no greater than that of galvanized chain. Given that grade 30 stainless chain is four times the price of galvanized chain, I don't see the value. It does stow more efficiently in the chain locker, reducing the cone-shaped piles that trouble shallow chain lockers.

Snubber

Skip this section if you have chosen a mixed rode (chain leader plus nylon rope); the nylon rope will provide enough shock absorption so long as at least 40 feet of rope is deployed. If you've chosen all chain, use a rope snubber to prevent the chain from grinding on the anchor roller and to absorb wave energy. Typically, a snubber will be about one boat length and one size smaller than the recommended anchor rode. (Snubber sizing guidelines are provided in Chapter 2.) The snubber is attached to the chain with either two rolling hitches, a camel hitch, or chain grab hardware described in Chapter 13. Multihulls always use nylon bridles to prevent yawing. (See Chapter 3.)

Swivels

While replacing my chain several years ago, I was surprised to find a small crack growing inside the stainless steel anchor swivel. Granted, it was 15 years old, but so was the chain. The cause, most probably, was that it had been mounted directly to the anchor and was side loaded every time the wind shifted. I installed the new chain without a swivel, and with proper chain alignment (see Chapter 13) and anchor recovery practices, it comes up straight 95% of the time. If you must have a swivel, newer designs by Mantus and Quickline/Ultra have eliminated many of the stress points and have proven dependable. Isolate the swivel from the anchor with shackles or a few links of chain to prevent side loading.

Picking Your Spot

There are many factors, but these are the most fundamental:

- **Depth.** Enough to allow for low tide. You must have enough rode to deploy a minimum of seven times the water depth, and more if wind is expected (Chapter 4). If significant wave action is possible, the water must be deep enough that breaking or steep waves are not created. It should also be flat, since sloping areas offer poor holding (Chapter 5). Circle the target area first, watching the depth sounder. Watch out for fishing gear floats and moorings (the rode or rudder may foul when you swing), old pilings, and submerged trees.
- **Protection from the Weather.** In the summer it's nice to anchor behind a spit of sand, protected from waves but open to a cooling breeze. But when severe storms are expected, seek protection from the wind. Trees can be very effective, reducing surface wind for a horizontal distance as much as 20 times their height. However, while the narrowest part of the creek may offer the best shelter, it may not give sufficient space for swing and limited dragging. A broad creek (150-200 yards) with tall trees is better. Remember that thunderstorms often bring an abrupt shift in wind direction; be familiar with local patterns.
- **Bottom Type.** Whenever possible, seek out sand or firm mud. Guidebooks often comment on the quality of holding, but don't rely on them since bottom conditions can vary over just a few yards and the guidebook author may have used a different type of anchor. Avoid coral, rocks, gravel, weeds, and soft mud when possible. These bottoms have either inconsistent or weak holding characteristics. See Chapter 5.
- **Hazards.** What will you drag into if the anchor fails? A marina, other boats, rocks, or a beach with breaking waves? Or perhaps a forgiving

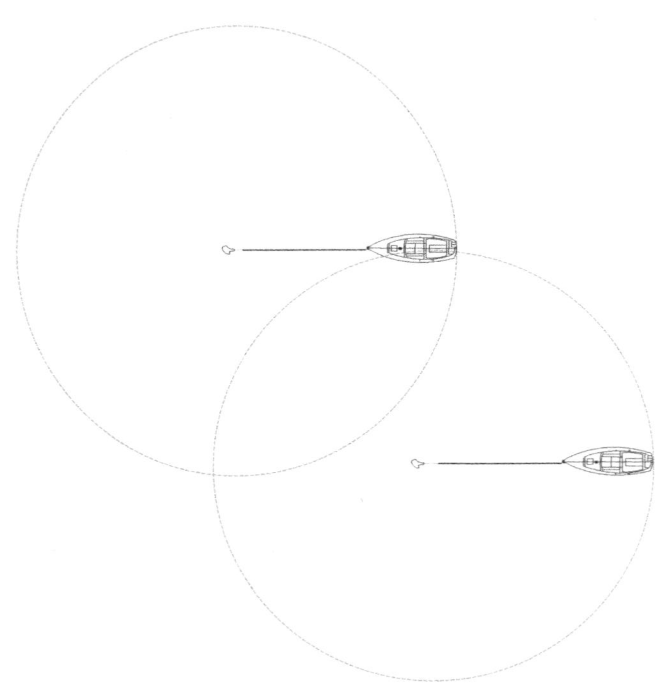

Proper staggering of anchor location maximizes the number of boats that can safely anchor in a crowded harbor.

mud bank? How much room do you have (a few hundred feet is a good minimum whenever possible)? If it is an open roadstead or harbor that becomes unruly in onshore conditions, will it be possible to raise anchor and leave in the middle of the night? Although it is common to find boats clumped together in one corner of a harbor, that doesn't mean it's the safest place. More often it's just a herd mentality.

- **Spacing.** Boats at anchor swing with the wind. Boats with equal scope generally swing approximately in unison, although differences in windage, keel design, and rope vs. chain rode result in considerable variation, particularly in light winds. In a crowded harbor, it is impractical to stay completely outside of the swing radius of other boats, but you can position yourself to minimize the risk of collision and conserve space. A good starting point is to lower your anchor approximately one rode length plus one boat length off the beam of a neighboring boat. After you let out scope, this will place you in a staggered position to one side, technically overlapping the swing radius of the neighboring boat, but with very low risk of actually touching. Of course, there is no reason to anchor this close unless you feel certain the harbor will fill up by evening. (To estimate distance, sight past your thumb with your arm outstretched—a man will appear the length of your thumb at 60 feet and the height of your thumbnail at 175 feet. Another method is to approach from well down wind, and use the height of the other boat's mast as a reference before plotting a parallel course.)

Placing the Anchor

The most common method in popular harbors is to lower the anchor along with 50 feet of chain, and go below to mix a drink. The second most common method is to drop the anchor along with 50 feet of chain, and then put the engine in reverse at about half throttle and plow furrows all over the harbor. Don't be those guys. Few things identify an

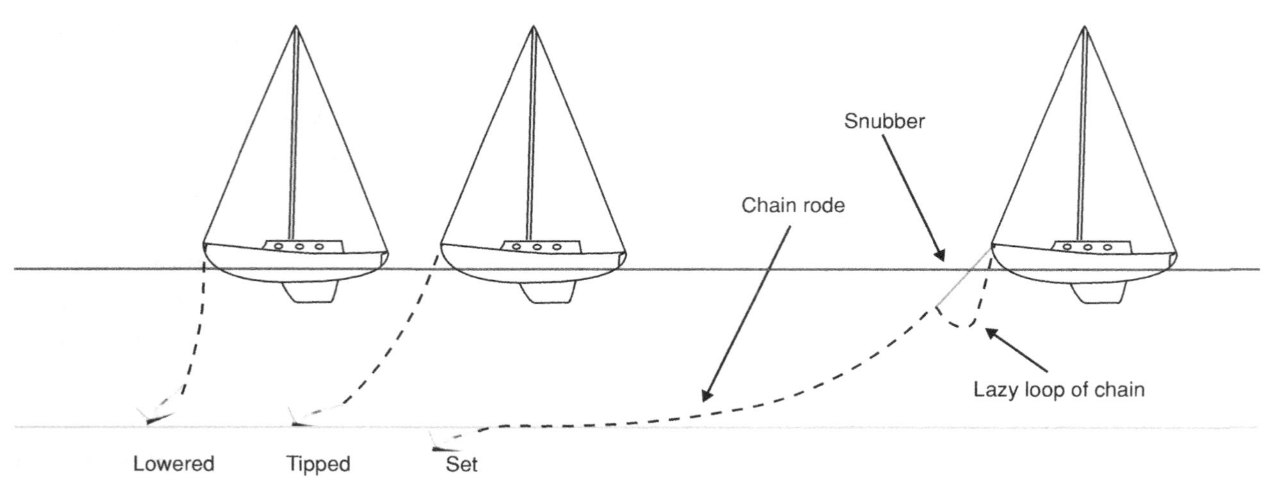

Lower the anchor to the bottom, gently tip it over, and lay the remainder of the chain out slowly to avoid fouling the anchor.

experienced cruiser more clearly than solid anchor placement technique.

1. Bring the boat into the wind over the target spot and stop.
2. Allow the boat to begin drifting to leeward at about 0.5 to 1 knot. If there is insufficient wind to cause this naturally, apply just a touch of reverse for a few seconds.
3. Lower the anchor until it just touches the bottom, adding a few more feet at a time as the chain begins to angle forward, away from the boat. The goal is to place the anchor right side up, with the fluke facing aft, and then gently tip it over. Since most modern anchors will align themselves properly as a result of the water flow when backing slowly, this procedure should land the anchor butter-side up, facing the correct direction, and without chain tangles. Continue to add chain very slowly until the angle is at least 45 degrees. Any anchor can be fouled by a pile of chain carelessly dropped on top of it.
4. Lower the required amount of chain more quickly. It doesn't matter if the boat drifts downwind at an odd angle during this step.
5. Attach the snubber (Chapter 2) before the rode draws tight. Ease sufficient chain so that the tension comes onto the snubber instead of the chain windlass; allowing the chain to come tight against the windlass can apply a damaging jerk. Place chafe gear on the snubber where it rubs on chocks and where it crosses the chain.
6. The boat is moving very slowly aft prior to snubbing and the anchor will take a light bite, gently stopping the boat. However, the anchor is not set. For initial setting, the rode length should be 7 to 10 times the depth of the water plus the height of the bow above the water; this is the scope. See Chapter 4 for a detailed discussion of scope.
7. If anchoring in very soft mud, allow the anchor to settle for 10 or 15 minutes before power setting. This will allow it to settle through the ooze and bite into firmer material below. The exception to this rule is the Fortress anchor, which should be lightly set immediately. See Fortress Anchors, Chapter 7.
8. Apply reverse at idle, backing at no more than 1-knot until all of the slack is removed from the chain and snubber. Take the engine out of gear as necessary. Note the GPS coordinates to the nearest 0.001-minute (about 6 feet). Speed should be zero after the slack is taken up.
9. Slowly increase reverse throttle from idle to the maximum intended over a period of about 30 seconds in firm bottoms. In very soft mud bottoms, increase the throttle more slowly taking as much as 2 minutes to reach full RPMs. In settled weather, 1/3 throttle should be enough and recovering the anchor in the morning will be easier, but don't hesitate to use full throttle if strong conditions are expected. Although the GPS may display a speed of 0.5 to 1 knots for few seconds, it should drop to zero. This small amount of movement is a combination of controlled anchor drag during setting process, straightening chain catenary, and bridle stretch. Again, note the GPS position. In Chapter 5 we'll investigate power setting and how to confirm whether and anchor is well-set. Soft mud setting is discussed in Chapters 4 and 7.
10. If the anchor takes more than about 20 feet (0.003 minutes by GPS) to set, it is not actually setting. It's probably upside down or fouled. If it does seem to catch after this distance, it is probably just caught on trash. Raise the anchor all the way so that you can check for fouling, and repeat from step one. Contrary to popular advertising, even modern roll bar anchors can be completely stable upside down in very soft mud; there simply isn't enough resistance pressing against the roll bar to force the anchor to self-right. Worse yet, the roll bar will fill up with sticks and trash, perhaps giving the misleading impression of a light set. A pivoting fluke anchor may just sled along (see Chapter 7). Hence the importance of Steps 2 and 3.
11. Secure the chain with a stopper or cleat as a backup in case the snubber fails or a non-locking chain hook (see Chapter 13) falls off as a result of brushing the bottom.
12. Cut the engine.

Like driving a nail into wood, a proper stroke is more efficient than the sloppy bashings of a teenager. Lower and tip the anchor down carefully, lay the chain out carefully, power set appropriately, and your problems will be few.

Tripping lines are seldom good practice because of the risk of the line fouling either your running gear as you drift over the anchor or fouling other boats moving through the harbor. The sole exception is rocky terrain where fouling is likely. Their use is described in Chapter 12, which discusses anchoring in rocks. Most fouling in muddy harbors, however, is the result of dragging; if the anchor is lowered and set carefully it will move only a few feet and the risk of fouling is very low. However, if the anchor is deployed carelessly and plows a long furrow across the bottom during the setting process, the anchor is quite likely to set under an old tree or cable. Thus, efficient setting practice reduces the risk of fouling.

A storm comes up and you're dragging? Your basic options are to add more scope (let the snubber go and add a fresh one), place a second anchor, or raise anchor and move elsewhere. All of these are troublesome, so focus on anchoring right the first time.

Windlass Safety

One of the easiest ways to lose or damage a finger is to get it caught between the chain and the gypsy. I've had only one bad experience, but it could easily have turned out differently. I was recovering the anchor in calm conditions, squatting on one knee near the windlass. A wake threw me off balance, my left knee landed on the up button, and my left hand against the spinning gypsy. Because my weight was on both my hand and knee, I couldn't quickly lift either, and the windlass spent a few scary seconds churning against my glove. Without the glove, I would have lost a tendon.

- Leather gloves. Relatively tight fitting. Sailing gloves will do.
- Never squat. Either stand, sit, or kneel on both knees.
- Consider a hand-held remote or a switch on the rail in place of foot switches.
- If the chain is not feeding properly, lower the anchor a few feet, removing any twists as it goes. Never touch the chain while recovering.
- If the rope/chain splice is causing trouble, re-splice using the irony splice (Chapter 13). If the chain itself is jamming, either the chain is stretched or the gypsy is worn. Find out which and replace it. A new chain is much cheaper than fingers.
- Open the windlass breaker before moving the chain on the gypsy with fingers or performing any other work that places your body at risk. This is even more critical if there is a remote switch.

Recovering the Anchor

Many sailors use the windlass to pull the boat up to the anchor and then break the anchor out, all without pause. You can get away with this in light winds, although it is a strain on the windlass. Use the windlass gently, with short rests, to avoid overheating. If there are significant waves it is dangerous to use the windlass directly, since the load on the windlass when the chain snaps tight will far exceed the safe working load. Technically, there should be a clutch to relieve this overload, but they are often seized with corrosion or adjusted too tight. A better procedure is required in stronger winds. If you have switched to grade 70 chain and downsized, careful practice is even more important,

Never grind the chain over the snubber.

because the windlass may now be considerably undersized (most were engineered for grade 30 chain). The following assumes an all-chain rode:

- Motor forward just enough to take the strain off the snubber. Retrieve enough chain to recover and remove the snubber. If you use the windlass to pull in the chain, never allow the chain to grind over the snubber; the rope will suffer serious but invisible internal damage, and will unexpectedly fail at some point in the future. Keep the snubber out from under the chain by lifting up and to one side. Sailing gloves are good, but a pair of PVC-coated gardening gloves (Atlas Fit) save wear and tear, keep your good gloves dry in cold weather, and provide superior grip on a muddy chain. Always protect your fingers; they are your crew.
- Continue motoring forward over the anchor, while the bowman gives direction to the helmsman, maintaining the speed below 1-knot. Because single-engine boats will have very little steerage at low speed, the bowman may have to recover just enough chain to keep the boat headed to wind.
- As the rode becomes straight up and down, the procedure differs based upon wave conditions:
    - If wave action is minimal, tighten the rode and allow the gentle bobbing motion of the boat to loosen the anchor for at least one minute. Tighten the rode some more. Repeat as needed until the anchor can be recovered without straining the windlass or the crew.
    - If the wave action is significant or the anchor well buried, waves and momentum of the boat supply the breakout power. If the rode is rope, cleat tightly and proceed to break out the anchor as described below. If the rode is chain, reattach the snubber to the chain and cleat tightly, maintaining enough slack in the chain that the windlass will not feel the force. I use a short dedicated "break-out" snubber with a plain chain hook for this. A pawl-type chain stopper, if rated for the load, works well. First, allow the bobbing of the bow to work the anchor loose. If this is not effective within 10-15 minutes, motor over the anchor at 1 to 2 knots, using the momentum of the boat and wave action to pull the anchor loose. With large chop, even with a short snubber, the up-and-down motion of the bow can create snatch forces beyond the breaking point of both chain and snubber if the boat is directly over the anchor. Thus, it is sometimes safer to use a scope of about 1.5:1. This greatly reduces the snatch force and is very nearly as effective at breaking the anchor free. Do not motor over the anchor at more than 1.5 knots; the momentum of the boat will create forces beyond the safe working load of the chain, anchor, and bowsprit/anchor roller. Considerable damage can result. Instead, be patient and be prepared to repeat the process several times. If the above methods are not successful, consider diving to take a look before breaking something through ham-handed applications of force. Most bent anchors are the result of forcing things when the toe is caught under an immovable rock.
- Once the anchor is free of the bottom, retrieve until just above the surface and check the rotation. If it is correct, stow the anchor. If the anchor is backwards, lower the anchor until it is a few yards in the water, and slowly backup. Most modern anchors will align themselves with the flow of the water and straighten out if lowered and recovered in this manner. If there are chain twists between the roller and the windlass, stop and lower the anchor to the bottom untwisting the chain as it goes. (Only touch the chain while lowering, and then with great caution.) See also Chapter 13, Anchor Twist.
- Scrape or wash down. When anchored in sticky mud, the anchor is commonly embedded with tenacious deposits. Left in place, they contribute to corrosion and may inhibit setting at your next stop. Some sailors swear by a seawater washdown hose, but I've been happy using a plastic scraper with an 18-inch handle. Likewise, mud can pack into the links of the chain; lowering and raising the anchor a few times will rinse off the bulk of the mud. Letting the boat hang at relatively short scope for a few minutes before raising the anchor, allowing the waves to lift and drop the

chain can help; in rough conditions this can put a terrible strain on the windlass, but ordinarily the chain comes up pretty clean on those days. How clean is clean enough depends on whether anchor locker stink will spread throughout the cabin. Once a year, while in a marina, lower the anchor and all of the chain, hose out the anchor locker, and hose off the chain as it is recovered. Never lower all of the chain in truly deep water—the windlass may not be able to manage the weight of the anchor plus the entire rode.

- Secure the anchor. An anchor on a bow roller can really get bashed sailing to windward. At the same time, securing the anchor on the roller by leaving tension on the windlass can wear the gypsy. A lashing can secure the anchor, but a better solution is a chain lock or chain brake. Be wary of stainless pins; these can bend and jam, and you won't notice it until you you're lowering anchor in the dark, or at least that was my experience on two occasions. After the second time I switched to a high tensile steel pin (a Philips screwdriver with a hole drilled in it for a retaining pin) for the chain lock, and a lashing on the anchor when needed.

Setting the Anchor Under Sail

In days past and today with smaller boats, this is the only way. If you sail long enough, your engine will fail due to a rope around the prop or dirt in the fuel filter. The procedure is fundamentally similar to our basic technique—tip the anchor over carefully, don't pile the chain on the anchor, and get the snubber on before the rode draws tight. But the lack of engine power makes maneuvering more difficult, and you really want to get the hook to catch the first time. Practice these procedures a few times with the engine running in neutral or in a wide open area. These are good skills to have, and when you really need them, it won't be the time to suddenly learn how the rules are different for your boat. Good communication amongst the crew (or planning if singlehanded) is vital to first effort success.

- In all but the lightest zephyr (less than 5 knots), ease sail and slow way down. Anything much above 1 knot downwind will apply too much shock load to the rode, even with a snubber in place. Do not stow the sails, because if the hook does not catch you will need to circle around and try again. Normally only one sail is required; whether jib or main depends on the balance of the boat. I find dousing the main and furling the jib is least dramatic; even loose, the main has a nasty tendency to fill and drive, since the boat may get sideways while drifting backwards. The jib, on the other hand, can be furled or dropped while drifting backwards, and unfurled or hoisted in moments if the anchor does not catch; you should be drifting backwards at only 1-2 feet per second, so you do have some time to recover the anchor, hoist, and regain control. Just make certain you have room to leeward.
- Hand-set the anchor with very light pressure when the boat reaches about 5:1 scope (when the rode length is 5 times the depth of the water plus the height of the bow roller). Then release and allow the boat to continue drifting back to 10:1 scope. This is conservative, to be sure, but you want the anchor to catch the first time. Let it rest at long scope for at least a few hours to allow the wind to settle the anchor in, since there will be no power setting. You can shorten up later.
- In stronger winds, the procedure is very similar, but everything happens faster. If the boat is drifting back too quickly, you may want to snubber the rode gradually starting at about 5:1 scope in order to maintain some control.
- In lighter winds, it may be advantageous to use the momentum of the boat to set the hook. Again, make a light set at about 5:1 scope before allowing the boat to continue downwind to full scope and snubbing firmly. Again, allow several hours for the anchor to settle in at 10:1 scope before shortening up.
- Downwind steering. If setting in light winds by sailing downwind, don't steer dead downwind unless you really want the chain to scrape the side of your boat or the nylon rode to get wrapped around the rudder. Instead, steer a curved course, kicking the stern to one side so that the chain does not run down the topsides and the rode is not directly under the boat.

- Supplemental Setting. The conservative approach is to rest at long scope and let the wind slowly set the anchor. Supplemental procedures can unset the anchor, and resetting with no engine is awkward. However, if severe weather is expected, deeper setting may be desirable, if for no other reason than to confirm the quality of the set. Light pressure can be applied by backing the sails; however, unless you have a multihull with considerable beam, this is ineffective. Hauling the rode up to short scope, and then letting the boat drift backwards at up to 1-2 knots will apply a force equivalent to a strong squall. This is very effective once the wind reaches 15 knots. Alternatively, a kedge can be taken off the stern and hauled tight to provide setting force, though it should not be left in place if any side wind is expected (see Chapter 11, Testing and Anchor for Big Wind and Fore-Aft Anchoring). A second anchor will also add security (see Chapter 10).

Anchoring without an engine can also be an emergency situation. In one of my more careless moments, I changed my fuel filters without remembering to reopen the shutoff valve when I was finished. The gasoline in the carburetors and line was just sufficient to get me between two stone jetties in a 25-knot crosswind, before both engines cut out about 20 seconds apart. The solution was to anchor very quickly.

- Momentum. If you can decide quickly, the boat will still move forward, allowing you to coast into an advantageous anchoring position. If I had wasted valuable time trying to figure out why the engines stopped, I would have lost momentum and slowly drifted too near to the leeward jetty for safe anchoring. Instead, I used what momentum I had to maneuver the boat as close to the windward jetty as practical. Take full advantage of stored momentum. It won't keep.
- Quick Deployment. The anchor must be ready to deploy within 30 seconds when maneuvering in close quarters. Any lashings that were placed for offshore sailing should be removed and the anchor should be secured by only a quick-release pin or simple lock. I only had to remove a spring clip and pull a pin—the anchor was on the bottom before the boat began drifting backwards.
- Scope. While it's tempting to begin snubbing the rode at short scope to see if the anchor is catching, resist the temptation. Nothing more than the lightest hand setting should be attempted until scope is at least 7:1—you're in a harbor, so it will be shallow and 7:1 won't be that far, perhaps 70 feet. Allow for rode stretch and setting distance.

With the boat anchored and my mind settled, it took only a few minutes to identify my foolish error, raise anchor, and enjoy the rest of the day, thankful to have dodged a bullet.

Raising the Anchor Under Sail

In light winds, the procedure is not much different than raising the anchor under power. Haul by hand as fast as you can, cleat the rode off short as the boat passes over the anchor, and hope the momentum is enough to free the anchor. If that fails, shorten up as much as possible and hope the bobbing of the boat will free it. If nothing happens within 15 minutes, take the rode to a winch and grind. If it's an all-chain rode, reattach the snubber and take that to the winch. Use a snatch block to create a 2:1 purchase if need be. This may seem like over kill and a lot to set up, but it's sometimes the best way to free a deeply set anchor, even if the engine is available, because the strain is slow and steady.

If the wind is blowing you will need to short tack up to the anchor using only the mainsail with the traveller lowered slightly. Even the most stubborn boat will come through the tacks reliably; when the rode pulls tight at each lay line, it pulls the bow around. If the harbor is crowded and losing control could result in a collision, ask for help or wait until the other boats leave. Never be in a rush.

Spare Anchors and Rode

What sort of anchors? Assuming the primary anchor is a conservatively sized modern scoop-type, a pivoting fluke anchor as both kedge (to pull the boat off soft groundings) and storm anchor for soft bottoms is a good choice. Fortress is my personal favorite, since they seem to set more reliably than others in the class and are considerably lighter, a boon when taking the anchor out in a dinghy. A third anchor is prudent if you'll be sailing far, the design dependent on your sailing waters; every experienced cruiser will admit to losing an anchor, often due to a stupid mistake. I'm guilty. The design of this third anchor has been debated to death—any modern anchor is as suitable as any other. At least one spare full-length nylon rode and one shorter nylon rode should be included, along with a spare set of dock lines and whatever spare line you have for contingencies.

A single, anchor, thoughtfully placed, will put you in good stead 95% of the time. In Chapters 2-6 we will work our way through the factors that determine if the anchor will hold:

- **Reduce the Load.** Chapter 2 quantifies wind load, dynamic loads, and methods to control them.
- **Reduce the Motion.** The anchor must lie quietly. Chapter 3 explains practical strategies for reducing yawing and hobby horsing.
- **Keep the Lead Angle Low.** The rode must remain close to the bottom. Chapter 4 quantifies how chain and scope interact to accomplish this. The negative effects of reduced scope are quantified and the positive effects of time are quantified.
- **Good Soil.** An anchor is never better than the seabed in which it is embedded. In Chapter 5 we explore bottom types and in Chapters 6 though 9 we quantify the actual holding power of anchors in a variety of seabeds, focusing not on sand, but on the worst case scenarios; soft mud and impenetrable bottoms such as cobbles and hardpan.
- **Multiple Anchors for Bad Bottoms.** Finally, when faced with exceptional conditions—either very poor holding or very strong weather—multiple anchors can be the best answer. There are many ways to do it wrong and a few ways that work well; we've quantitatively tested all of them and will walk you through the minefield, debunking myths along the way (Chapters 10 through 12).

Good anchoring is simple to summarize and complicated in execution. I've enjoyed working my way through the minefield, one step at a time, testing gear in hand.

Chapter 2: How Much Load?

FOR MANY YEARS, ABYC deck hardware load recommendations have been the gold standard, and yet over the years, observation and testing by multiple investigators have confirmed that the actual wind load is 3-5 times less than ABYC values.

My 32-foot, 10,000-pound catamaran became a test bed. (This work was later confirmed with a 24-foot trimaran and a 36-foot monohull—the trends were the same.) First, I determined the wind-only portion of the load by anchoring with a very long nylon rode in a well-protected harbor. With no waves exceeding a few inches and the gusts averaged out, wind load figures were, in fact, about 4.5-5 times lower than the ABYC figures. How can this be? And just like that, it became clear to me that understanding the forces involved is central to understanding anchoring, and experimentation would be the only way to separate fact from guesswork. Engineering design starts by understanding what must be accomplished, and for ground tackle design, how much the anchor must hold.

Testing continued in an open roadstead with 8 miles of fetch in 6-7 feet of water using an all-chain rode. "Why so shallow," you ask? "Surely it is poor practice to anchor where steep or breaking waves are possible?" Very true. However, for test purposes, I wanted to make certain that steep waves were a factor, and I did not test in large breaking waves. Additionally, the test area is a popular summer anchorage, and once in a while, cruisers are surprised by an unexpected wind shift or thunderstorm.

Table 1

Snubber Data

PDQ32 Catamaran
1/4-inch G43 chain rode

Fatuige Failure Probable

Horizontal Peak Load, Pounds

Rode Type

Windspeed Knots	60' x 8mm Wind Only	Climbing Rope 8mm x 35' Bridle	3-Strand 1/2" x 30' Bridle	3-Strand 3/8" x 6' Snubber	3-Strand 1/2" x 6' Snubber	1/4" G43 Chain No Snubber	3/8" BBB chain No Snubber	3/8" BBB chain 10x22 Float	1/4" Amsteel As Rode	ABYC Values 40-foot monohull	Yawing No Bridle or 1/4" G43
10	29	34	38	42	47	54	40	see discussion	142	133	60 (15 degrees)
15	62	73	104	115	130	150	110	see discussion	340	300	220 (30 degrees)
20	111	125	150	258	292	360	300	see discussion	650	533	500 (30 degrees)
25	173	224	234	475	537	662	620	see discussion	NA	833	
30	254	310	465	708	800	1,035	1,000	see discussion	NA	1,200	
35	330	415	520	960	1,141	1,409	1,361	see discussion	NA	1,633	
40	420	528	600	1,254	1,490	1,840	1,778	see discussion	NA	2,133	
45	519	650	815	1,587	1,886	2,329	2,250	see discussion	NA	2,755	
50	627	786	1,006	1,959	2,329	2,875	2,778	see discussion	NA	3,090	
55	744	933	1,218	2,371	2,818	3,479	3,361	see discussion	NA	3,361	
60	871	1,091	1,449	2,821	3,353	4,140	4,000	see discussion	NA	4,000	
	WLL 1/2" rope exceeded										
Breaking Strength, including bridle angle		6,480	13,500	4,400	7,500	7,650	11,000	11,000			
Fatigue strength, including bends		1,037	2,160	704	1,200						
Design limit, including allowance for single leg loading		622	1,512	704	960	2,600	2,650	2,650			
% reduction in peak force		69%	65%	30%	19%	basis	3%	nil			

Anchoring should be about a plausible worst case scenario.

A variety of snubber materials were tested, including 3-strand nylon and dynamic climbing rope. Both grade 43 chain and oversized grade 30 chain were tested. To test single-line snubbers, I replaced my usual nylon bridle with a non-stretch Dyneema bridle to eliminate shock absorption (catamarans always use a bridle to avoid excessive yawing).

To test the affect of sailing at anchor, also referred to as yawing or horsing around, we ran additional tests with no bridle. Yawing increases the load both by increasing the wind profile (the boat becomes more sideways to the wind) and by impact when the chain snaps tight during the swing. Yawing can also loosen the anchor by jerking it from side to side, liquefying the soil (see Chapter 4). The results are summarized in Table 2. There's a lot of information packed in there, so before we dig too deep, let's review the data, column by column.

Table 2 Summary

Shaded cells represent weather conditions where the snubber or rode would likely fail due to fatigue within 30-100 days of storm exposure, ignoring the effect of chafe. In general, the data below 40 knots were measured, and the data above 40 knots were extrapolated, using the relationship force ~ wind speed^2. All values are momentary peak loads observed during a 10-20 minute test period. The test boat was anchored at 10:1 scope with V tandem anchors in firm sand to prevent shock absorption due to dragging. The test site was exposed to an 8-miles fetch in only 6-7 feet of water; few real-world anchorages are this harsh.

- ***Wind Only.*** The wind-only load was estimated by using a 60-meter climbing rope rode plus a long bridle in a nearby location, but protected from waves by a jetty. If a ½-inch rope rode were used it would eventually fatigue at 55 knots. The wind load is about four times less force than the all-chain example.
- ***8mm Climbing Rope Bridle.*** Climbing rope, designed to absorb the energy of climbing falls with minimal impact force, provides maximum wave and gust damping. However, it is thin and will eventually fatigue at 50 knots. The load is reduced 69% relative to the all-chain example.
- ***1/2-inch 3-Strand Bridle.*** The peak load is reduced slightly less (65%), but with stronger rope, the bridle can endure for weeks at 65 knots.
- ***3/8-inch x 6-foot Snubber.*** Because it is too short to dissipate much energy, the peak load is only reduced 30% and the snubber will fatigue at 30 knots.
- ***1/2-inch x 6-foot Snubber.*** A traditional short snubber selection, the force is only reduced 19%. Endurance is improved by 5 knots to 35 knots. Small wonder these commonly fail during squalls in exposed anchorage areas; if chop builds up in the anchorage, they begin working well above the fatigue limit and will fail within a few thousand peak cycles. The snubber is simply too short to dissipate the wave energy.
- ***1/4-inch G43 (grade 43) Chain, No Snubber.*** The base case. The peak forces are very high, comparing well to ABYC working load values. At 50 knots the working load of the chain is exceeded, assuming the anchor didn't drag first. This verifies the ABYC design basis.
- ***3/8-inch BBB (grade 30) Chain, No Snubber.*** This chain has a working load limit similar to ¼-inch G43, and was tested to evaluate the effect of catenary in shallow water. There was a slight improvement in damping in lighter winds, as long as the chain maintained some curve, but no significant difference in storm conditions. The larger grade 30 chain would fatigue in similar conditions to grade 43 chain.
- ***3/8-inch BBB Chain With Buoy.*** The reduction in force attributable to the buoy was trivial.
- ***1/4-inch Amsteel Rode (Dyneema).*** Only limited testing was required to confirm that it was horrible, with impact loads higher than chain.
- ***ABYC Values.*** The current ABYC Table 1 gives recommendations only for storm and

Table 2

Snubber Data

PDQ32 Catamaran
1/4-inch G43 chain rode

Fatuige Failure Probable

Horizontal Peak Load, Pounds
Rode Type

Windspeed	60' x 8mm	Climbing Rope	3-Strand	3-Strand	3-Strand	1/4" G43 Chain	3/8" BBB chain	3/8" BBB chain	1/4" Amsteel	ABYC Values	Yawing
Knots	Wind Only	8mm x 35' Bridle	1/2" x 30' Bridle	3/8" x 6' Snubber	1/2" x 6' Snubber	No Snubber	No Snubber	10x22 Float	As Rode	40-foot monohull	No Bridle or 1/4" G43
10	29	34	38	42	47	54	40	see discussion	142	133	60 (15 degrees)
15	62	73	104	115	130	150	110	see discussion	340	300	220 (30 degrees)
20	111	125	150	258	292	360	300	see discussion	650	533	500 (30 degrees)
25	173	224	234	475	537	662	620	see discussion	NA	833	
30	254	310	465	708	800	1,035	1,000	see discussion	NA	1,200	
35	330	415	520	960	1,141	1,409	1,361	see discussion	NA	1,633	
40	420	528	600	1,254	1,490	1,840	1,778	see discussion	NA	2,133	
45	519	650	815	1,587	1,886	2,329	2,250	see discussion	NA	2,755	
50	627	786	1,006	1,959	2,329	2,875	2,778	see discussion	NA	3,090	
55	744	933	1,218	2,371	2,818	3,479	3,361	see discussion	NA	3,361	
60	871	1,091	1,449	2,821	3,353	4,140	4,000	see discussion	NA	4,000	
WLL 1/2" rope exceeded											
Breaking Strength, including bridle angle		6,480	13,500	4,400	7,500	7,650	11,000	11,000			
Fatigue strength, including bends		1,037	2,160	704	1,200						
Design limit, including allowance for single leg loading		622	1,512	704	960	2,600	2,650	2,650			
% reduction in peak force		69%	65%	30%	19%	basis	3%	nil			

working anchors; characteristic wind speeds were suggested in earlier editions, and the values between these were extrapolated for purposes of comparison only. Refer to Table 1 for actual ABYC H-40 Table 1 recommendations.

- ***Yawing.*** The ¼-inch chain rode was attached to the center of the front cross beam with no snubber. Although forces were not recorded, they were about the same as with a Dyneema bridle. Yawing increases the wind force and can loosen the anchor in poor bottoms.

What else did we learn? First, that rode tension is very difficult to gauge by eye. During one light wind test with all-chain and no snubber, an express cruiser wake interrupted my measurements. Although I felt nothing more than a light nudge, the 2,000-pound load cell exploded, probably at about 6,000 pounds, judging from the deformation of the surviving shackles. There was very little sound and no one else onboard even noticed. I've performed thousands of failure tests on climbing and sailing gear, and even with gauges telling me the exact strain at every moment, there is generally very little visual change suggesting impending failure, unless you know exactly what to watch for. Just because you are not feeling strong shocks and loud noises, as the boat bucks at anchor, does not mean the snubbing force is not thousands of pounds. You simply can't tell by looking at the chain or by the feel of the boat, unless there is something elastic in the system that you can see stretch.

ABYC Table 1 recommendations are sound for all-chain rodes. When anchored with no snubber (all chain), as soon as the wind reached 15-20 knots, the chain became effectively straight and the maximum impact forces were close to the ABYC working load values. This represents the worst-case scenario for boats anchored in a shallow, open area with long fetch, steep non-breaking waves, and all chain rode. Obviously, extreme loads are very dangerous, no matter how strong your anchor and chain. We need to reduce these loads.

The wind load alone was about 4.5 times less than the ABYC values, and the rope and long snubber loads were three times less than ABYC values. This agrees well with data collected by other investigators, including Don Dodds, Robert Smith, and Rick Neeves. Although the exact values obviously depend on the specific rode design, boat, and situation, it is an established fact that actual loads can be greatly reduced.

Current Force

In addition to the wind and waves, a strong tide can significantly increase the load. The force required to move our test boat through the water at 2 knots is only about 25 pounds, which is trivial in comparison to wind and wave loads, and often is dismissed by sailing writers. However, this is not the whole story. For example, if the current is moving strongly from south to north, and the wind is strong from the west, the current will press against the keel of the boat at a severe angle (high force) and cause the boat to take the wind at a slight angle (higher force). This conflict in direction also increases yawing, as the wind and current fight for

Table 3

Table 3 assumes 6 to 12-foot depths, exposure to non-breaking waves generated by a several mile fetch. If the water is over 20-feet deep and the scope is long, the short snubber case becomes similar to the long snubber case (Chapter 4). The load is about 25% greater for power boats and 35% greater for catamarans.

Horizontal Working Load at 60 Knots--Assorted Rode Types

	Horizontal Working Load, Pounds					
	Boat Length, Feet					
Rode Type	25	30	35	40	50	60
Wind Load Only	261	508	653	871	1,161	1,451
Rope	314	611	785	1,047	1,396	1,745
Long Snubber	327	636	818	1,091	1,455	1,818
Short Snubber	975	1,895	2,437	3,249	4,332	5,415
Chain Only	1,238	2,408	3,096	4,128	5,504	6,880

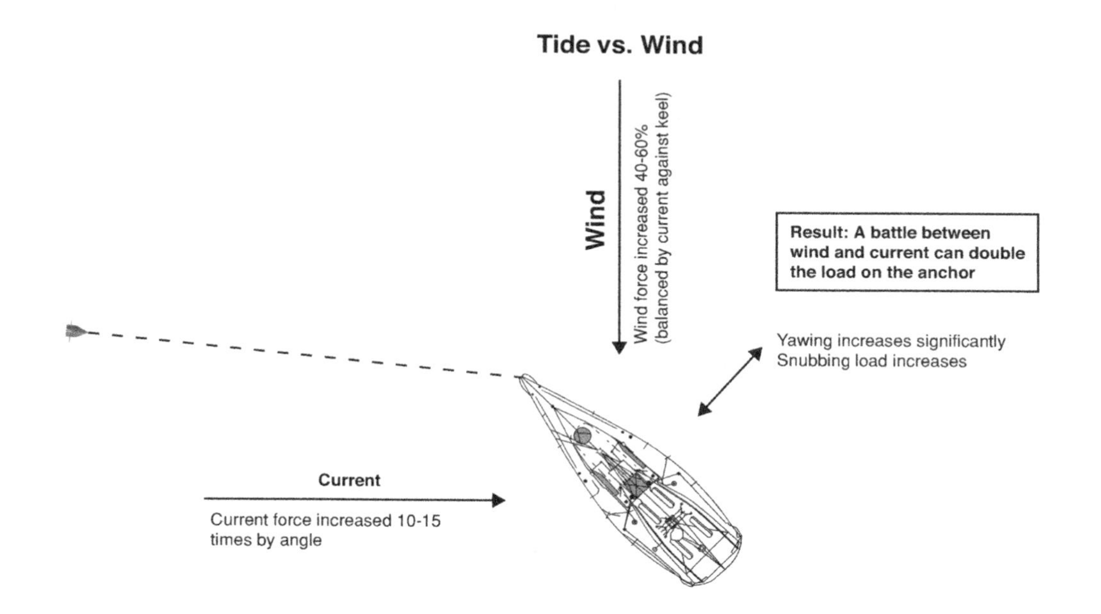

control. The result is a bizarre dance that is difficult to analyze, some of the force being transfer to the keel but some taken by the rode; allowing an additional 50-100% load is prudent in severe cases.

Snubbers

Short Snubbers

A chain grinding on the rollers or bobstay is noisy and destructive, and snatch loads are a hazard to bowsprits and windlasses. Common practice is to unload the windlass by attaching a short length of line to the chain rode with a chain grabber (see Chapter 13) which is led over the roller or chocks and back to a bow cleat. Because such a line is too short to effectively absorb surge energy, it does not reduce peak rode tension and must be stronger than the chain it snubs if it is expected to have a reasonable fatigue life. Study the 6-foot x ½-inch example in Table 2; the load is reduced only 15% and the rope may fail from fatigue in a 35-knot storm. If downsized for better energy absorption, it will be operating far beyond its safe working load and will fail even sooner (see the 6-foot x 3/8-inch example, failing at just 30 knots). More

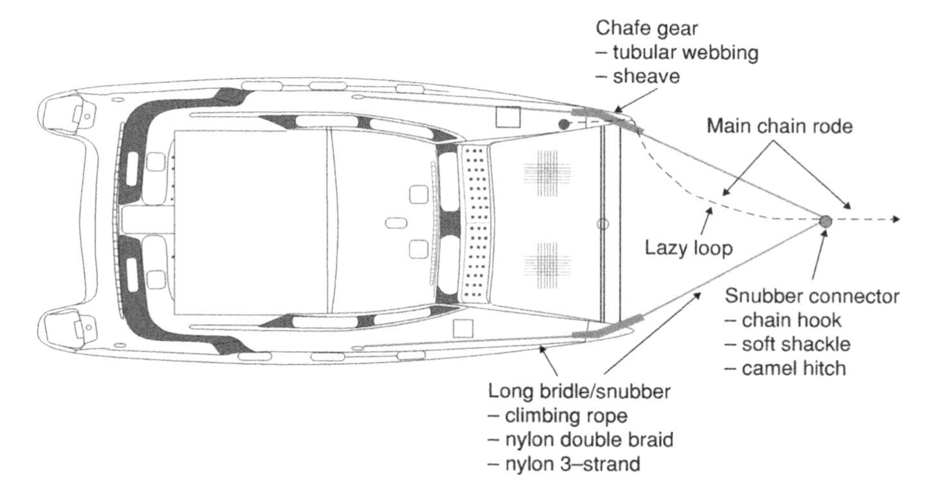

Long bridle as used on Shoal Survivor. The snubber connector is kept off the bottom in shallow water by attaching it the bridle to the midships cleats. In deeper water or strong winds it is attached to the bow cleats. The chafing gear is 1-inch tubular nylon webbing. Another way to keep the snubber connection off the bottom is to attach a small fender to the chain near the snubber connection to lift the rope off the bottom; even a 3" x 12" fender is enough. See Chapter 13.

importantly, each time a wave or gust exceeds the holding power of the anchor, something must give; if force is not absorbed by the rode and snubber, then the anchor must move through the bottom to dissipate energy. In soft mud we have calculated and observed that the anchor can move 2-6 inches during each surge, often several times each minute during a severe storm (50 knots). This amounts to 30-60 feet per hour, assuming the anchor does not trip in the process. Unfortunately, both experience and testing suggest it will trip, the result of striking buried debris or crossing a soft spot in the bottom (Chapter 8 and Appendix III).

Long Snubbers

Typically one boat length or a bit more, long snubbers also unload the windlass. Additionally, however, they reduce peak anchor loads in shallow water by 50-70%. In order to function properly, the snubber must be matched to the boat and ground tackle, just as fishing line and lure weight must be matched to a fishing pole: too long is awkward, too short lacks the length to dissipate shock; too thick is durable but little different from chain, and too thin is vulnerable to fatigue. A simple conceptual basis is that the snubber must be long enough to stretch the height of a wave (3-6 feet) while staying within 10-15% of the breaking strength; 25-50 feet of 3-strand nylon is a good starting point.

Example. Assuming a year-round cruiser sees a powerful squall every other week and two good storms each month, there will be about 100,000 significant surge cycles within two years, a time period commonly used when evaluating snubber life (see fatigue rate graph in Chapter 13). On our test boat we found that an 8 mm climbing rope bridle (double line) reduced the load 69%, has an acceptable fatigue life at 50 knots, and the breaking strength of the combined legs is 75% of that of the chain. Imagine how well this reduces fatigue on every, link, pin, and shackle of your ground tackle? A ½-inch 3-strand bridle reduced the load 65%, while increasing the fatigue life considerably—a better choice in windy areas.

Slack In The Chain

There must be enough slack to allow the snubber to do its work. This must be at least 25% of the length of the snubber. Traditionally, generous slack was deployed to create a lazy loop, required to keep a common chain hook in place. As a result, tension would never come on the chain at the bow unless the snubber failed. In the case of a single line 3-strand snubber, twisting of the rope as it stretches can result in the chain lying over the snubber (see next page). If the chain becomes tight, chafe is rapid. A long lazy loop discourages this, but does not prevent it entirely. (See Chapter 11.)

What is the correct snubber size? While every anchoring situation and boat is different, cruiser experience with dynamic climbing rope and 3-strand nylon snubbers indicates a single-line snubber sized according to the formulas below should last a full-time cruiser 2-3 years and the occasional cruiser 5-8 years (length in feet; displacement in pounds).

Don't let the chain grind over the snubber when retrieving or deploying. It will cause hidden internal damage to the snubber. Always lift up and to the side.

A long bridle slides easily inside tubular webbing chafe gear.

- ***Snubber length = 1.3 x boat length.*** Increase the length about 20% for single braid (less stretch). Decrease to one boat length for climbing rope (more stretch). These are minimum lengths; longer is better, up to about 60 feet.
- ***Snubber diameter = .008 (length) X (displacement/7800)^0.25.*** For catamarans, increase the diameter 20% and use a bridle, to correct for increased windage and reduce yawing. Monohulls using a bridle can reduce the bridle leg diameter 20%.

And for those that prefer to simply pick a number from a table, I have calculated some examples (see Table 4).

Practical Notes on Using a Snubber

- Protect against chafe and sharp turns. I use tubular nylon webbing where it passes through chocks and where the chain may rub. Others have used sheaves to reduce friction and heating.
- If the anchor roller is well designed, it may be the lowest chafe option. Make sure the side plates are smooth and well flared; the yacht will yaw and the snubber will rub.
- The anchor roller should not be cantilevered too far beyond the bow unless very well-supported; it will have to carry a downward load of 500-1,000 pounds for a 40-foot boat, depending on wave action, and possibly more during anchor retrieval.
- Do not retrieve a snubber under a loaded chain. Extreme pressure from the chain can ruin a snubber in seconds by causing hidden internal damage. Heavy chafe gear (tubular webbing) can protect snubber from abrasion, but this is not a substitute for proper handling.
- Attach a long snubber to the midship or stern cleats in light winds to keep the connection to the rode off the bottom (it can chafe or snag on rocks). When the wind pipes up, ease more chain out and move the snubber attachment to the bow cleats to increase stretch, reduce chafe, and increase scope. (Long Snubbers, Chapter 13.)
- Keep a back-up snubber on hand, one size larger. If a serious, prolonged storm is predicted, pre-rig the backup with about 6 feet of slack (Chapter 11). This is also handy if you need to increase scope; instead of laboring to remove the loaded snubber from the chain, simply cast it off and rig the backup after increasing scope.
- Never use non-stretch materials for a bridle or snubber with an all-chain rode. I used an Amsteel bridle to generate the no-snubber data, and the loads were frightening even in moderate winds. When the chain snaps tight it felt like

This chain did not start out wrapped over the snubber; the rope stretched and rotated under load. (They are recovering the anchor at this point—the snubber was longer, the lazy loop was shorter, and at some point the chain was able to flip over.) Possible solutions include a long lazy loop, a braided rope snubber, or a bridle.

The combination of trade winds and a chain over the snubber did this in a single night.

Table 4

Snubber Examples

		Monohull--Examples			Monohull--Cruiser Experience										Catamaran		
		Catalina 36	Islander 44	Hunter 50 cc	Pacific Seacraft 34	Pearson 53	Morgan 41.6	not reported	not reported	Fomosa	Columbia	Cabo Rico 38	Van De Stadt	Sail Mag Story	Lightwave 38	PDQ 32	Stiletto 27
	length, feet	36	44	50	34	53	41.6	67	55	41	50	38	47	45	38	32	27.00
	weight, pounds	15000	28000	37000	13500	77000	27000	64000	44000	28000	28000	21000	30000	26000	12000	7800	1700
		Calculated Examples															
snubber length, feet		47	57	65	44	69	42	87	72	53	65	49	47	59	38	32	35
single line	in 16th inches	5	8	9	5	12	7	15					8	8			
diameter	in mm	9	12	15	8	19	12	23					13	12			
bridle	in 16th inches								8	6	7	5			7	5	3
diameter	in mm								13	9	11	8			10	8	4

Actual Practice	Pacific Seacraft 34	Pearson 53	Morgan 41.6	not reported	not reported	Fomosa	Columbia	Cabo Rico 38	Van De Stadt	Sail Mag Story	Lightwave 38	PDQ 32	Stiletto 27
snubber length, feet	45	25	50	35	75	8	30	30	20	10	40	35	15
diameter in 16th inches	8	16			8	8	6	10		5			5
diameter in mm			10	22					11		10	8	
	3-strand	3-strand	climbing rope	3-strand	3-strand	3-strand	3-strand	3-strand	climbing rope	3-strand	climbing rope	climbing rope	double braid
					bridle	bridle	bridle	bridle			bridle	bridle	bridle
comments				stretch didn't last		failed				failed			
				too short		too short				too short			

Calculated examples were derived using these formulas:

— *Snubber length = 1.3 x-boat length.*

— *Snubber diameter = .008 (length) X (displacement/7800)^0.25.*

— *Catamaran diameter increased 20%*

The lower box describes actual cruiser usage. The shaded cells highlight the most likely cause of failure; in all cases it was a snubber too short to absorb wind gust and wave energy.

a firm bump… and I destroyed a 2,000-pound load cell! I've also used polyester, and it is nearly as bad.

- Attach the snubber before setting the anchor. The windlass can take quite a thump if the boat drifts back on it during anchoring setting.
- Coiling a 3-strand snubber can cause it to twist the chain (twists from coiling become active under load), causing the chain to wrap around the snubber and chafe. Always coil lines in a figure 8.
- Three-strand rope can twist and slightly unlay under load. This doesn't happen when a 3-strand line is used as anchor rode because it is secured at both ends. However, as a snubber, the chain can rotate, allowing the chain to drape across the snubber and chafe. We prefer single braid, double braid, or climbing rope snubbers, because these materials are non-rotational under load. A bridle or a longer lazy loop also works.

A Precautionary Note. If switching to high tensile chain allows you to downsize—and often it does—remember that the same downsizing does not apply to the rope portion of the rode. The conundrum is that modern windlass designs may accommodate grade 43 and grade 70 chain, but they do not fit the rope that matches the stronger chain. Using an irony splice (Chapter 13) helps in the case of grade 43 chain, but you will still be significantly under strength for grade 70 chain. For combination rodes that will pass the splice through a windlass frequently, grade 30 chain is a better choice, since it is compatible with the correct rope size.

Rope Rode

I used a combination rope and chain rode for many years with two different boats. The Chesapeake Bay is the ideal environment for rope, with very little chance of cutting, since there is no coral and the rock is either in flat planes or rounded cobbles rather than broken boulders which can cut. For the most part, it's sand and mud. As a result, I'm unaware of any local anchor rode cutting incident related to the bottom. Where coral and sharp rocks are present, the traditional consensus is that rope adds risk. On the other hand, many have cruised tropical areas and even sailed around the world using a combination rode, with the

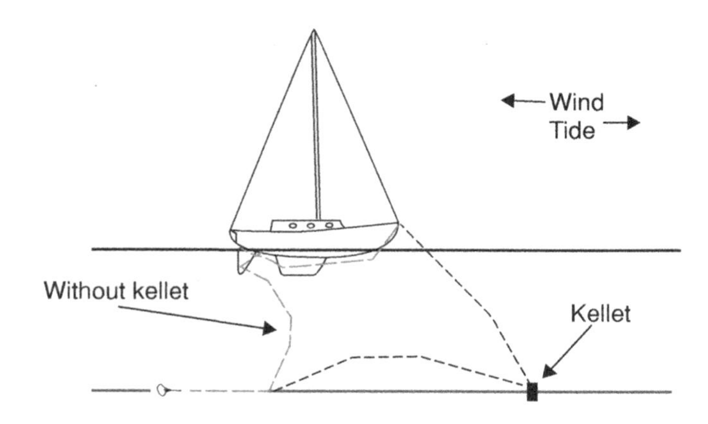

important caveat that they deployed enough chain to keep the rope off the bottom, typically 100 feet or more. The need for a snubber is eliminated; the nylon absorbs the shock. The boat will yaw (also known as sailing at anchor or horsing) a bit more, lacking the inhibiting effect of chain dragging on the bottom. Yawing increases strain on the anchor, jerking it from side to side, and although this is partially offset by the shock absorbing value of nylon, it contributes to loosening the anchor by disturbing the soil and preventing proper consolidation (more in Chapter 4). In a crowded harbor, you will need to stay a little farther away from your neighbors because of the yawing. (See Chapter 3 for discussion on reducing yawing.) In very light winds, the boat will drift about aimlessly.

A rope rode brings up less mud, but it cannot be cleaned completely with a hose, resulting in musty smells. Leave it on deck to dry for a short time before stowing. Since nylon is affected by UV, vary the sections that are exposed.

Perhaps the greatest hazard is the tendency of a current to wrap the rode around the rudder, propeller, and keel. I am aware of numerous cases where the rode was seriously damaged by sawing back and forth on the relatively sharp trailing edge of the keel, in one case cutting clear through the rope in a matter of hours. Intelligent use of a kellet at about two times water depth can minimize this risk. The kellet can be lowered on a spare snatch block or attached with a rolling hitch.

Be wary of using a kellet if coral or rocks are present. The function of a kellet is to keep the rope low, often right on the bottom, greatly increasing the odds of wrapping the rope around something sharp.

Those who sail coral-infested water with combination rope/chain rode are careful to allow only the chain to touch the bottom, and they never use a kellet.

A combination rode is easier to handle than chain in the absence of a windlass, but with a windlass, chain is easier to handle. A chain rode is heavy, affecting trim and increasing hobby-horsing to windward; on a large, ballasted monohull, 500 pounds for 300 feet of 3/8-inch grade 30 chain, windlass, and related gear may not be too noticeable, but even 100 pounds for 100 feet of 1/4-inch grade 43 chain and windlass may hamper a light multihull or small monohull. Finally, smaller boats (less than 30 feet) have considerably lower cutting risk because the tension on the rode is less; the rode size for a 25-foot and 35-foot boat is generally the same (1/2-inch nylon 3-strand) because of handling requirements, even though the rode tension is only half and the displacement only one third for the smaller boat. In general, chain rodes do not make sense below for boats smaller than 30 feet.

Curiously, both chain and rope sized by traditional guidelines have about the same capacity to absorb energy up to the working load limit (WLL). "How could this be?" you say. "Nylon stretches and chain does not!" There are several factors at work. First, the chain will typically be somewhat stronger in absolute terms than the rope it is spliced to, but more importantly, the chain can operate at a higher fraction of the breaking strength than nylon rope can, while still achieving an acceptable fatigue life. The result is that the chain will typically have a WLL 4-5 times higher than the rope. In the case of our test boat in shallow water, without a snubber, the chain will be working at 2,778 pounds (2,600 pound WLL) at 50 knots, while a rope rode would be working at only 744 pounds (709-pound WLL). Second, chain does stretch (1.5% at the WLL), and nylon doesn't stretch as much as you think unless overloaded (only 5% at the appropriate WLL). Thus, they are both operating at the same fraction of their energy absorption limit, which makes sense. They will have similar fatigue durability in a storm, catastrophic chafe of the nylon rope excepted. (See Appendix V.) That said, the strain on the rest of the gear will be greater with an all-chain rode and no snubber.

Polyester Rode

Polyester rode has some popularity in England and Europe. It has a significantly greater fatigue life (see Chapter 13), is not weakened when wet, and is less subject to abrasion. On the other hand, it has 3-5 times less stretch than nylon, contributes nothing to catenary, and in my testing allowed brutal impact forces, roughly the same as chain with no snubber. As an extension to a very long chain rode in very deep water (>40 feet), it is acceptable—it does have some stretch and the 300 feet of chain already deployed provides considerable shock absorption. It will reduce unnecessary slingshot motion sometimes associated with very long nylon roads. But as a substitute for nylon in a conventional combination rode, it is a serious mistake.

Chain catenary reduces the pull angle and absorbs some shock. In the shallow waters where I tested snubbers, the chain lifted off the bottom in 15 knots and was bar-straight by 20 knots.

What about deeper water? There are two factors at work. One is the amount of chain required to keep

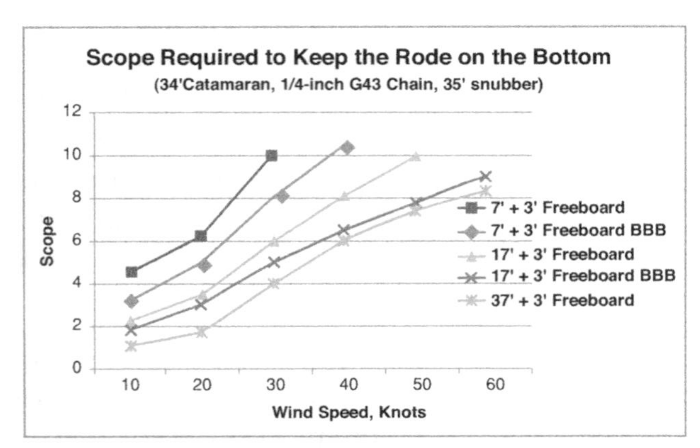

Figure 1. It takes 20 feet of water and 7:1 scope to keep the rode on the bottom. Heavier chain helps.

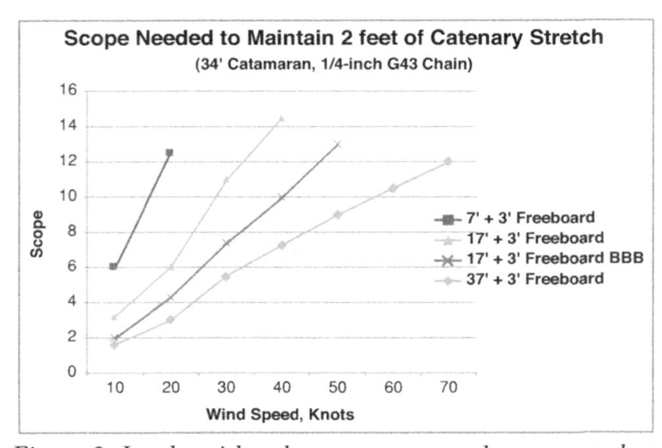

Figure 2. It takes either deep water or very long scope to keep significant curve in the chain in strong winds.

the chain on the bottom most of the time. In Chapter 4 we will learn that even minor wiggling can reduce anchor holding capacity by loosening the soil. To reduce peak force, however, what matters is whether the chain maintains enough curvature to absorb the shock of gust and wave impact. Coincidentally, both are provided only by deploying a generous amount of chain (200-400 feet), whether the result of long scope or deep water; it doesn't actually matter which. Any less, and in strong weather the chain will draw tight and impacts will transfer directly to the ground tackle and bowsprit. Heavier chain, such as BBB/grade 30, reduces the required length 10-20%. A cruiser anchored in shallow water will need to rig a long snubber every day, while in deeper water short snubbers are sufficient for settled conditions. In strong conditions even the boat in deep water will need to add scope; whether a long snubber is also needed depends on the depth of the water (less than 40 feet) and exposure to waves. In storm conditions, boats anchored in shallow, exposed waters need to relocate.

But wouldn't these plots be different for a larger boat? No, they are actually relatively constant, based on testing and theory. So long as the strength of the chain is matched to the wind load using a basis similar to the ABYC ground tackle tables, the weight of the chain goes up in exact proportion to the load (twice as much strength requires twice as much steel) and the shape of the curve is constant, not changing with the size of the boat.

High Tensile Chain

Aren't grade 43 and grade 70 chains brittle? First, anchoring "snatch" loads are not impact loads as understood within the study of brittle fracture. They are quite gradual when compared to a hammer blow. Second, high strength alloy chain is more elastic, stretching considerably farther within its safe working load and before yielding than grade 30 chain. This increased elasticity reduces the potential for dangerous shock loads. For example, the minimum elongation at failure (NACM Welded Chain Specification), a measure of toughness, is 15% for grade 30, and 20% for grade 43 and grade 70 chains (See Appendix V for data summary.). High strength chain is not made from hardened steel, but rather lies at the low end of spring steel temper. Clearly an alloy coil spring is better suited to absorbing repeated bumps than a coil of mild steel. The value of these superior properties are confirmed every day in the transport industry, a truly brutal application, where alloy chains have been used to secure heavy loads across billions of miles of highway. This has generated an enormous pool of experience, untold millions of times more comprehensive than the scattered experiences of a few sailors. In factories high strength chain is used for overhead lifting and the use of grade 30 chain has long been prohibited by regulation; the risk of sudden failure is higher with lower grade chain. And thus, counter to the belief of conservative writers, high strength chain (grades 43, 70, and 100) is safer than grade 30 chain for a given strength rating.

Even Heavier Chain

"What about heavier chain, something larger than the minimum recommendation? I understand the additional weight and catenary will absorb impact." Yes, to some extent, but generally not enough to matter. In my test example (Table 2) with ¼-inch chain, catenary was effective up to about 15 knots, after which the chain was effectively straight. When I switch to 3/8-inch chain (ridiculously heavy for an 8,000 pound, 32-foot catamaran—an exaggeration tested for illustration only) the wind speed at which the chain became effectively straight increased by 6 knots, and the difference in ride was noticeable only between 15 and 20 knots. Basically, the heavier chain was equivalent to adding 4 feet of ½-inch nylon snubber, an insignificant improvement in shallow water, since a snubber is needed either way. In deeper water testing (20 feet), it required 25-30 knots of wind to effectively straighten the heavier chain, after which shock absorption was greatly reduced. However, this difference will be important to the sailor who anchors in deeper water and seldom anchors out in breezy weather. He will need a snubber only in stormy weather and thus may find heavy chain easier to use. He won't gain much holding power unless the water is quite deep, since the buffering effect of the heavy chain is nil in the strong conditions where it is really needed, although he might feel as if he has. He will also need to be careful about his use of snubbers; because the chain is absorbing the shock in moderate weather, he may feel comfortable with a short snubber, just sufficient to unload the windlass and quiet the chain.

When the wind and chop comes up and the boat begins to buck, the snubber will fail, it will come as a surprise, and he will blame it on old rope, the heating of nylon under extreme load, or some other factor which misses the point entirely. The snubber was simply overloaded because it was too short to have any chance of absorbing the energy. Moreover, in truly deep water—over 40 feet—even the lightest chain will provide all the required buffering, and it will be far easier to carry enough if a higher grade is used. Thus, heavier chain is only of real value in a window between 20-30 feet in moderate weather, which turns out to be the most common anchoring depth for many sailors. Whether heavy chain is for you depends on both where and how you cruise.

Chain Locker Size

The boat we have is often the limiting factor. Chain lockers are often tragically small, and adding a windlass only makes this worse; the chain must have a minimum free drop to avoid jamming, and chain loves to form a nice neat cone under the windlass. First, rope does not pile in this way, so using rope as some portion of the rode saves space. I suggest carrying only enough chain to anchor 95% of the time on all-chain. For the rare deep harbor, a rope extension will serve well, and will be suspended well above the bottom out of harm's way. Second, high tensile chain allows more length than grade 30 (but about the same weight), often giving the nod to higher grades. Stainless chain is less prone to mounding, but the higher cost and risk of cracking are deterrents.

Kellets

A kellet can also be used on chain. Although the weight is centered rather than distributed, a kellet is dynamically similar to an equivalent mass of chain. The kellet is awkward to handle and more likely to dance around the rode in rough weather, although it is cheaper than more chain.

Buoys

"What about a buoy near the snubber attachment, like a mooring ball? I've seen this in Maine and California and they swear it helps with waves." In an open roadstead, exposed to large waves or large steep chop, a buoy helps the bow rise to waves by supporting the weight of the chain. It can also reduce the sharp up-lift on the anchor due to hobby horsing.

Holding is actually reduced in sheltered harbors. In testing we saw no measurable effect unless the chop was over two feet. When the wind was moderate, it bobbed on surface and the load was light because chain catenary is still effective. When the wind becomes strong enough to straighten the rode, it pulls under and again has little effect. In fact, by lifting the chain it reduces the amount of wind required to straighten the chain and lift it off the bottom, reducing the effective scope. The overall impact is at best neutral and generally negative.

A buoy can't help in shallow water. If the waves are large they will be breaking and you need to move. The weight of the chain and its effect on hobby horsing will be minimal, because there isn't much chain. Finally, if the buoy is located far enough from the boat to actually submerge under tension, it reduces scope by lifting the chain. More scope and a redundant snubber is the better answer.

In deeper water the math is better, although there are still challenges. First, the fender must be large enough to support the chain once it is lifted off the bottom, which in 20 feet of water will be over 100 pounds for my PDQ 32. By comparison, the Taylor Made 10" x 26" Big B fenders I carry, suitable for boats 35-45 feet long, provide only 75 pounds of buoyancy. Second, because it must be considerably forward of the bow for good effect—at least 30 feet, and farther if we expect it to absorb

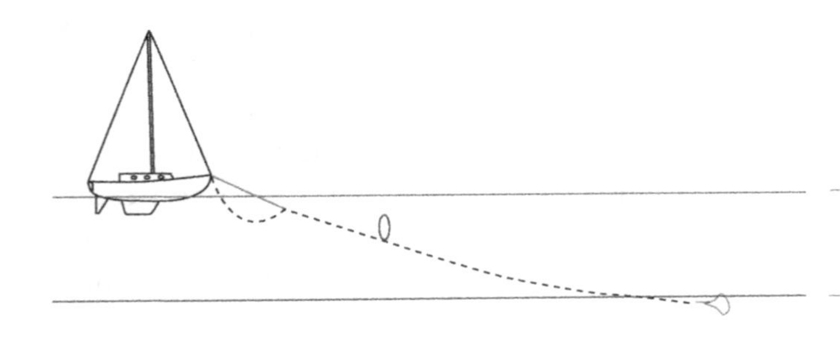

energy by submerging—it will reduce effective scope by lifting the chain.

I only tested this with a load cell once, in 15 to 20-knot winds, 14 feet of water, and 2-3 foot chop. The buoy submerged but was not pulled under. The load on the rode was reduced about 20%, although I also increased the rode length by 40 feet in the process of deploying the fender. I did not dive on the anchor, so the effect on chain movement is unknown, although according to Figure 2, with 5:1 scope, it probably remained on the bottom. The effect on the bows lifting and plunging was similar to moving a crewman away from the bow; possibly noticeable, but not certain or dramatic. My conclusion? With sufficient scope a buoy reduces anchor up-lift due to waves, reduces rode tension, and reduces pitching in open roadsteads during moderate winds. The improvement is modest and depends on the boat. In strong conditions, the required buoy will be larger than that carried by most cruisers and the improvement in ride will be minimal, and effective scope will be reduced. In the case of permanent moorings, the anchor can withstand up lift, scope is short, the chain is heavy, and the buoy can be much larger. In this one case the benefit is considerable, explaining why this is common practice for moorings, but not for anchoring. On the other hand, it did reduce yawing once the wind picked up, the result of increased underwater drag, an important benefit in some cases, as long as you can add a little scope to offset the up-lift.

Yawing

Yawing (also known as sailing around or horsing). Of the many variables that influence anchoring, this varies the most between boats. Other than good holding ground, few have more influence on keeping the hook on the bottom. Although crashing about can certainly increase the force on the anchor, the greatest risk is disturbing the anchor and liquefying the soil. See Chapter 3.

PDQ 32. To increase yawing, I continued testing using a chain rode, but replaced my customary catamaran bridle with a single attachment point at the center of the main beam; this increased yawing from 5-15 degrees to 20-35 degrees. Rode tension measurements show no significant increase compared to prior testing using non-stretch, presumably because the chain was not directly aligned with the wind and waves while it was yawing, only when it was centered. In light winds the chain dragging on the bottom dampened the swing, but this faded as the wind strengthened and chain lifted off the bottom. However, the effect on the anchor is more difficult to evaluate. In the test conditions—anchor well buried and wind up to 20 knots—the chain was also buried and diving confirmed that the chain was probably not moving quite far enough underground to actually be transmitting the twisting action to the anchor shank.

Corsair F-24, nylon rode. Again, we skipped the bridle to encourage yawing. By adjusting windage (reacher on a bow sprit) and underbody (center board and rudder) we were able to increase yaw to 80-120 degrees, behavior we have observed in flighty boats in the field. The rode tension increased in direct proportion to the increase in area caused by getting sideways to the wind, sometimes more than double.

Hunter 36, all-chain rode, no snubber. We put a tender on the bow to increase windage forward, causing yawing up to 90 degrees in 20 knots. Load increased 25-40% due to slightly increased windage. Occasionally, at the end of a swing a gust would straighten out the catenary, we would feel a great thump, and the bow would snap around as if tacking. The swing had not truly reached the end of anything—it is simply following an arc—but when the catenary snaps out with no snubber in place it can feel that way, and the resulting force can be double the baseline.

Slow vs. Rapid Forces

There are four competing processes affecting the stability of an anchor. First is the common observation that a slow pull is more effective for extracting a deeply buried anchor than a quick pull. The result of combined viscous and inertial effects, the difference in force required for anchor extraction ranges between 15-60%, depending on soil type and depth. Second, the relatively rapid pulsing of waves reduces anchor holding capacity over time by liquefying the soil and preventing effective consolidation. This is primarily a problem when a shallow-set anchor is assaulted by steep chop at short scope; deeper set anchors tend to be insulated from the rapid jerking by the chain buried in the seabed. When recovering an anchor we take advantage of this weakening by positioning the boat directly over the anchor, tightening the rode, and using the bobbing of the bow in the waves to pump the anchor vertically. Third, there is soil consolidation wherein the soil slowly reforms around the anchor, regaining some of the strength it lost when disturbed during setting. Finally, there is a synergistic effect, where the reconsolidated soil encourages deeper setting of the soil by providing a better bite. (This is primarily a soft mud effect.) See Chapter 4 for detailed discussion.

How Strong Does Our Gear Need To Be?

Assuming you have chosen a suitable snubber (or are anchored in suitably deep water with all chain so that the catenary is effective), it appears the working load on your anchor system during a severe storm is actually about 30-50% of the ABYC storm anchor recommendation. In my case, because I use a long climbing rope bridle, I know my working load will never exceed about 1,350 pounds even in a severe storm, only 50% of the 2,600-pound WLL of ¼-inch grade 43 chain. However, I'm not suggesting downsizing—deck gear and chain should be sized conservatively in case of snubber failure—only demonstrating that the working load on the entire system is greatly reduced through intelligent use of a snubber.

With a proper snubber, my anchor only needs to hold 1,350 pounds in the most severe storm, not the 4,000 pounds all-chain rode would require in the same shallow anchorage. This lower figure is achievable in most bottoms with conventionally sized anchors. The latter, however, is unachievable in soft mud, and in firm sand and mud bottoms that can hold an anchor under such strain, the gear will be stressed beyond safe limits. If the anchor doesn't drag, it will be so deeply buried that recovery will be a major project or impossible. Thus, the real benefit of using a snubber is that we apply a lighter hand to all of our gear. Can the same goals be accomplished with rope or heavy chain? Certainly, but given the limitations and vulnerabilities, the chain plus snubber combination seems to be the most robust and dependable approach to reducing anchoring loads. We can summarize our choices thusly:

Rope

Probably the best choice for lighter boats with no windlass. Also used successfully by well-travelled cruisers. Use a chain leader equal to the greater of one boat length or the maximum common water depth.

- Excellent shock absorption
- Lightweight
- Economical
- Limited cutting and abrasion resistance
- Keel wraps are problematic in tidal areas
- Sailing at anchor and swinging are increased
- More scope is required

Chain

Popular on cruising boats equipped with windlasses for ease of handling and reliability.

- In shallow water (<20 feet) a snubber is required anyway, so the chain grade is not too important, as long as it is strong enough and the snubber is appropriate.
- In moderate depths (20-30 feet), grade 30 chain eliminates the need for a long snubber in settled weather. If the snubber fails in moderate weather, grade 30 chain can eliminate hard snubs. Conservative scope is still required.
- In deep water (>30 feet) heavy chain loses its advantage because even grade 43 provides enough catenary if the scope is sufficient. (See Chapter 4.)
- Multihulls tend towards lighter chain because of weight sensitivity and because they often anchor in shallow water. Additionally, they use a combination bridle/snubber anyway, so this does not add rigging complexity.
- Heavy boats will lean towards heavier chain because the difference in weight (about 100 pounds) is acceptable, they anchor in deeper water, and because it reduces the consequence of snubber failure in a prolonged storm (when anchored in deep water).

The popular argument that weight is better spent on the anchor than on chain is off the point; snatch loading and proper anchor size are separate issues. The rode must prevent snubbing, and the anchor must be sized for the load.

On the balance, a chain rode with a nylon snubber seems to offer a good compromise of reliability, versatility, reduced yawing, and ease-of-use when anchoring in shallower waters, though smaller boats that will handle the anchor by hand are better served by a combination rode. For the way I sail, on the generally shallow waters of the Chesapeake Bay, a long snubber and 100 feet of grade 43 chain backed by 200 feet of rope is a lightweight, robust combination. This allows me to anchor using all-chain 90% of the time, and hobby horsing is reduced. I use a bridle anyway (catamaran), which provides good shock absorption even in very shallow water. I avoid the downsides of excessive weight and of hobby horsing. For a larger boat and deeper harbors, increase this to 200 feet of chain, but the principle is the same; carry only as much chain as you use frequently and use rope for the occasional deep harbor. If you chose all chain, remember to secure the bitter end with a lashing so that it can be released under load if need be. If this anchor point is too deep into the bilge to reach from the deck, splice on a length of rope just sufficient that it can come up through the hawse pipe for easy access in an emergency.

Horses for courses.

Chapter 3: Stop Horsing Around

A FEW WEEKS AGO I witnessed the most spectacular case of sailing at anchor (also known as yawing or fishtailing) I have ever seen. If not for the lack of sails, the visual impression was that of an engineless boat tacking up a narrow channel. Back and forth she went, turning 120 degrees each time the end of the rode was reached. The bow would ease around and the boat would merrily sail 200 feet in the opposite direction. They spent the night like that, going back and forth, like sleeping inside a floating metronome. An anchor alarm would be useless, since the boat was all over the harbor. It was also rude; they took up far more space than needed, and no one nearby slept that night—they were kept awake, wondering when he would come barging through. The cause? An oversize dinghy on the bow acted like a small sail forward, there was no dodger or bimini to provide windage aft, and as a result the windage center of effort was well forward of the underwater center of resistance. The boat naturally turned away from the wind, swinging back and forth. Add to that a nylon rode, which rather than damping the motion as chain does by dragging along the bottom, actually contributes by storing kinetic energy like a spring, and she met all of the requirements for a real dancer.

Yawing

The only time I've had an anchor fully disengage from the bottom was a Danforth, with a nylon rode and no bridle. I had anchored my beach catamaran 50 yards off a river beach, sails up but sheets loose and the rode tied to only one bow. The wind increased, the boat began zigging, and the anchor popped loose. My girlfriend witnessed my finest speed swimming, as I attempted to run down a beach cat under full sail. Fortunately, the anchor caught again 100 feet away and the boat jerked to a stop. But the lesson stayed learned. No leaving sails up and always use a proper bridle.

What can be done to quiet the nervous boat? Reducing windage forward and adding windage aft helps. Increasing underwater resistance forward and decreasing water resistance aft helps. In the interest of experimentation, I dispensed with my usual bridle, secured the mooring line to the center of the front beam (a surefire way to make most cats sail about) and tested some common methods.

All Chain Rode. The best single step you can take towards reducing yawing in light winds is to switch from rope to chain. In very light winds, the chain stays relatively motionless on the bottom and so does the boat. As the wind increases the chain will gradually lift, but even then chain creates drag as it moves along the bottom and through the water. However, in strong conditions the chain is off the bottom and only changes that influence the

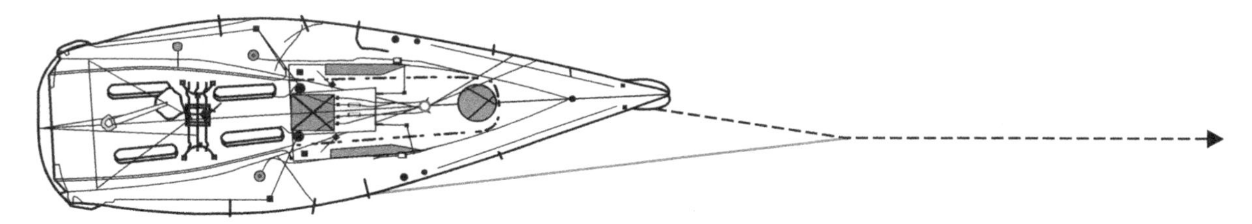

An off-set rode is particularly helpful when wind and waves come from different directions.

aerodynamic balance will reduce yawing. When a gust comes, the catenary will be pulled out of the chain, and when this coincides with the end of a swing, the inelastic nature of chain makes for a violent snubbing, as though the chain had reached the end of something. In fact, the boat is only traveling an arc described by the length of the rode. If the rode is nylon, the turn is smooth and gradual since there is no catenary to suddenly pull tight.

Use a Bridle. Catamarans represent an extreme case. When moored by the center of the front beam they are very nervous at anchor, the result of wide beam and shallow keels. Add a bridal attached to the bows, with legs greater than 150% of the beam, and they sit very quietly. Monohulls also benefit, though the improvement is less dramatic. Curiously, the bridles fitted on many charter cats are shorter than this, which makes them easier to use but more nervous at anchor.

Bridle angles greater than 120 degrees actually increase the load on each leg above that of a single line due the inefficiency of the bridle leg angle. At 90 degrees, depending on the angle of pull, the maximum load on either leg will be 70-100% of the total, and at 30 degrees 57-100% of the total. The load can always be 100% on a single leg due to yawing; with wide catamaran bridles this seldom happens because the angle is wide and yawing is very limited, though on monohull bridles, single-leg loading is the norm.

Specific to catamarans, it can be handy to use a very short bridle when tied to mooring ball in fair weather. If the legs are short enough, the ball can be held between the hulls, avoiding the noise of the ball banging on the hulls in calm winds. The boat will yaw more. Lengthen the bridle in storms to avoid over straining the bridle and to reduce yawing.

Offset Rode. In the presence of tide or waves from the side, moving the rode even slightly to one side will keep the wind on one side, eliminating yawing. Attaching a line with a rolling hitch and taking it to a midships cleat is sometimes effective. This can also make it worse, so be prepared to adjust or cast it off. This can also be accomplished with a bridle.

Remove the Dinghy From the Bow. Many sailors hate carrying a dinghy on davits. They don't like the look, they're concerned about bad weather, and all that weight aft increases hobby horsing. Sometimes the boat is simply too small for davits. But carrying a dinghy on the foredeck adds windage in the worst possible place, the exact opposite of a riding sail. A dinghy left in

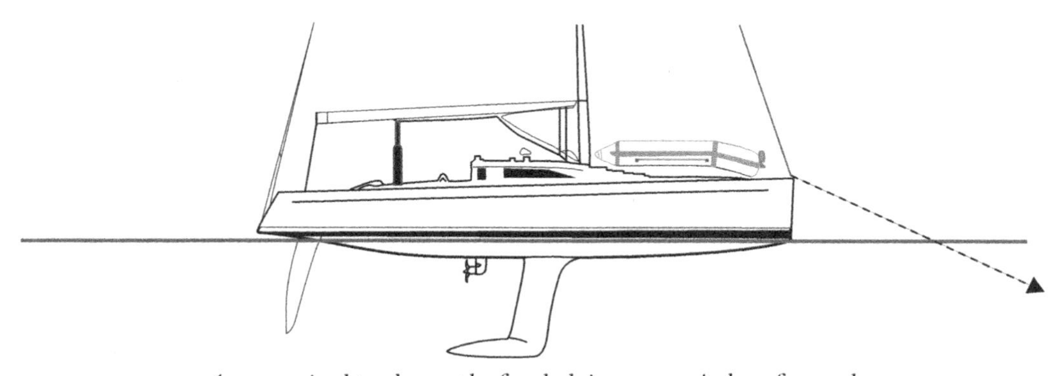

An over-sized tender on the foredeck increases windage forward.

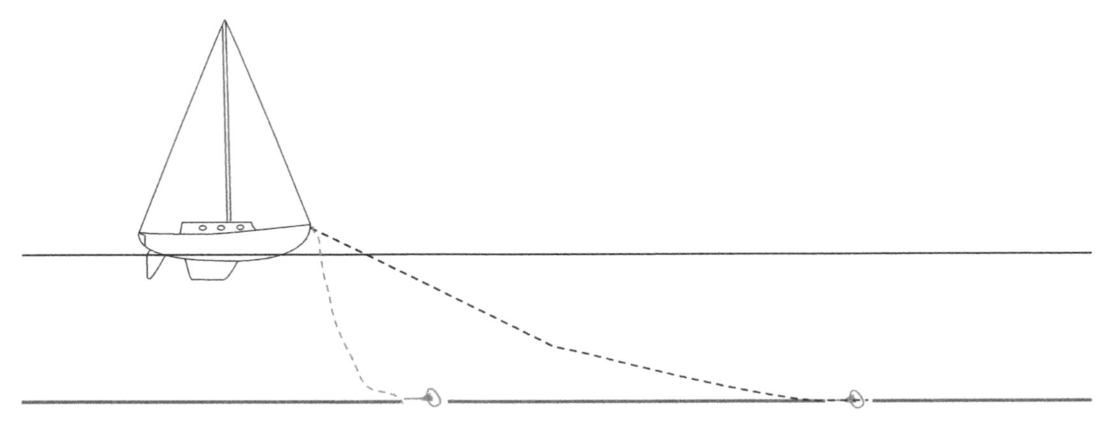

Hammerlock mooring

the water will whip around in storm, sometimes dragging the boat around and frequently flipping it over; at the very least keep it close to the transom, out of the wind.

If a fierce storm is expected, deflate and bundle, take the dinghy below, or take it ashore. On davits, on the other hand, it actually helps stabilize the boat and can stay there in all but hurricane conditions.

Hammerlock Mooring. This is an old-school method, fully relevant to today's nervous boats. Lower a second anchor on 1.25:1 to 1.5:1 scope, preferably a type that can generate some hold on very short scope (the Lewmar Claw is excellent for this because it always digs some, while many others will just skid at ultra-short scope). For example, a 25-pound Claw on 20 feet of line in 10 feet of water (14 feet from the bottom to the deck) is about right for a 35- to 40-foot monohull. It won't set, but it will provide considerable drag as the bow tries to fall off to one side or the other, stopping yawing before it starts. A kellet can also be used in this way, but a second anchor is more effective and may serve other purposes. In fact, a hammerlock mooring is one of the best uses for the typical double roller bowsprit; anchor from one, hammerlock from the other. Because of the great difference in scope, tangles are avoided.

There are downsides. With a reversing tide or in light winds, the hammerlock anchor can foul the main rode, although this is very unusual. If it does tangle with the main rode, so long as the rode is chain, it will simply ride it like a kellet. Never use a hammerlock mooring where it can cross the rode of another boat; it will snag, perhaps trip the other anchor, and things will get very ugly. If the bottom is sensitive, containing submerged vegetation or coral, a hammerlock mooring will be destructive. If it works too well, it can pull you out of swing synchronization with other boats in a crowed harbor; in this case, just lift it up until you adjust, and then lower it again.

A hammerlock mooring can also be converted into a V tandem by easing the secondary rode as the wind shifts. See Chapter 10, V Tandems for Soft Bottoms.

In-Line Tandems. Not effective. Some sailors—unknowingly or misinformed—set two anchors in a row, in the belief that this gives them more holding power. In Chapter 12 we will debunk this theory for most bottoms. Can the second anchor can serve as a sort of kellet, reducing yawing? The fallacy with this is that typically a smaller secondary anchor is attached to the primary, and the sheer presence of that secondary makes the primary anchor much less stable. As soon as the boat yaws, you end up anchored only by the secondary anchor, which is not your best anchor. Additionally, in-line tandems are generally too close together to function as a hammerlock mooring.

Bahamian Moor and V Tandem Anchoring. Setting two anchors in broad a V will greatly reduce yawing, but there are downsides including increased complexity, potential for tangles, and swinging out of synchronization with other boats in the harbor. Try to resolve yawing problems with other methods.

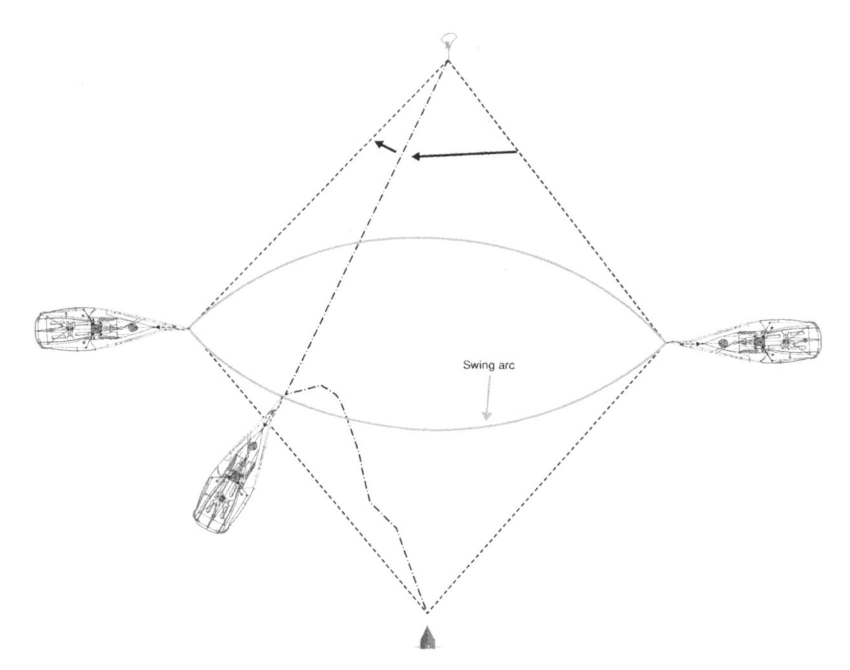

Bahamian moor. The swing arc can be further restricted by placing the anchors farther apart, but the load on the anchors increases exponentially as the included angle approaches 180 degrees, causing anchors to drag.

However, if you really need to sit still, these methods are described in Chapters 10 and 11.

Stern Anchor. If you sincerely do not believe the wind will change direction, this is a simple answer. Of course, if there are other boats nearby, they will swing and you will not. Even worse, if the wind switches to the beam, the loads become enormous, the ride becomes rough, and one of the anchors will drag (see Chapter 11). This is for narrow, well protected waterways only.

Stem Snubber Attachment. Attaching the snubber to an eye located near the water line increases scope, reduces swing radius, and reduces sailing around. However, it demands increased diligence to avoid grinding the chain over the snubber during recovery (Chapter 1), and leaves the snubber continuously exposed to sun and dragging through the water when sailing, unless you also reach down and disconnect when not in use, which can be quite a reach. Perhaps the greatest advantage is avoiding chafe around a bobstay or over a poorly designed anchor roller.

Alternative Anchor Rodes. Chain has the advantage of abrasion resistance and catenary weight, at the cost of poor shock absorption and considerable weight. Nylon is superior at absorbing shock, but is vulnerable to abrasion

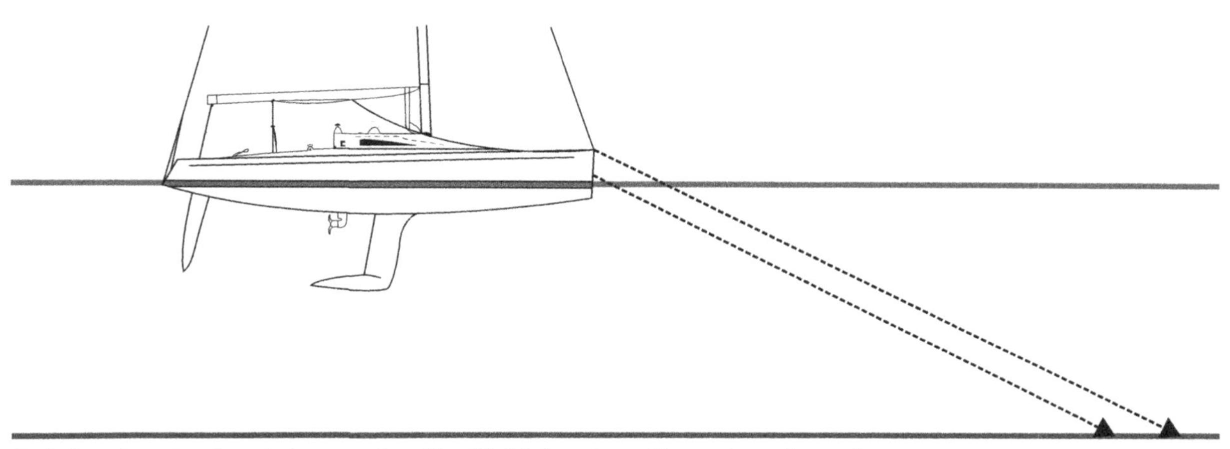

Rode length and swing circle are reduced by 10-30 feet, depending on boat size and scope.

and can lead to considerable yo-yoing in strong conditions if the rode is very long, say over 200 feet. Some have theorized that polyester might be a better compromise for very long rodes, reducing the surging that nylon allows. In England and Europe, polyester rodes have gained some popularity. Although I have not tested polyester rodes at length, I did test them alongside the snubbers and chain during the Chapter 2 exercise. In short lengths—up to 150 feet in shallow water—polyester was more jarring than chain, because there was no catenary effect and not enough stretch to provide effective shock absorption. On the other hand, if the polyester is only used to extend a 300-foot chain rode in deep water, where there is already considerable catenary affect and enough polyester to provide some additional stretch, this is a good answer. Surging is minimized, shock absorption is still acceptable, and weight is saved.

Riding Sails. Sailrite sells kits. The Finn Delta from Banner Bay Marine is a more advanced design that has done well in independent testing. It will add some windage and needs to be hauled very tight in a blow.

Lift a Kick-Up Rudder. If the rudder can be easily lifted, this eliminates lateral resistance aft and will quiet the most nervous boat. I once owned a high-strung racing catamaran, and the key to quiet anchoring was to keep the centerboard down and the rudders up. In other cases, lifting both the center board and the rudder is effective. Centerboard up and rudder down is always a mistake since you have moved the center of resistance aft. Experiment.

Adding a Drogue or Fender to the Rode. Some cruisers have reported success attaching either a fender or a speed limiting drogue (a small sea anchor, about 2 feet in diameter) to the anchor rode about 20-30 feet forward of the boat, where it will typically stay in the water. I tested both a Seabrake GP24 weighted with 2 feet of chain and a large fender and found them to be less effective than the hammerlock mooring, but not prone to fouling on the bottom. The deeper the water, the better they work.

Horsing

When over 150 feet of nylon rope is deployed, boats will sometimes have a tendency to surge fore and aft with the gusts. On its own, this increases rode tension, but most often it is not observed separately but rather as a contributor to increased yawing. A hammerlock mooring or V-tandem anchor helps. It can also be reduced by using a longer chain leader, which results in less nylon. Plaited rope also contributes, because it is more elastic; stick with 3-strand.

Hobby Horsing

Rocking may not alarm your neighbors like yawing, but it disturbs the anchor. Particularly at short scope, persistent upward tugging disturbs the soil above the anchor, reducing holding capacity beyond the negative effect of short scope alone.

In Chapter 2 we noticed significant increases in rode tension when the period of the waves and the natural pitching motion of the boat became synchronized. Even boats that are not prone to rocking can be set in motion by the sharp downward pull of the rode as each wave passes when anchored at short scope. In order to avoid skewing the data (Chapter 1, Table 2) by this depth, weather, and boat-specific phenomenon, I lengthened scope to as much as 20:1 to break the rhythm, and I used data taken in differing sea states. A wave period of a little less than 2 seconds and a wave length of 1.5-2 boat lengths would set our 32-foot test boat rocking, increasing the pull on the anchor by 10% (rope) to 30% (all chain). At short scope the difference was greater and the chain was rhythmically lifted from the bottom. Although designers fight this type of resonance through hull shape and weight distribution, specific attributes generally make it worse: long overhangs, deep keels, slender ends, and weight in the extreme ends.

This not generally a problem in protected harbors; depending on wind speed, a fetch of at least a mile is required to build waves of the critical period. The effect is also most pronounced and dangerous at short scope, in shallow water, with all-chain rode. There is little give, and when the bow surges up and boat moves back with the passage of a wave, the catenary snaps out of the rode and the bow is yanked sharply downwards. This can explain the sudden onset of violent motion involving yachts anchored in 6-10 feet of water with a mile or more fetch in a storm. Within 10 minutes a nasty chop rises and boats start to drag. This may also explain the large improvement in holding when scope is increased; holding is improved somewhat by the lower digging angle, but often that alone cannot account for the marked improvement, since a well set anchor in consolidated ground has a distinct advantage over an anchor that is on the surface as a result of dragging. However, the hobby horsing motion is disrupted the instant rode tension is reduced while letting out more rode, and the increased rode length often breaks the rhythm, dropping the load by as much as 50% and allowing the anchor to bite. The increased scope does not apply the same downward yank on the bow and corresponding upwards yank on the anchor, the catenary won't straighten with the same timing, and the resonance is diminished.

A weighted drogue or a fender attached to the rode 20-30 feet in front of the bow can also help break the rhythm.

- Anchor in Deeper Water. Waves will be less steep and the increased rode length will dampen the short period movements.
- Reduce Weight in the Extreme Ends. Carry only as a much chain as you use 90% of the time, using rope rode for the remainder. Use primarily rope for the secondary rode and store the secondary rode and anchor (hopefully aluminum) away from the ends. Keep only light items in bow and stern lockers. If there is a dinghy on davits, choose a light dinghy with modest motor.

Yawing and rocking at anchor is more than inconvenient and uncomfortable. An anchor that is in motion—even a small fraction of an inch every few minutes—sits in a soup of agitated water and muck, while an anchor that is allowed to rest quietly benefits from the soil slowly settling in around it, regaining its original strength and building suction. In the next chapter we will see that this agitation can reduce the potential holding capacity of an anchor by as much as 50% and is a leading contributor to anchor dragging.

Through the actions suggested in Chapters 1 through 3, the anchor load has been quantified, suitably reduced, and the anchor is resting quietly on the bottom. But is it truly sitting still, and what is really going on down there, under the muck?

Chapter 4: Scope, Cyclical Loading, and Soil Consolidation

THERE ARE THREE times in the life of an anchor when scope matters: initial setting, long period surges during extended setting, and sort period disturbances during wave strikes.

Initial Setting

The shank must stay on the bottom until the anchor is fully set. Fortunately, since rode tension is low during the first part of the setting process, chain catenary is sufficient to keep the shank on the bottom, even at relatively short scope. In Chapter 5 we'll discuss power setting and how much force is applied, but in general it is equivalent to a 25-35 knot wind. With a rope rode there is little catenary, so scope during setting should be at least 10:1.

Reverse Catenary

In sand and particularly in soft mud, pivoting fluke anchors become deeply set, and the rules underground become somewhat different. The chain begins to take a reverse catenary curve, as the resistance of the chain dragging through the mud imparts a recurve arc to the rode. Eventually, the anchor can dive no deeper because the force required to drag the shank and chain down exceeds the downward pull of the anchor. With a deep-diving design such as the Fortress, this can easily be 2-5 feet under the bottom and the reverse catenary

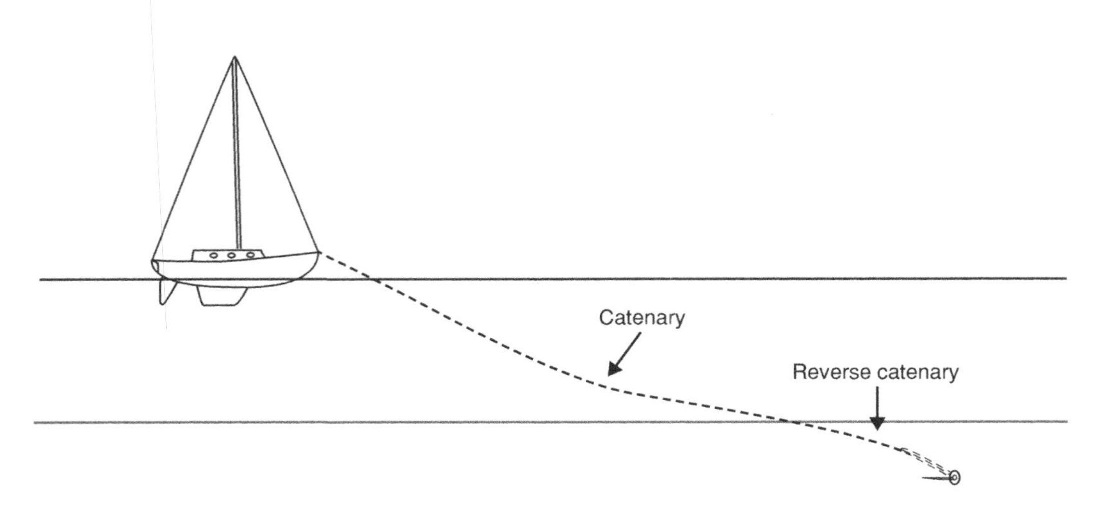

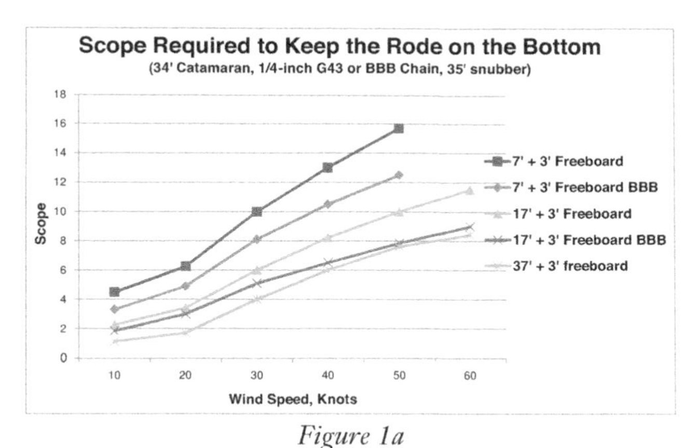

Figure 1a

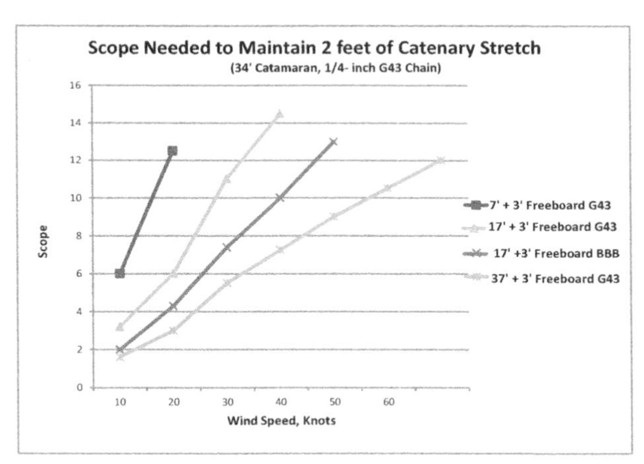

Figure 2a

angle becomes pronounced. Other anchors do not set this deeply in most bottoms.

All of this, however, is dependent on maintaining the pull horizontal to the seafloor throughout the entire setting process, which in extreme conditions includes the storm itself. When the chain eventually lifts—and it will—the angle on the seafloor begins to match the reverse catenary angle and the anchor can dig no deeper. The holding capacity will never exceed the wind strength which caused the rode to rise significantly and consistently above the seafloor, because the anchor is prevented from digging deeper as the storm builds. This is not to say the anchor will suddenly fail. A deeply buried anchor can operate with some uplift in stable soils (soft mud is different—we'll get to that soon), so long as it does not exceed the reverse catenary angle. It simply won't go deeper or hold any more.

Short Scope

For anchors that bury less deeply, the picture is less bright. Figures 3a shows how severely short scope reduces holding capacity. Unsurprisingly, the pivoting fluke anchor retained most of its holding capacity even with considerable uplift. This correlates rationally with the common difficulty of recovering a deeply set pivoting fluke anchor. Scoop and claw anchors lose holding capacity dramatically below 7:1 scope. Interestingly, even multi-ton stockless ship anchors behave in a similar manner, confirming that the effect is largely independent of weight. Remember that this is based on the actual scope at the bottom; there is always some catenary so the effective scope will always be slightly greater. Additionally, the average measurement variability is 15-30%—Figure 3a includes data averaging and only reflects trends among related designs. I have

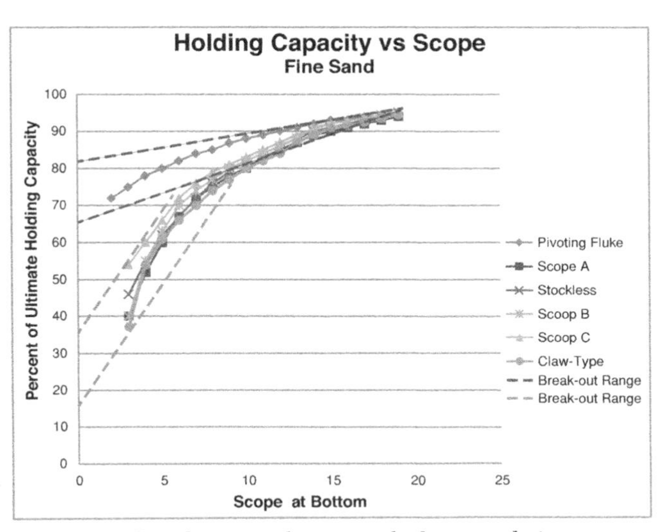

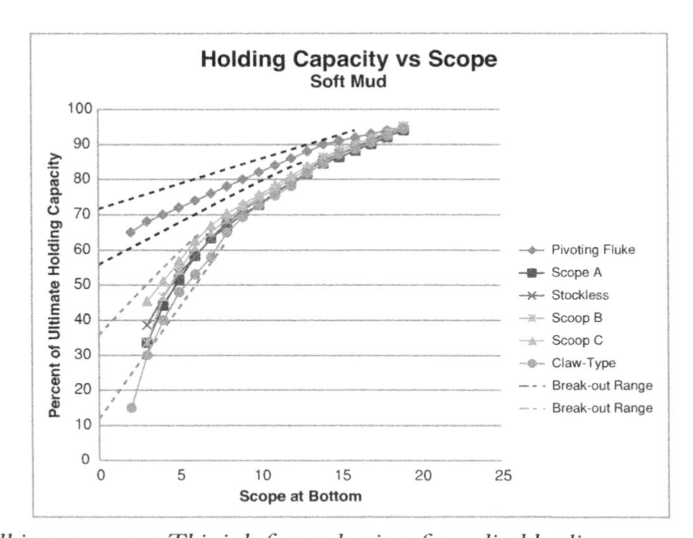

Figure 3a. Based on actual scope at the bottom, chain catenary will increase scope. This is before reductions for cyclical loading.

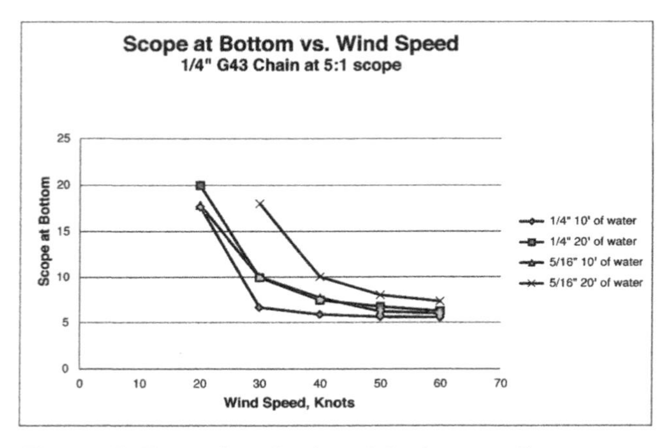

Figure 3b. Even when the chain lifts there is still some curve. However, that too fades as the wind builds.

not discriminated among related designs because the data overlap.

Although the reduction in holding capacity is dependent on seabed material and design, the general trend is that once the rode lifts significantly above the seabed, holding falls rapidly. With a good design in stable soil, the hold may still be sufficient. But no matter what the literature or fellow cruisers say, by 5:1 actual scope at the bottom, holding capacity is only a shadow of what it was at long scope.

Fortunately, a chain rode will help keep the rode angle low, even as it begins to lift from the bottom. In very shallow water the chain becomes effectively straight by 30 knots, and the calculated scope is very nearly the same as the actual scope on the seabed. In deeper water more curve is retained, although whether it is enough to help depends on the depth, the anchor characteristics, and the seabed. Heavier chain helps considerably in the 15- to 30-foot depth range. In storm conditions, however, the scope will still be reduced very significantly, perhaps dangerously so unless the scope is greater than 5:1 or the water greater than 30 feet deep.

Decoupling Gusts from Snubbing

In deep water there is a time delay between the impact of a gust or larger wave and the boat being forced back on a tight rode. During testing of dockline forces for another project, an interesting finding was that gusts striking the beam of a boat generated the same peak line tension as a bow wind, even though the total force was 4-6 times higher with the beam wind. The reason, of course, is that the keel and rudder prevented momentum from building when the boat was forced sideways across the slip. The same dynamics are at work here; although the catenary is not responsible for dissipating the gust energy—mathematically it can't be—the friction of the boat through the water can. Additionally, by the time the boat comes up against the chain, the gust has dissipated or the wave has passed. As a result, deep water gives a smoother ride in moderate winds. The cautionary note is that when the wind becomes sufficient to straighten the chain, this buffering can quickly vanish.

Soaking the Anchor in Soft Mud Bottoms

For longer than I can remember, probably generations, it has been Chesapeake Bay lore that the longer an anchor soaks, the better it will hold.

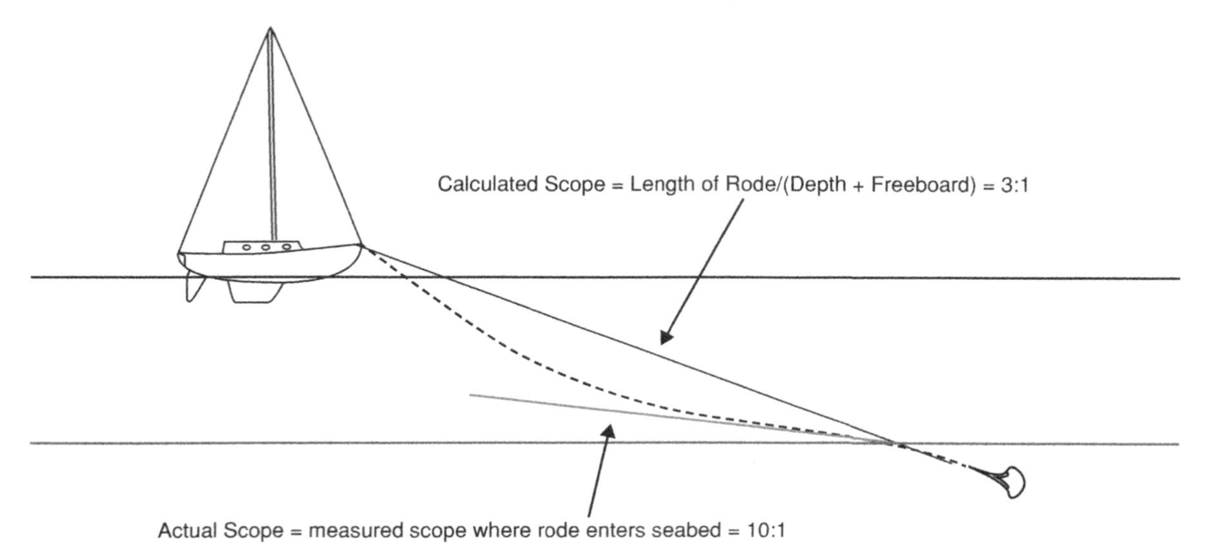

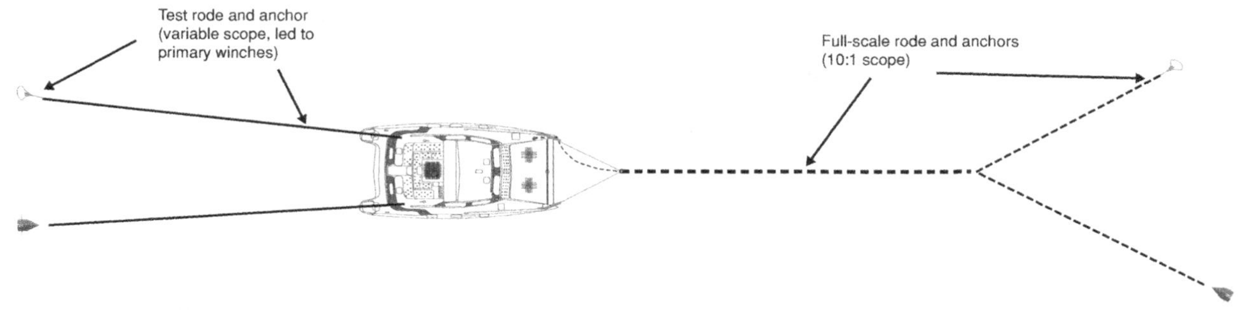

The test rig. Anchor with a pair of full size anchors, and then slowly tension the test anchors using winches and wind oscillations.

Often an older generation anchor—and perhaps undersized as well—would utterly fail to set when first deployed. However, the sailor knew if he waited 30 minutes before applying significant force, the anchor would dig in and hold through reasonable weather. The empirical interpretation was that time allowed the anchor to sink through the surface ooze down into the firmer mud below, and the steady tugging of the rode would also help it settle in. It was also known that the anchor would improve over time as a boat stayed in one place for days or weeks. We've all hooked an old tire or sunken branch and then struggled with the suction force that developed over time. How much is lore and how much is supported by science and testing?

Offshore oil platform operators and anchor manufacturers (Exxon and Vyrhof) have studied the effects of both time and cyclical loading of drag anchors (the classification that yacht anchors fall within, as opposed to dead weight, piles, and embedment anchors) on multi-ton anchors. They report consistent improvement in ultimate holding capacity and stability for anchors over time and with exposure to cyclical loads, ranging from 25-50%, depending on the combination of factors. Additionally, experience tells cruisers that if our anchors failed at the low forces suggested by soft mud testing (Chapter 6 and Appendix III), half the fleet would drag every time the wind topped 20 knots, and that's just not what we see.

I began my test program using a collection of small anchors that I have used for anchor studies for many years. They have proven themselves consistently able to deliver results that are scalable to their full-size brothers (see Chapter 6). A 2-pound Mantus Dinghy serves as a surrogate for scoop anchors and a Fortress Guardian G-5 serves as surrogate for pivoting fluke anchors. Thoroughly tested as part of a Practical Sailor review of dinghy anchors (August, 2016), I have a solid background in both general behavior and quantitative holding power for these anchors in the soft mud and fine sand of the Chesapeake Bay. We also tested a 35-pound Manson Supreme and a 13-pound Mantus. All testing was performed at 20:1 scope to mimic the effect of chain rode keeping the anchor on the bottom. The rode was polyester double braid, so that the actual rode angle could be known and not influenced by chain catenary.

Securely anchored (Fortress FX-16) in a number of soft mud locations, we pulled the smaller anchors using the primary winches. First, a baseline was established by pulling each of the 2-pound anchors immediately after deployment using a slow, steady pull. We also tested the holding capacity of anchors that had been left to soak for an hour without any initial set to establish if settling time alone made any difference. We then tested anchors that had been set 10 minutes after deployment to 70% of the holding capacity established in the baseline test, allowing each to soak without loading for one hour, after which time they were pulled each until they dragged. Finally, we tested the effect of cyclical loading over a period of hours, mimicking the effect of moderate wind and wave action. Again, each anchor was set to approximately 70% of the holding capacity established by the first test. However, this time we applied cyclical loading two ways; by pulling with a winch 10 times for 10 seconds with a 10 second rest between pulls to simulate wave action, and also by allowing the

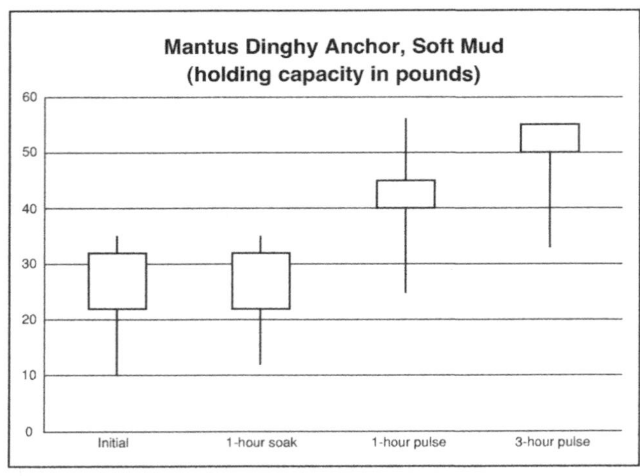

Figure 4 Anchors placed in soft mud can improve dramatically over time.

small anchor to carry the side load as the boat gently yawed from side to side, to simulate long period wind load fluctuations; because the test boat sits very quietly on a bridle and because of the stern anchors, this yawing only occurred with minor wind direction oscillations, with a 5-15 minute period. At the end of the experimental time period, we pulled the anchors until they dragged. We then repeated this testing with a 35-pound Manson Supreme in soft mud. All tests were repeated at least four times. As with all anchor testing and soft mud, variability is the rule. We moved our test boat through a range of 100 feet to avoid disturbed soil, but always within the center of the same broad creek (Warehouse Creek, off Eastern Bay, Chesapeake Bay). We recorded the maximum tension, but all data analysis and plots reflect the tension 30 seconds after winching stopped, because static holding is a better measure of anchor holding and stability.

Soaking alone made no appreciable difference. This is not surprising since the 2-pound anchors were just sitting on top of the ooze and the 35-pound Manson Supreme only sank about two inches. The mud may be soft, but there is a lot of surface area to support the weight. Anchors that had soaked for an hour did set more quickly, but the final holding capacity was no different than if the anchor had been set when first deployed. Thus, soaking and settling alone is a myth.

The short pulls with the winch—simulating the effect of waves and yawing—resulted in holding capacity degradation ranging 30% to no change, confirming that yawing and hobby horsing not only increase peak rode tension, they also loosen the anchor. There was not enough rest time between pulls for the soil to consolidate and the net effect was to further disturb and weaken the soil. Cyclical loading nearly always results in a reduction in holding capacity, the result of reduced soil consolidation in mild cases, and soil liquefaction in severe cases. Deep burying reduces this vulnerability by increasing the soil overburden pressure and because the friction of the chain through the seabed buffers the jerking on the anchor. Long scope helps by changing the pull direction; the soil is stronger the more horizontal the pull. Snubbers help by reducing peak loads.

However, if the anchor was lightly set soon after deployment and then subjected to very slow pulls with long rests in between—simulating the slow rise and fall of the wind—holding capacity increased dramatically. The improvement was variable, from a low of no change (2-pound Mantus with set-and-soak for one hour in soft mud) to a high of 500% (2-pound Mantus after 3 hours of slow cyclical loading in soft mud), with the average after 3 hours of slow cyclical loading in soft mud being 122% better. The 35-pound Manson Supreme showed an 80% improvement. The improvement will be less in firm bottoms and less as the anchors get larger (multi-ton anchor improvement with time and slow cyclical loading is generally 20-35%).

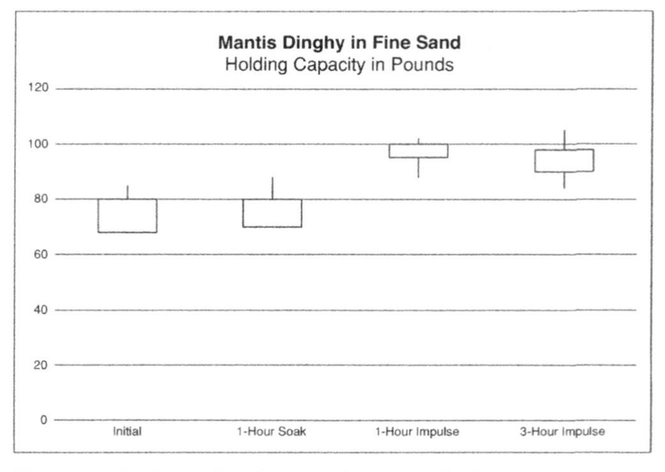

Figure 5 Anchors placed in sand improve little over time.

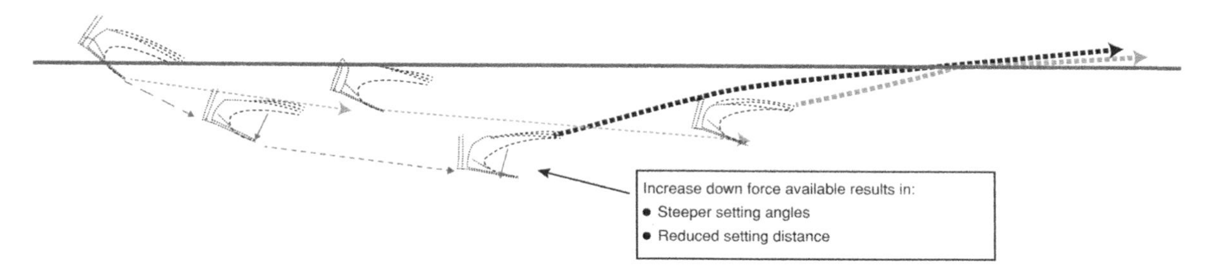

In actual practice, I doubt many anchors are ever simply soaked and allowed to settle; the boat drifts back against the anchor and causes a light set, and then the wind pulses every 5-20 minutes, adding more encouragement. This confirms generations of Chesapeake Bay sailor experience.

I repeated this experiment in fine sand with the 2-pound Mantus only. The improvement was considerably less (23% average), more consistent, and took less time. Full scale anchors should behave about the same, since settling, variation of bottom firmness with depth, and mass are not important factors.

The theory, specific to the soft mud of the Chesapeake, is that pure downwards settling provides only a tiny contribution, while the real mechanism is compaction and stiffening of the layers above the anchor. This gives the broad tail portion of the fluke improved grip, allowing the anchor penetrate both deeper and more directly with each pull. Anchors commonly have trouble setting when the density of the soil increases too quickly and the surface material is weak; the wide heel of the fluke can't generate enough downward pressure to force the toe deeper.

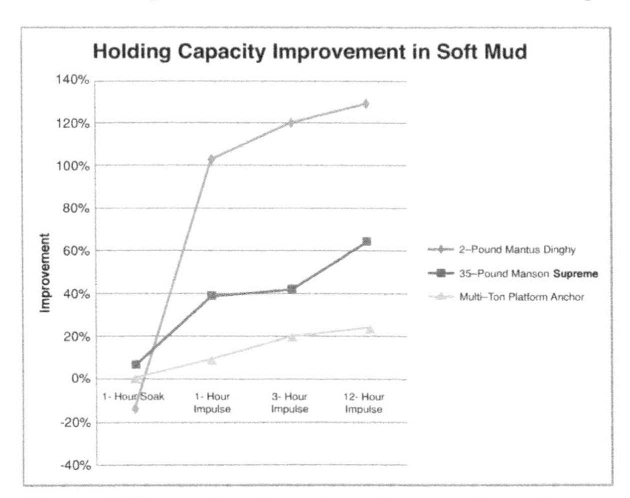

Figure 6 The smaller the anchor, the more slow pulsations and time help.

However, through slow consolidation, a region of compacted soil is reestablished above the anchor, resolving the dilemma and driving the anchor deeper. This also explains why a long resting period between pulses is required; the soil needs time to consolidate between pulls. The reason we saw greater improvements than reported for oil platform anchors is simply that we are working in unconsolidated layers near the surface, while the multi-ton anchors are already in deeper, firm soil.

Veers, Resetting, and Dragging

Since the soil consolidation is a local effect, how does the reinforcement we measured relate to pulls at an angle? Veering has not been extensively studied by the platform anchor folks because their anchors are not subjected to veering loads; they are multipoint anchors and the anchor only sees a pull in one direction. Additionally, many of the large anchor designs are comparatively fragile when exposed to side loads and can easily be damaged during deployment or recovery if side loaded.

First, the consolidation effect is primarily in front of the anchor, although it does seem to proceed to the sides as well to a lesser extent. Second, the greater portion of the holding capacity improvement is not from soil consolidation as much as from deeper setting. In the little bit of veer testing we did, it seemed that in a gradual shift of up to 120 degrees, the anchors smoothly rotated and had effectively the same strength as before the shift, indicating the anchors stayed down and that the increase in holding capacity is relatively durable. With just a little time allowed for reconsolidation, the force required for recovery seemed to be in similar proportion to the final holding capacity; weak anchors came right up, and even that little 2-pound Guardian required using the dinghy engine to recover from every good set; no amount of arm power I could muster in a tippy inflatable was going to make it budge.

Scope Counts

I also tested at shorter scope. There was no improvement with long period cyclical loading, most likely because the angle prevented the anchor from going deeper. Additionally, a shallow anchor agitates and softens the overlying soil. I then tested short pulls on shallow set anchors. In soft mud, whatever hold had been achieved gradually weakened, the anchors beginning to drag at 25% to 40% of the initial setting load. Typically the 5:1 holding capacity was only 20-30% of that achieved at long scope with soaking time. Obviously, short scope and yawing or hobby horsing make a very dangerous combination, and is certainly a leading cause of dragging. Although we understand the arguments for shortening scope in crowded harbors, in soft mud this must be delayed until the anchor is well-set, which may be many hours. Furthermore, anchors that had gained holding capacity as a result of slow cyclical loading lost most of what had been gained when scope was reduced.

The danger of relying on this slow, deeper setting is that if the anchor is overloaded and required to reset, you're starting all over again. This can happen if there is a strong 180° reversal in direction or if the anchor is simply overpowered. Once it comes to the surface it has to start digging all over again, but it will not have time to progress through the graduated three-hour setting and soil consolidation process, will have only half the holding capacity it had before it was ripped loose, and is likely to drag across the harbor an alarming rate. Additionally, scoop anchors will be clogged with sticky mud and pivoting fluke anchors will not reset if on their backs (the flukes jammed with mud in every trial). Better to make sure you don't drag. And just how do we accomplish this?

If the risk is the approach of a storm, try setting the anchor in the direction of the greatest anticipated wind. Alternatively, you can set two anchors in a V (see Chapter 10). In soft mud in violent weather, this may be the only practical way to ensure both good holding capacities by the individual anchors, and prevent the destruction of that hard-won deep setting power.

In soft mud, full-scale anchor holding capacity typically improves 50-75% over time as a result of the steady tugging of the wind. The obvious corollary is that it pays to anchor early, at least a few hours before the thunderstorms arrive. The most effective power setting is not immediately after the anchor is deployed, but rather should be delayed at least 15 minutes and potentially repeated after several hours. The only way to know how well an anchor is set is to test it vigorously, and you should calculate what "vigorously" means with your boat in relation to wind speed (see Chapter 5). If the rode does not stay on the bottom during setting, the additional setting and consolidation will not happen. Shorten up later if you must, but consider staying at long scope for at least a few hours and then shortening up before dark.

In-Line Tandems

These present a very special solution for impenetrable rocky and hardpan bottoms only, which we will discuss in detail in Chapter 11. Perhaps the leading reason they fail is inadequate scope. Briefly, when anchors are asked to scrape over cobbles and hardpan, most of the hold they generate is not from burying, but rather depends on weight to generate friction, and any lifting at all reduces holding power to nearly zero. Additionally, when there are two anchors in a row, the first anchor feels all of the normal uplift force but only half of the setting force, since it is towing the second anchor. Thus, for in-line tandems the scope must be double that recommended in Figure 2a, and that guidance is absolute. A scope of 20:1 is not excessive in shallow waters, and at least 15:1 in deeper water.

Rudeness

Swing room becomes an issue in a crowded anchorage. It is vital that all of the boats have approximately equal scope so that they swing in unison with wind changes. If you lay out 10:1 scope in 20 feet of water in fair weather, when all of the others have anchored on 5:1 scope, you have monopolized an area the size of two football fields, since you will not be swinging in unison with other boats. That's kind of greedy. Based on the weather, the effectiveness of your ground tackle, and the type of bottom, decide how much scope you actually need. Are other boats likely to drag on such short scope? Sometimes you need more scope and a crowded harbor isn't the safest place in a storm. Moving is often the best option. But in fair weather ask around, find out how much scope others are using, and if it seems safe, shorten up.

This same reasoning applies to setting two anchors in a V and to Bahamian moors, discussed in Chapters 10 and 11. In this case the swing is either truncated or eliminated entirely, taking the boat out of synchronization with the other boats. Fortunately, in most cases where two anchors are actually needed, either neighbors will be few because of severe weather, or in the case of a narrow channel, they may be anchored in the same manner. "But I got here first, and I am anchored in the way I feel safe." Latecomers won't like it, but they are required to stay clear, in both tradition and law. Decision No. 124-5861 (1956) in U.S. Admiralty case law states: "A vessel shall be found at fault if it . . . anchors so close to another vessel as to foul her when swinging . . . (and/or) fails to shift anchorage when dragging dangerously close to another anchored vessel. Furthermore, the vessel that anchored first shall warn the one who anchored last that the berth chosen will foul the former's berth." Notice that the first boat anchored is given certain rights, but that these evaporate as soon as they begin to drag. Additionally, Admiralty Court decisions have a consistent precedent of apportioning blame if either party could reasonably have reduced the risk of collision or damage. Thus, you have a responsibility to remain engaged in the situation and handle your boat as required to keep everyone safe.

It's complicated. I understand the need for short scope in crowded harbors and its practicality in settled weather in deep water with all chain rode. But it is also apparent that when anchoring in soft mud, short scope brings a triple penalty during the critical soil consolidation period; the angle is poor for deep setting, soil consolidation is prevented by yawing and hobby horsing, eliminating potential improvements, and anchor holding capacity is always diminished at scope. Arrive early, set properly at long scope, and wait to shorten up until the anchor is well settled, bearing in mind that your well-set anchor may come loose if the chain starts jerking upwards. Make sure you have room to lay enough scope to keep the chain on the bottom before serious wind comes up. Watch out for hobby horsing if the water is shallow.

Lots to consider.

Chapter 5:
Just How Good is That Bottom?

WE DON'T EXPECT A nail to hold in rotten wood and we can't expect an anchor to hold in bottomless ooze. We can't drive a nail into metal; some bottoms are just too hard. We don't expect much from a nail driven into end-grain wood; slopes and rubble-filled bottoms are poor as well.

Chart information provides some clues. Sand and mud are generally good, but it depends on the modifiers; fine sand is strong, but coarse sand and light coral sand can be very weak. You can build an ornate sandcastle with fine, wet sand, but coarse sand and gravel just collapse in a pile. Mud can be soft ooze that will reach your waist if you try to walk across (through?) it at low tide, or a nice sticky muck suitable for mud pies. Clay can be impenetrable. Tides and storms can change a bottom, and even if the chart information is correct, it often varies from spot to spot. I visited places where others have reported excellent holding, but winter storms had scoured away the sand, and the clay that remained couldn't be penetrated with a screwdriver. I've anchored where others reported dragging through ooze all night, yet in the morning I had difficulty breaking my anchor loose. At best, chart information and guidebooks provide a hint. In out-of-the-way locations, you're on your own.

Table 5

	NOAA Chart 1, Nature of Seabed					
Main Descriptor				Modifiers		
S	sand			f	fine	+
M	mud			m	medium	
Cy	clay			c	coarse	-
Si	silt			bk	broken	
St	stones			sy	sticky	+
P	pebbles			so	soft	-
G	gravel			sf	firm	+
Co	cobbles			ca	calcerous	
Sh	shells			hd	hard	-
Wd	weed			S/M	layers (sand/mud)	
K	kelp			lrg	large	
Grs	grass			wh	white	
Sn	shingle			bl	black	
Oz	ooze			gr	gray	
Oys	oysters			drk	dark	

Sounding Lead

Traditionally, a manual sounding lead was packed with grease, and the material that attached itself to the grease was examined. Presumably, this allowed you to distinguish between sand, shell, and mud. However, I've never understood how this 1/32-inch sampling is going to tell me the difference between sticky mud and ooze. Back in the day, they had to use the sounding lead anyway. Today, I doubt it's worth the time it takes. If you're really curious, you can dig a better sample with your anchor in just a few minutes.

Boathooks, Paddles, and Stakes

Just how soft is the mud? The U.S. Navy used to have a practice where they would send couple of guys out in a small boat with a blunt stake and a hammer:

- Very dense sand: more than 50 blows/foot.
- Sand: 25-50 blows/foot.
- Hard clay: more than 16 blows/foot.

- Consolidated mud/clay: 4-16 blows/foot.
- Soft mud: 2 blows/foot.
- Very soft mud/silt: you don't need the hammer.

During testing, my method has been to explore the proposed test area by kayak, probing the bottom as I go (the test boat has a 3.3-foot draft and most testing was in 5-7 feet of water). If I can push the paddle in more than 18 inches with one hand while reaching well out to the side (10-15 pounds of force) I rate it as very soft mud, suitable only for testing and moderate weather. If I can only push it in 1foot with one hand, it is ordinary Chesapeake Mud (which I gather is relatively soft), suitable for all weather with good anchoring methods. Stiffer than that, just anchor as usual, and it will hold. I also look at the stuff that comes up with the paddle; sticky is good, but if it rinses off on the way up, that's bad, indicating poor cohesion.

Setting

Your first concrete information about bottom conditions often comes when you lower the anchor and back down on it. What can we learn from this simple act? When the anchor first hit bottom, did the chain go suddenly slack with a jerk, or was it gradual? A quick stop indicates a firm bottom; whether that is good sand or mud, or difficult shell and rock is unknown. When the slack came out of the chain and the snubber took the load, did the chain snap bar-tight, or was the tightening very gradual? A sudden catch indicates either a good set in a nice firm bottom, or that it caught on a rock, which may not be good. Did the chain and snubber rise and fall while backing, as though the anchor was rhythmically catching and releasing? This is a sure sign that you're on shells, smooth rock, or pocketed but impenetrable clay. Is there grass floating on the surface in the wake of the anchor? Weeds. If the tension seemed to increase gradually over a period of 10-15 feet, this suggests a soft but workable bottom; anchors take 10-20 feet to fully set in very soft mud. On the other hand, if an anchor takes more than 20 feet to catch, it is not setting properly. It is either upside down, fouled, or you are backing down too quickly. When in doubt, pull the anchor up and look at what it is carrying.

How do you know if the anchor is well set and how much it will actually hold? It's not always practical to dive under water and lay eyes on the anchor. In soft mud areas the visibility is usually terrible, the water can be too cold or too deep for practical diving, and often it's just bloody inconvenient. Moreover, without detailed knowledge of the soil mechanics, do we really know what we're seeing in any quantitative sense? You can only observe the surface—is there a hard layer or layer of shells a foot or so down that the anchor is already resting against? Better, we can translate our power setting information into a proof test.

First, calculate the reverse thrust capacity of your boat. You can measure this at the dock by using a load cell—this is how I do it—but as a first approximation, multiply your engine horsepower by a factor relating efficiency to reverse thrust, given below. Propeller fouling, even very slight, can greatly diminish this force. Outboards have less thrust in reverse because exhaust discharged through the propeller hub causes partial ventilation (forward thrust is much better).

- Inboards, fixed blade propeller: 25 pounds/horse power.
- Inboards, folding blade propeller: 20 pounds/horse power.
- Outboards, high thrust (Mercury Big Foot, Yamaha 9.9 High Thrust): 14 pounds/horse power.
- Outboards, average: 10 pounds/horse power.

Compare this thrust with the estimated working load from Table 6. This table assumes that you are anchored at 7:1 scope and are using either a boat-length snubber or anchored using a heavy chain rode in water 20 feet deep; either provides significant damping of waves and wind gusts and allows us to use 1/3 of the ABYC recommendation for horizontal loads on deck to estimate actual rode tension.

Power boats typically add 5 feet of length to compensate for greater windage.

Table 6

Rode Load with Long Snubber or Equivalent (1/3 ABYC H-40 Deck Gear Loads)

	Horizontal Working Load, Pounds					
	Boat Length, Feet					
Windspeed, Knots	**25**	**30**	**35**	**40**	**50**	**60**
15	42	58	75	100	133	167
20	62	87	112	149	199	248
25	116	163	209	279	372	465
30	160	233	300	400	533	667
42	240	467	600	800	1,067	1,333
50	341	663	852	1,136	1,515	1,893
60	490	933	900	1,200	1,600	2,000

Catamarans typically add 5-8 feet of length to compensate for greater windage.

Example: Our 32-foot test catamaran has twin 9.9 hp engines generating 280 pounds of thrust in reverse.

- Windage is equivalent to a 40-foot monohull, or about 279 pounds at 25 knots.
- Thus, power setting tests the anchor to 25 knots.

Example: A Hunter 31 has 21 hp with a fixed blade propeller, generating about 525 pounds of thrust in reverse.

- Windage is about 510 pounds at 42 knots.
- Thus, power setting tests the anchor to about 42 knots.

You have proof tested the anchor to hold this much wind, in the direction of the test, right now. If the scope is long and the boat is neither yawing nor hobby horsing, holding capacity should build over time. If the scope is short and the boat is active, holding capacity may diminish. Finally, power setting does not tell you about wind shifts or whether the anchor has reserve capacity above the setting force.

Weeds

First of all... don't. There are too many places where destruction of submerged vegetation has caused ecological damage. Anchor somewhere else.

If the anchor can penetrate, it can be very strong indeed. More often, however, the anchor is only caught under the root mat, and it will pull off a chunk and drag in a severe storm. There's little way of knowing, other than swimming down and looking at the anchor. For more discussion, see In-Line Tandems, Chapter 12.

Very Soft Mud

Common in tidal creeks, it can be perfectly acceptable in settled weather if the shelter is sufficient. However, the holding strength is very poor (see Chapter 6) and a V tandem rig with two anchors may be required in strong weather. See Chapter 10 for rigging details.

Sand

It depends. Fine mineral sand with just a little mud mixed in is the gold standard; a conservatively sized anchor will hold nearly as much as the rode can stand, maybe more, and anchors stay put (Chapter 11). On the other hand, light coral sand, river-rounded sugar sand, light gravel and fine shells behave more like ball bearings, allowing anchors to move around, often without the benefit of deep setting; they are insufficiently cohesive (they don't stick together) to give a good bite and drive the fluke downwards, so the anchor drags along near the surface, not completely buried.

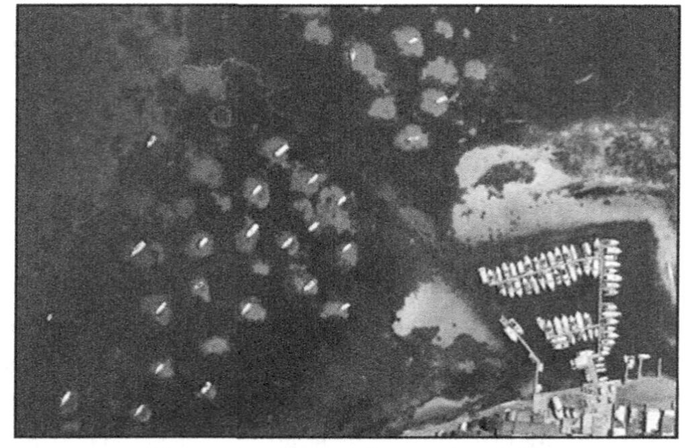

Vegetation damage in mooring field.

Anchor rigging methods are like those for soft mud, requiring a soft snubber and allowing for movement (Chapter 10). Worse yet is sand over hardpan, impossible to see, only detected by observation of the surrounding area; are there sedimentary rocks in evidence, or is the sand in a sheltered area between outcrops? The anchor may seem to bite, but it will be prevented from setting deeper under increasing strain (Chapter 12).

Rocks and Coral

Anchoring in coral is either frowned upon or illegal. Rocks don't allow anchors to penetrate in the normal manner, and when the boat starts dancing around in the wind, even a good pocket or solid hook can lose its grip. In the worst case, the rock forms a smooth pan, where only friction is available. The best alternative is to relocate to a sand or firm mud bottom. If you must anchor over rocks, special rigging may be required, as described in Chapter 12. The bottom line is that bottoms where anchors cannot reliably dig and bury are unpredictable. Experience and diving are your guides.

Avoid Slopes

First, there is the matter of scope; if the slope is deeper towards the boat, the scope is reduced by the amount of the bottom slope. Second is firmness; if the slope is steep you can also bet it's also very hard or it would not have held the slope. Move to a flat spot.

Long Stay or Severe Storm

Consider lightly setting the anchor and then lifting it back up to see what it brings. Also, driving a pole or boathook down through the bottom can provide valuable clues. Before setting anchors to secure an offshore platform, the soil is always surveyed. Is it hard or soft? On a soft bottom, do you hit shells or sticks or anything that feels crunchy as you push deeper? Drag the pole from side to side. Does it feel smooth, lumpy, or gravelly? Push straight down with one arm extended (about 10-15 pounds); if the pole penetrates more than 1 foot the mud is soft, if it penetrates over 2 feet it is hopeless. Does the hook bring up grass? Go for a swim if it comes to that. Use all available information, not just local knowledge, which I've found to be notoriously variable in quality, just like the bottom.

Throughout the rest of the book we will be immersed in data and discussion of anchors, rigs, and how to optimize our grip on the bottom. However, at the end of the day it comes down to whether the anchor can work in the bottom you have chosen. It can never be better than the material you have given it to work with. Choose wisely.

Chapter 6: How Much Does an Anchor Hold?

THE LAST THING I want to write is a review of anchor testing and holding capacity by brand. I've done anchor testing for magazine reviews, and sifting the data is like herding cats, only worse and with more variables. I've tried hard to list anchors alphabetically when there is no reason for a strong preference because most modern designs are very good, differing only in the details of the compromises they have made. But the topic can't be avoided entirely, because too many reviews and too many vendor claims are based on a best performance in perfect sand, rather than in the real world of poor sets and imperfect bottoms. A typical anchor review will list the "maximum force held," which is another way of saying it is the best the anchor can possibly do on a good day. What matters to a cruiser is more complicated:

1. Does it set reliably? A design that exhibits moments of brilliance intermixed with poor performances is difficult to judge.
2. Does it reset reliably? Closely related to #1, but not always. Pivoting fluke anchors are challenged in this area, but they will often rotate to face the load to some extent if the turn is gradual. When deeply set, they powerfully resist unsetting. Finally, as a secondary anchor or kedge, does it even matter since the direction of pull will not change?
3. Holding capacity on a poor day, with a mediocre set, in a marginal bottom. Not how much the anchor will hold when perfectly set in firm sand, but rather the minimum it will probably hold if it "sorta" felt like it was set after you backed down against it. A major consideration for soft mud anchors.
4. Short scope holding. Perhaps this is only important if you really need to push the limits of scope in crowded anchorages. The first three factors probably take precedence, although this depends on your habits.

There are secondary issues as well; how does it fit in the bow roller, does it bring up a ton of mud, is it prone to fouling on trash or rocks, and does it break out easily? With good sand bottoms, an appropriately sized modern anchor is very secure. Chapter 12 is devoted to rock, hardpan, gravel, and weeds. In this chapter will focus on a common nemesis of secure anchoring; very soft mud.

Holding Capacity in Soft Mud

In August 2014 there was a significant testing effort on the Chesapeake Bay in Solomons Island,

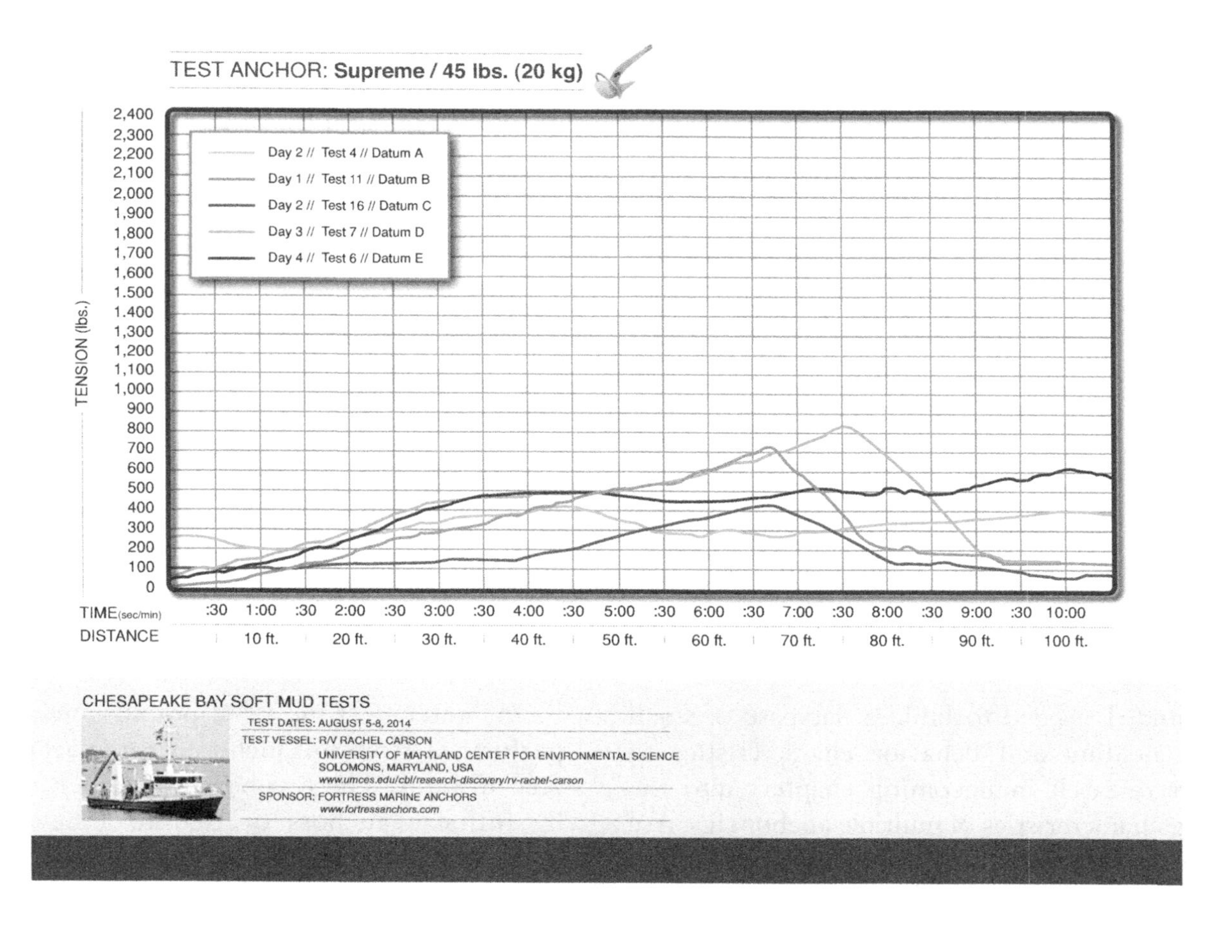

Maryland, sponsored by Fortress Anchors, conducted aboard a University of Maryland research vessel, and witnessed by several respected impartial observers. I like this data set because all of the pull data is available and because I know the area personally. Although the area certainly plays to the strength of the sponsoring company's product line, that does not imply the data is inaccurate, and the third party oversight was intimate. The data also confirmed what area sailors have always known about very soft mud in general and the Solomons Island area specifically; that even a conservatively-sized anchor of modern design isn't always enough. Some of my testing was in the same area and produced similar findings. (The complete data set is reproduced in Appendix III.)

For example, in the above test, the practical holding power of the Manson Supreme was a little over 400 pounds in soft mud, not the 800 pounds attained on the best effort. That best effort required almost 80 feet of dragging and may have been the result of hooking a buried log. More importantly, the sailor had no way of knowing which of the five sets he actually had. He probably would have re-anchored after test 11 (120 pounds holding), feeling that the anchor had not set. In fact, because my boat has only 280 pounds of thrust in reverse, I would not have been able to distinguish between the other sets or knowing if the anchor would hold more than that in a storm. To make matters worse, 45 pounds is a pretty big anchor for a 32-foot catamaran; 35 pounds is more common, which would likely hold about 325 pounds, or only about 30 knots of wind.

Before we get into a panic, holding is also increased by soak time and cyclical loading, as discussed in Chapter 5. Most cruisers are aware of this, if only at a subconscious level. For example, the data suggests a 25-pound Delta would generally drag with about 200 pounds setting force, which I know is true; my Delta would often drag if I applied full reverse, about 280 pounds. On the other hand, the same undersized anchor often held in 25-30 knots after a few hours gently tugging against the wind, which is over 300 pounds. However, because this is variable and common to all mud testing, rather than blindly adjusting data, we will simply hold this information in our back pocket as a safety factor, mentioning it but not adjusting the data or our recommendations.

In this testing phase my goal was to develop a database of holding power for both full-scale and smaller 2-pound anchors for several reasons. First, by testing I could confirm the theory that both small and full-scale anchors perform in direct ratio to their weight in a wide range of sand and mud bottoms common to the Chesapeake Bay. Numerous investigators have reported that holding capacity is proportional to weight^X, with the exponent ranging from 0.92 to 1.1. Put another way, an anchor that is twice as heavy, assuming equivalent design, will hold roughly twice as much.

Second, I needed to build a database of small anchor holding and behavior characteristics to support research in upcoming chapters into the holding characteristics of multiple anchor rigs. Are they better than single anchor rigs? If so, under what circumstances and by how much? Eventually, I would need to drag multiple anchor rigs until failure, and there is simply no practical or safe way to drag a combination of well-set, full-size anchors. Large tugs can have trouble with forces like that, since two 45-pound anchors can hold upwards of 10,000 pounds in firm sand. Thus, I chose to study more manageable, smaller anchors that could serve as surrogates for their larger brothers. I have no expectation that a small anchor will behave the same as a larger anchor in difficult to penetrate bottoms or in the presence of weeds, but that wasn't relevant to the testing I had in mind.

Finally, if the data turned out to be consistent, I could combine the data from the 2-pound anchors with limited data from 35- to 45-pound anchors to estimate the behavior of larger anchors in a variety of bottoms and rigging situations. The eventual focus was rigging methods, and testing must translate to real-world numbers if the information is to be of any practical use.

I tested three representative bottoms: gravelly beach sand (Sandbox, Great Falls, Maryland) for ease of photography and to work out our systems; fine, firm sand (Herring Bay, Chesapeake Bay) to test high load holding; and typical soft creek ooze (Rockhold Creek and Warehouse Creek, Chesapeake Bay) for a taste of the real world. I picked locations with deep, consistent bottoms since these reduce variability. I did not measure forces on the gravelly beach—dry sand doesn't handle like wet materials—though it was obvious what we could drag with one hand, what required effort, what two men couldn't budge, and what was unstable.

Further testing was conducted on gravel over hardpan, cobbles, and rock. However, the results on these bottoms are too variable for quantitative analysis. It also became clear that different bottoms require different rigging details; see Chapter 12 for rock, weeds, and cobbles.

In water testing of 2-pound anchors was performed from an anchored catamaran in 5-7 feet of water. The test boat was either anchored by full-size anchors or tied to the dock to prevent movement. Anchors were pulled using the primary winches; while one tester moved anchors about while snorkeling and watched the anchors strain, the other recorded load readings. We used a 6-foot chain leader with a polyester rode at 10:1 minimum scope (20:1 for single-line tandem rigs), and thin polyester slings for secondary rodes. We understand the significant benefit of all-chain rodes in moderating sudden veers on soft bottoms—the chain must be dragged over and through the sand or mud, creating some forward pull and smoothing the transition—and so during veer testing we maintained about 10-30 pounds of tension to help the anchors

2-pound anchors, from left to right: folding grapnel, Lewmar Claw, Mantus Dinghy, and Guardian G-5.

rotate through the turn. Each rig was tested three times, recording the maximum force at 0, 30, 60, and 90 degrees.

Pivoting fluke anchors are variable in their ability to rotate to face new loads. If set in firm sand and then pulled at a 90 degree angle without a slow transition in the direction of pull, the anchor often pulled out sideways without rotating, with the holding force approximately 70% of the setting force—not much if set by a weak sailboat engine. However, setting in mud is a long, slow process, and if moderate load is applied while the direction is changed, the Guardian anchor often cut its way cleanly around, like a hand saw responding to a gentle twist from the carpenter's hand. The Mantus, Mason, and Claw anchors shifted very reliably to face new loads.

Guardian, 32- vs 45-Degree Fluke Angle

To investigate the effect of fluke angle on holding (Fortress anchors are adjustable to 32 degree and 45 degree settings) I modified our Guardian anchor so that it had a fluke angle of 32 degrees on one side and 45 degrees on the other. In sand the 45 degree setting did not allow proper burying and was much less stable. In mud, our results were mixed; if there were firmer layers or debris, the 32 degree setting was more reliable, though the 45 degree setting was much stronger in optimum conditions. A full-scale anchor is less affected by small debris, supporting the Solomons testing observation that a 45 degree angle can be much stronger.

However, because of the uncertainty in bottom conditions, we think the cruiser is generally better served by the 32 degree angle, reserving the 45 degree setting for storm preparation over a well-known soft bottom. All of the test data reported here was collected using the 32 degree setting. (Note: I do NOT recommend modifying anchors in this way—this was for testing only, and the anchor was weakened by the modification.)

Guardian G-5, Fortress Anchors

With the greatest fluke area and the Fortress reputation for high-holding in sand and mud, it was little surprise that it put up the biggest numbers. I was pleasantly surprised at its ability to track though the 90 degree shift in many bottoms without resetting; as long as the transition includes significant pressure, it simply cut its way around.

However, during a prompt 90 degree shift or reversal in firm sand or other material that prevented a proper set, it occasionally released, typically at 70% of the force with which it was set. It reset in a short distance, unless jammed by a shell or mud, which unfortunately, is common. In soft mud the anchor buried deeply and a release at low force during a shift was never observed. The best policy with pivoting fluke anchors is to set them hard and deep.

Lewmar Claw, 2.2-Pound

With less fluke area, it didn't put up big numbers. However, it is impossible to deploy wrong, short of dumping a huge pile of chain on it. We cast it in every careless way we could think of without fouling or failing to set, and it gave more repeatable resistance at short scope than any other anchor. This makes it an excellent choice for hammerlock mooring and when nothing else seems effective. However, its holding power, particularly in mud, is limited. Nonetheless, it found a permanent home as our favorite kayak fishing anchor. It's so easy to use and far more effective than canoe anchors.

Mantus Dinghy Anchor. Strong and sure to track through shifts, the dinghy felt as though it were nailed to the bottom. We even used it as a lunch hook for our 10,000-pound catamaran on good sand, observing how it held when really challenged. Though it would start to drag when the wind topped 20 knots and the chop started to build, the holding remained steady and the force held was substantial for such a small bit of metal. By the end of a summer of testing, the Mantus replaced our 20-year old battle-proven Guardian G-5 as our dinghy anchor, not because it was as strong—the Guardian has much greater holding capacity in good bottoms—but because it was easy, small, suitable in more bottoms types, and strong enough.

I also tested mushroom anchors and folding grapnels while I was at it. They were horrible, holding 4-10 times less, not worth even showing the data. Even in good sand, it was easier to drag these anchors to me than to wade over to them.

I then pulled two 35-pound anchors (Manson Supreme and Lewmar Claw) to failure in soft mud, to establish whether the test area was comparable to the Solomons Island test area. The results were consistent with the Solomons Island data when corrected for weight.

Is small anchor testing accurate and relevant to larger anchors? After months of comparing small anchors with large anchors, I think so within the strict limits of the bottom types investigated. Small anchors will always have difficulty engaging hard or weedy bottoms, but in uniform sand and soft mud I found they compared very well with their big brothers, with which we have long experience.

Holding Capacity

The consensus of manufacturers (Fortress, Bruce, Manson, Mantus) is that holding power in soft substrates increases in approximate proportion with mass (exponents range from 0.92 – 1.05). While there are differences between models and manufacturers, a 35-pound Mantus should hold roughly 18 times more than a 2-pound Mantus, and a Fortress FX-16 should hold 4 times more than a Guardian G5. If we compare our soft mud 2.5-pound Mantus result (36 pounds) with the 45-pound Mantus result (500 pounds) using a 0.92 exponent, the scale-up error is about 9%. The same is true for the Guardian/Fortress comparison and the Claw comparison; about 5-20% scale-up error. The drag-in distance to full holding was proportional to physical size, a trend supported by U.S. Navy testing; Solomons Island anchors took 30-40 feet to develop full hold, while these small anchors took 5-15 feet. These are averages; variations between runs were often 50% or more, just like the Solomons Island test data. The most common cause for variation in all locations was trash in the mud. Still, I think this is pretty darn close.

How Small Anchors Behave Compare to Their Big Brothers

- Holding power was proportional to weight, within 20%, for all models.

Table 7

		2-Pound Anchor Holding Power		
		Guardian Fortress	Claw Lewmar	Dinghy Anchor Mantus
Actual Weight	**(pounds)**	2	2.6	2.6
Material		Aluminum	Galvinized Steel	Stainless Steel
Fluke Area	**(square inches)**	47	13	38
Holding Capacity	**straight-line**			
	mud	94	8	35
	sand	> 600	25	160
Holding Capacity	**90 degree**			
	mud	70	7	36
	sand	420	25	160

Table 8

Typical Worst-Case Holding Capacity in Very Soft Mud.

(Holding in other bottoms, including firm mud and sand, can be as much as 8 times greater.)

(Based on slow rate pulling. Soaking combined with cyclical loading will increase peak holding strength about 60% in soft mud. In fine sand and firm mud the increase will be about 25%.)

	Hold by Size, Typical Worst Set			
Anchor Type	**25-pound**	**35-pound**	**45-pound**	**55-pound**
Pivoting Fluke Anchor, 32° (by FX-Number for Fortress)	540	740	925	1100
Scoop Type	235	320	400	490
Plow Type	175	240	300	360
Claw/Bruce	205	280	350	425

- Guardian. The smaller version is slightly more reluctant to get started on firm bottoms, but reliably digs right out of sight once started. It is also more prone to clogging with debris.
- Claw. Very similar to larger models on all bottoms.
- Mantus. Very similar to larger models on all bottoms.

Overall, the burying behavior, turning behavior, and relative holding power of these pint-sized anchors in consistent sand and soft mud is proportional to full-size anchors. This allowed me to move forward with testing rigging designs using 2-pound anchors.

I reviewed published test results of full-size anchors, discarding anywhere objectivity was not certain or the full data set was not available. I also ran limited tests of my own in a variety of bottoms. I searched not for the best possible result, but rather for minimum holding capacity the sailor can reliably expect if the anchor felt like it was set with available engine horsepower. In my case, this would be the worst result over 275 pounds. Included are my long-term experiences in soft mud areas, where for years I could not get a solid set with a 25-pound Delta, but I can reliably set a 35-pound Manson Supreme or Fortress FX-16. (The 275-pounds reverse thrust of *Shoal Survivor* is greater than the first and less than the second). Likewise my experiences with breezy weather (300-

Table 9

Typical Worst-Case Holding Capacity in Gravel Over Hardpan.

	Hold by Size, Typical Worst Set			
Anchor Type	**25-pound**	**35-pound**	**45-pound**	**55-pound**
Pivoting Fluke Anchors (by FX-Number for Fortress)	Very low	Very Low	Very Low	Very Low
Scoop Type	90	125	160	200
Plow Type	50	75	100	120
Claw/Bruce	90	125	160	200

Table 10

Typical Worst-Case Holding Capacity in Cobbles and Rubble. Variable, Determined by Cobble Break-Out Force.

	Hold by Size, Typical Worst Set			
Anchor Type	**25-pound**	**35-pound**	**45-pound**	**55-pound**
Pivoting Fluke Anchors (by FX-Number for Fortress)	Very low unless they catch, then very high			
Scoop Type	150	200	200	no data
Plow Type	100	100	150	250
Claw/Bruce	150	200	350(dug through)	500 (dug through)

Table 11

Typical Worst-Case Holding Capacity in Rocks

	Hold by Size, Typical Worst Set			
Anchor Type	**25-pound**	**35-pound**	**45-pound**	**55-pound**
Holding capacity is determined primarily by whether the hook catches. A 2-pound hook can easily hold to the breaking limit of either the rock or the anchor. Heavier anchors are more likely to get a secure hook, and they offer more friction when dragging between hooks. Extremely variable. • Scoop anchors scrape consistently but occasionally have trouble hooking. • Claw/Bruce anchors scrape less consistently, but hook more solidly. • Pivoting flukes are more variable and vulnerable to damage in rocks. • Plow anchors can hook but often glide over edges and small rocks when on their side. • Northill and yachtsman anchors are very effective at hooking pockets and small edges. I have a 12-pound Northill that is one of my favorite anchors in rock. It is not a good choice for a general-purpose anchor because the exposed fluke can be fouled by the rode when the boat rotates with the tide.				

to 500-pound load), which often caused significant dragging with the 25-pound Delta but never with the 35-pound Manson Supreme or Fortress FX-16. In a strong storm (1,000-pound load) I need both a pivoting fluke anchor and my primary to be secure (see Chapter 10 for a description of rigging two anchors for soft bottoms). To calculate the holding capacity for other anchor sizes, the rule of holding capacity is proportional to weight^0.92 was used. This rule only applies well to uniform sand or mud bottoms, and not to cobbles or rocks.

Finally, there is the old saw that "the chain holds it." Certainly, a long length of heavy chain contributes by providing scope and shock absorption, as quantified in Chapters 2 and 4. When the wind shifts, often the chain will carve an arc through the mud, never fully aligning with the anchor. However, the old wives' tale that chain alone is enough is not remotely true. First, cited examples are invariably in relatively light winds. Second, the end of the chain is still secured at the anchor, and the appearance that the chain held the boat is a bit like suggesting that a pulley holds the rope and that the bitter end is secured is irrelevant. Finally, it ignores the fact that in strong winds it is mathematically provable and easily observed that at normal scope the chain is lifted clear of the bottom by a modest breeze. So much for friction. However, to confirm this I dragged sections of ¼-inch and 5/16-inch chain through both sand and soft mud just to see. Friction ranged 4-7 pounds per 10-foot section for ¼-inch chain and 5-10 pounds per 10-foot section for 3/8-inch chain. Assuming that you have 20 feet of chain actively on the bottom when the wind actually blows, this amounts to no more than 20 pounds of addition holding capacity. So while catenary helps with waves, and sideways dragging through the mud helps buffer direction shifts, in no real sense does the chain hold the boat, other than as a colorful figure of speech.

Combining this information with the working load data estimates in Chapter 2, and soil consolidation estimates in Chapter 4 (judiciously applied), you should be able to estimate whether you are likely to drag in a specific situation and whether the anchor you have is sufficient for your cruising area. This data will resurface in Chapters 10 and 12 when we estimate the holding power of full-scale multiple anchor rigs, which in good bottoms are beyond practical measurement.

Chapter 7:

Anchor-Specific Observations: Setting a Fortress, Roll Bars, and Angles

Fortress

It seems strange to dedicate space to a single anchor design. Strange, except that in soft mud Fortress anchors have demonstrated the ability to hold 5-10 times more per pound than any other type of anchor. Their high-strength aluminum construction makes even very large sizes easy to handle and row out, making them a very popular choice for kedge and storm anchors. Danforth also makes an excellent line of pivoting fluke anchors. Because they are made of steel they are somewhat heavier, but they share the same basic performance attributes. Most of my conclusions and practices apply equally to both. Unfortunately, there are a few downsides to lightweight anchors. Only by understanding them we can use them to their full potential.

Setting in Very Hard Bottoms

If the bottom is too hard, rocky, or covered in weed, pivoting fluke anchors are a poor choice. My advice is to use a modern scoop-style anchor.

Setting in Soft Mud

The difficulty in setting a pivoting fluke anchor in very soft mud is that the flukes are broad and light while the shank is blade-like and attached to heavy chain. As a result, the chain, shank, and crown sink below the flukes, giving the flukes a slight upward angle. Thusly positioned, the anchor can sled along the surface points-up, never catching. Large mud palms help, forcing the flukes down once forward motion begins, but there is more we can do:

- Mud Palms. These are hand-sized flukes attached to the crown of the anchor on either side, their purpose is to drive the main flukes into the bottom. If you have an older Fortress or Guardian anchor without mud palms, contact Fortress and they will send you a pair. They significantly improve soft bottom setting performance.
- Set on Short Scope. By reducing the scope to between 3:1 and 4:1, the shank is lifted ever so slightly out of the mud, the flukes swing down, and the anchor begins to bite. The moment

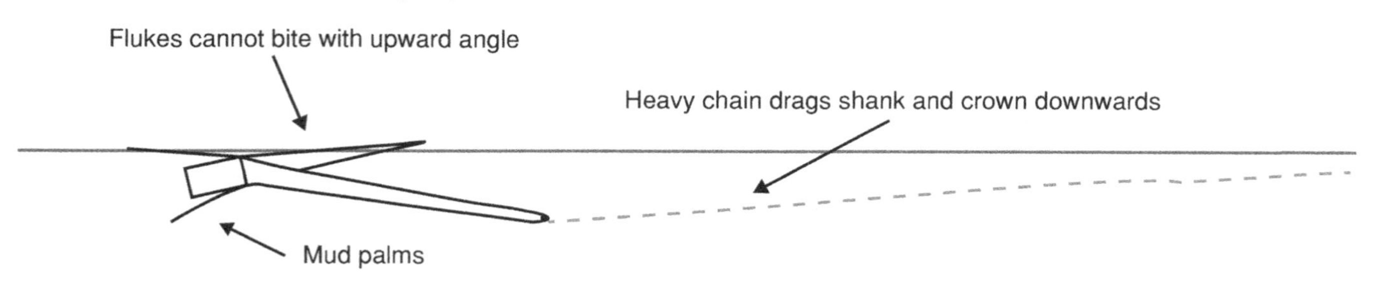

the rode begins to tighten, let out rode to provide about 7:1 scope and set at slow speed, just like any other anchor. Once the anchor is set deeply, scope can be reduced if needed.

- Lighten the Shank. More to the point, lighten the chain so that it does not drag the shank down. The chain leader on a pivoting fluke anchor should always be grade 43 or better to minimize weight. Heavy chain provides no benefit for deep-diving anchors, since it is the underground reverse catenary that controls their behavior, and a fat chain only restricts diving. The rode will almost certainly be fiber when used as a secondary anchor or kedge. Review the reverse catenary discussion in Chapter 4 regarding why catenary is a minor factor for deep diving anchors like the Fortress. Clearly, any chain dragged underground by the deeply-set anchor provides no catenary effect.

Wind Shifts

Common criticism of Fortress anchors is that they do not like direction changes. It is true that a shallow-set Fortress anchor will pop out in a shift and may have difficulty resetting, particularly if clogged with mud or shells. This is common in firm bottoms since most sailboats lack the power to set a conservatively sized pivoting fluke anchor below the surface. Dive on a few sets after applying full reverse to witness just how true this is. It's not that the anchor can't go deeper or that the anchor cannot hold much greater force; if you had 10 times the horsepower the anchor would set many feet underground and hold incredible force. But most sailboats simply haven't got the power to set it deeply in anything denser than medium mud. In fact, pivoting fluke anchors set deeply in soft mud have been tested to hold approximately 70% of the setting force in any direction before moving (observe the short scope capability of Fortress in Chapter 4). This is not our favorite anchor for use where we expect wind and tide shifts, but it is far from delicate when deeply set. This will be obvious the first time you try to retrieve one after a good blow.

The obvious corollary is to not excessively oversize Fortress anchors. These are very high-holding anchors and the sizes recommended by the factory are very conservative. In the recommended size, it is difficult

A Dyneema Chafe Leader makes rowing out a second anchor much easier.

to set below the surface in sand or firm mud, and it is only when well buried that the Fortress is reliably able to resist wind shifts. This is counterintuitive, but in my experience a smaller Fortress anchor is in some ways more reliable than a larger model, because it sets more deeply. Fortress recommends going up one size for storms, but they don't mean afternoon squalls, they mean an honest-to-goodness tropical storm or hurricane conditions in exposed locations, and even then, the standard size anchor is ordinarily enough, considerably higher in holding power than other designs at vendor-recommended sizing.

Tripping Line

Obviously useful for recovery if stuck under a rock or a log, although these occurrences are very unlikely in mud and sand bottoms where a Fortress anchor should be used. I tested recovery using a tripping line attached to the crown as a way to reduce recovery force for anchors set very deeply in mud. It didn't work. It seems that the mud palms function like the barbs on an arrow, and the retrieval force using the tripping line was about the same as pulling on the shank in the conventional manner.

Dyneema Leader

A Dyneema Leader. A Fortress rigged as part of a V tandem in mud may not require a chain leader at all. The primary rode is typically all-chain; it is strong, cut-proof, fits a windlass, and is well proven. It requires a long snubber in shallow water (not enough catenary), but otherwise, it's pretty foolproof. V tandem rigs in mud (Chapter 10), on the other hand are a very special case:

- Low-Risk Bottom. Any sharp items (few) in the mud are mobile and will shift away from the rode under pressure.
- Motion Is Controlled. While cutting is always a concern, the boat will not be yawing back and forth.
- Not the Sole Anchor. Should it fail, there is still the primary anchor.
- The V Tandem or Kedge Is Not in Daily Use. It may only be used a dozen times each year, even by full-time cruisers.

By replacing the chain leader with Dyneema, we realize additional advantages:

- Deeper Set. In soft mud a thin rode encourages the anchor to set more deeply, reaching the underlying firmer mud. Testing has shown that a wire rode results in about 25% deeper setting and 25% more holding capacity. Holding in wind shifts is also improved.
- Lighter. A second anchor or kedge often must be carried around on deck and set from dinghy or kayak. Chain is beastly heavy and is a hazard to the gelcoat. Safety on deck is improved because you no longer have to use one hand for the anchor and one hand for the rode. One hand remains free for balance.
- Smaller Anchor. I'm not suggesting tiny, just eliminating up-sizing for storm anchoring.
- Less Weight When Lowering. Just the anchor.
- Less Weight When Raising. Just the anchor.
- Less Mud. Dyneema does not bring up mud.
- Fewer Fittings. Splice eyes in both ends (Brummel for chafe), luggage tag it to the nylon rode, and use the existing shackle on the anchor.

The caveats? This is not for everyone or for every situation. A Dyneema leader only makes sense if the following conditions can be met:

- V Tandem Rig. With a single anchor, the boat yaws from side to side continuously, grinding the rode along the bottom. In a V rig, the rode will move very little, if at all.
- Soft Bottoms With No Large Rocks (scattered shells and small mobile rocks are acceptable).

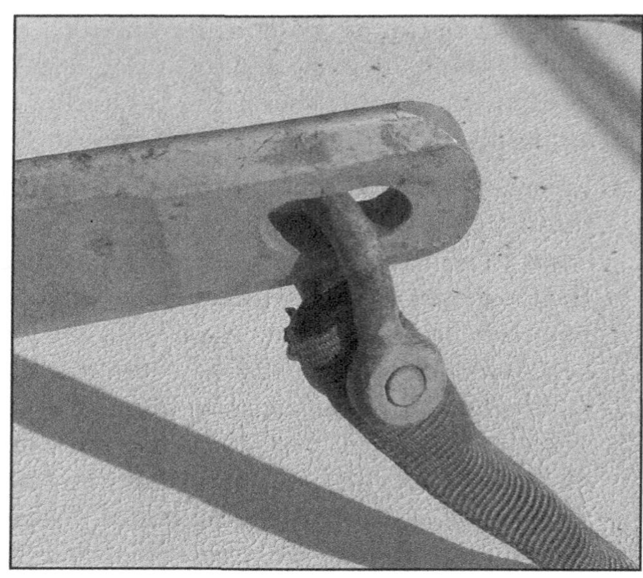

Tubular nylon webbing makes a very durable, free-floating chafe guard. The cover is secured only at the anchor end, by melting a hole and threading the shackle pin through the cover and rode eye inside.

- Short-Term Anchoring. In fact, V rigs are not well suited to long stays because the rodes are prone to tangling and winding together after dozens of wind shifts and tide changes.
- No Strong Tide. A Fortress needs the weight of chain to get it to the bottom when there is a strong tide. Made of aluminum with very large flukes, a Fortress anchor can glide on the current, never reaching the bottom. However, since soft mud bottoms seldom occur in areas with strong tide (the tide scours the mud away), this is an unusual problem to have when the Fortress is really needed.

Threading tubular webbing over the Dyneema leader greatly increases cut resistance, making it about as abrasion resistant as steel cable. Because the webbing is thick, floats separately from the Dyneema core, and is not under tension, even a sharp knife can't hurt it. If it rubs on a rock, the chafe guard slides or rotates with the rock, preventing abrasion. Finally, the webbing cover overcomes the handling and cleating problems of naked Dyneema or steel cable; the covered line is far more cleat and hand-friendly. Wire cable, on the other hand, is vulnerable to fatigue and cracking of individual wires. I have tested the Dyneema/webbing combination side-by-side with steel cable on a chafe test rig and found the wear and cut resistance is better in most scenarios. When the webbing gets too scruffy, it can be replaced for only $0.25/foot; the underlying Dyneema is preserved as good as new.

How long does the leader need to be? I have been testing using a 20-foot Dyneema single braid leader, entirely covered in webbing. The remainder of the secondary rode is ½-inch nylon rope. This is enough to follow the anchor underground and protect against cutting in all high-load areas. When recovering the anchor, it is enough to reach the deck, allowing easy hauling and cleating for break out.

The cross stock on this Northill anchor adds considerable holding capacity the moment it contacts the bottom by resisting being pulled through the soil sideways.

Roll Bar Anchors

A roll bar is a simple way to ensure an anchor will always roll over and engage, without leaving anything above ground for the rode to foul on. Properly executed, they also increase holding capacity, reduce over-burying, and ease break out. So what do we mean by "properly executed?"

Clogging

Although vendor videos show impressive reset characteristics, in really sticky mud many anchors become so clogged with mud that resetting is either delayed or prevented. In part the fluke is clogged, but more critically, the balance is upset, tipping the anchor backwards and preventing the toe from reengaging the bottom until the mud rinses out. The presence of a roll bar exacerbates the problem by holding mud in the aft section of the fluke. Unsurprisingly, there have been scattered reports of dragging related to this phenomenon. When deeply set during testing, both Rocna and Manson Supreme frequently came up completely clogged with mud. Mantus avoids the problem by spacing the roll bar well away from the fluke on wings—I never saw one clog. Spade avoids the problem by doing away with the roll ball entirely, achieving self-righting properties and deep setting through expensive fabrication methods (hollow shank) and a weighted tip (at the cost of fluke area). Not a major issue in anchor selection, but thumbs up for Mantus and Spade.

Self Righting

In truly soft mud, the roll bar has nothing to press against, and the anchor can remain stable upside down for some distance. The larger Mantus roll bar seems to help with righting, and the Manson Supreme seems to have some advantage in blade shape and weight distribution for self-righting. Spade seems immune to this problem. However, the bottom line is that good deployment practice, described in Chapter 1, will eliminate this problem for all designs.

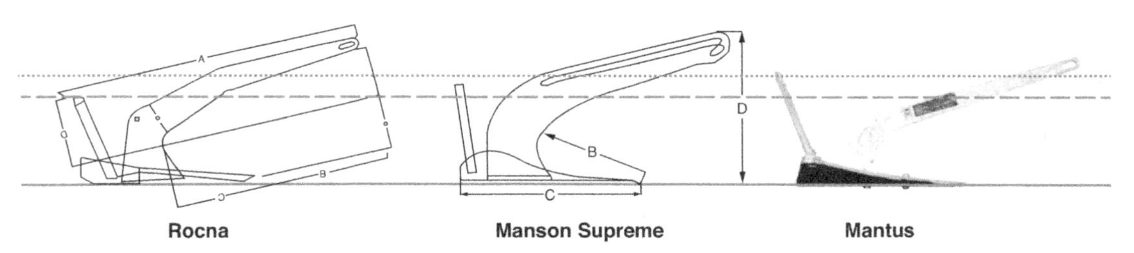

Roll bar height, bar diameter, and rake angle all affect holding capacity.

Although Mantus roll bars have been bent during testing, they are covered by a lifetime warrantee and are very easily replaced or straightened in the field.

Roll Bars and Cross Stocks Add Holding Capacity

I tested the holding capacity of a Mantus anchor both with and without the roll bar attached. The roll bar increased holding capacity by 20-40%. While resistance from large chain restricts anchors from setting deeply while adding nothing to holding capacity, a large stock like the Northill cross stock, or a large roll bar can make a significant contribution. They do this without the anchor burying deeply, which has two benefits:

- Easier Break Out. I love my Fortress anchor in soft mud, but the high recovery force is a disincentive to using it as my everyday anchor. Obviously, you can't have it both ways; an anchor that digs deep and functions at 3:1 scope is going to resist recovery.
- Less Reverse Catenary Effect. As an anchor digs deeper, the chain takes a curve and the fluke becomes progressively more parallel to the surface and stops digging, and ironically, stops holding. It just planes across, horizontally, with less resistance coming from the fluke and more from the chain and roll bar. The more resistance an anchor can develop from drag devices such as stocks and roll bars, the less deeply it must set and the steeper the fluke angle remains. (See Chapter 8)

The Mantus roll bar is unusual both for its large diameter and because it spaced away from the fluke on wings (others are welded to the fluke). As a result, the roll bar is pulled through fresh soil, undisturbed by the fluke, creating disproportionate holding capacity. Mantus and Rocna roll bars are raked backwards to prevent lifting the anchor as

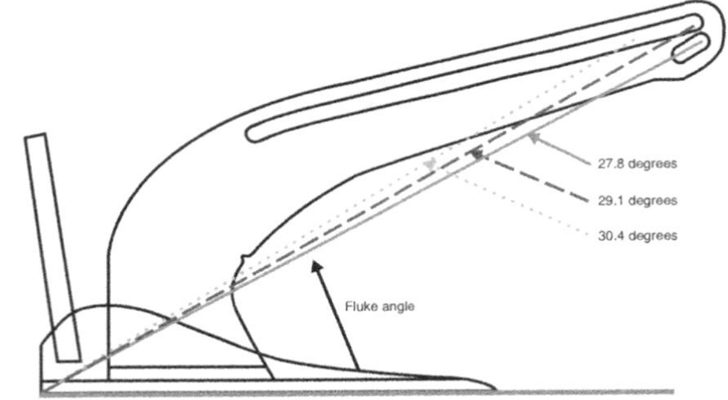

Fluke Angle. In anchors with a rock slot, the angle varies according to the rode attachment location.

it buries. Does the large, raked Mantus roll bar represent a positive design trend? Time will tell.

Accessories like cross stocks and roll bars are not just for righting, they also serve vital holding functions. As long as they do not impede burying by lifting the anchor, clogging or disturbing the flow around the fluke, they are not all negatives. Other designs employ kick-ups on the heel of the fluke or flanges angled inwards or outwards.

Angles

A rock on a rope is simple, but modern anchor design is deceptively complex, every angle and dimension affecting balance and penetration. But there is one angle that correlates with both setting speed and short scope performance; the angle of the fluke to the shackle eye when the fluke is just buried, known as the fluke angle. In theory, the sharper the angle, the faster an anchor sets and the better it cuts through hard layers and trash. Resetting ability also benefits. Alternatively, a blunter angle should

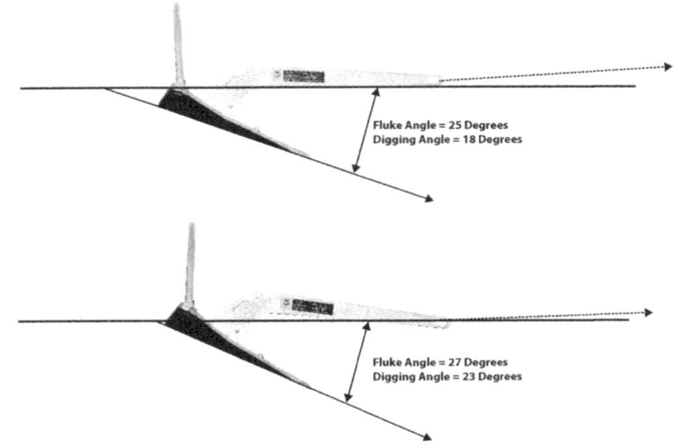

Because the fluke angle changes the attitude the anchor takes while digging, a one degree change in fluke angle results in a 2-3 degree change in digging angle.

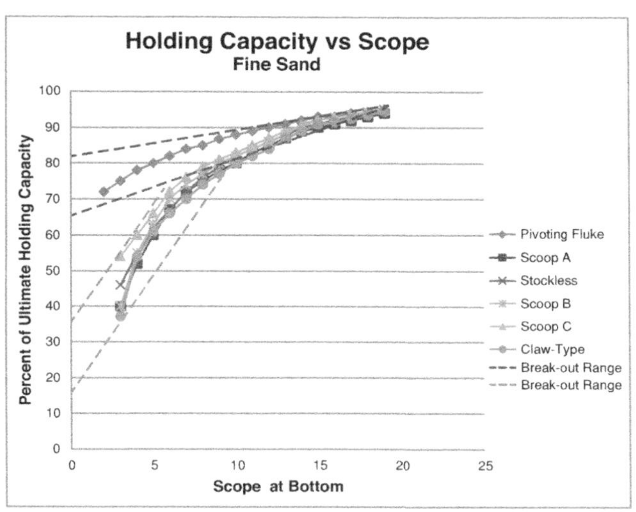

Figure 3. Based on actual effective scope at the bottom.

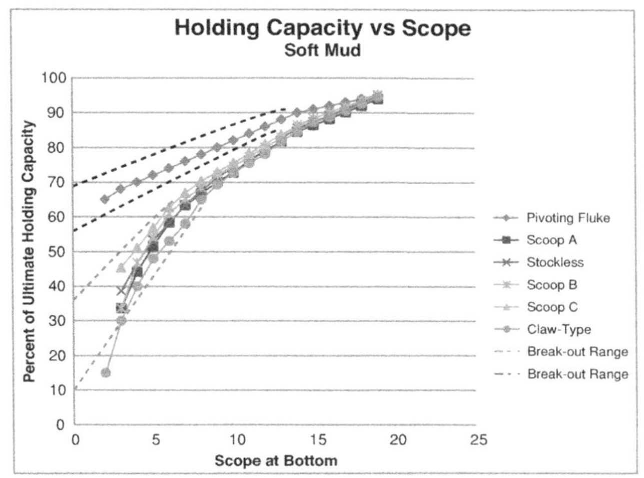

Figure 4. Based on actual scope at the bottom. Cyclical loading further reduces short scope capacity in soft mud.

promote deeper setting, more holding capacity, and better short scope performance.

To further study the effect I modified two anchors by varying the fluke angle as follows:

- Manson Supreme by attaching the rode to either the shackle hole or several locations along the rock slot.
- Mantus by drilling alternative shackle holes.

In each case, as the fluke angle was increased, setting became slower, the anchor became less able to dig through hard layers and push rocks aside, and resetting became less dependable. At the same time holding capacity increased 40-150% within the range of 25-32 degrees (the range of good setting performance), depending on the soil, anchor design, and scope. Visually, it was obvious that even a very small change in fluke angle resulted in a disproportionate change in the attitude the anchor took as it dug into the ground (about 2.5 times greater). The larger the angle, the more the heel of the fluke would jut upwards and the shackle end of the shank would angle downwards toward the bottom. Unsurprisingly, successful scoop anchor designs employ a very narrow range of fluke angles.

However, this is not to say that the lower-angle anchors had less holding capacity in all circumstances, because there are many other design variables. The changes illustrated in Figures 4 and 5 are relative to baseline holding capacity, which for all scoop anchors was very good (see Appendix IV for long-scope test data). Far more important is the macro trend—short scope = reduced holding capacity (Figure 4).

• Claw-style anchors have relatively low fluke angle when rolled upright, but a very high fluke angle when on the side. When rolled upright the broad face is prone to tangling on trash and can have trouble penetrating hard beds. Finally, although the 15 degree digging angle is very low, the side flukes are twisted and remain at a much steeper angle. Thus, the setting angle and short scope performance are similar. A different animal.

•• Pivoting fluke anchors begin setting at a very steep fluke angle and then pivot to the stated angle. Conventional anchors begin with a more blunt angle, which declines as they rotate into position and bury. Although these anchors are sometimes poor when there is weed or trash on the surface, once they get started they cut through trash in the soil. Reset capability is unreliable if the anchor becomes clogged with trash or sticky mud. However, if deeply set, they hold strongly enough that resetting is not generally necessary.

••• The Fortress anchors are adjustable to 32 or 45 degrees. The 32 degree setting is suitable for sand or mud. The 45 degree setting is only suitable for soft mud.

•••• Direct comparison of angles may not be appropriate. The second fluke and stock combine to put a lot of weight on the toe during penetration.

Table 11

Anchor	Measured Fluke Angle	Short Scope Holding Capacity	Setting Speed	Resistance to Trash Fouling
Claw	17-50 degrees	Fair	Fast	Low *
Fortress	32 degrees	Excellent	Fast	High **
Fortress	45 degrees	Outstanding	Medium	High ***
Manson	28 degrees	Very Good	Medium	High
Mantus	25 degrees	Fair	Very Fast	High
Northill	28 degrees	Good	Very Fast	High ****
Rocna	27 degrees	Good	Medium	Medium
Spade	26 degrees	Fair	Very Fast	Very High

This encourages fast penetration and makes it an effective weed and rock anchor. The anchor does not penetrate deeply, but this is OK—when the stock engages it adds a lot of resistance. The fatal shortcoming is that one fluke is always exposed, and if the tide spins the boat it will be fouled by the rode.

At short scope, Fortress, Danforth, and Manson are the champions as of this writing. Mantus and Spade, while the fastest setting anchors, should be given at least 5:1 scope at all times—even more if the rode will be lifting.

But is short scope holding capacity everything? Certainly not. The ability to penetrate hard bottoms or cut through shells and trash is often more important, creating circumstances where Mantus and Spade are the best choices. Really, is there any good reason to anchor in such a way that the actual scope at the bottom is less than 7:1? Not for most of us.

Easy break out is also a virtue, although it always involves a trade-off. As recently as the 1980s, before chain windlasses became commonplace on smaller boats, ease of breakout was a major selling point. Now short scope and fast setting are the buzz words. Unfortunately, the features that make for easy breakout, also reduce short scope holding capacity:

- Plow Shapes. They can cut vertically, just as they cut horizontally.
- Horizontal Stock. The Northill stock adds a lot of holding capacity when it buries, but it also prevents over burying. The Fortress stock is tiny when compared the fluke area and does not restrict deep burying.
- Heel Kick-Ups and Roll Bars. Like stocks, these increase holding capacity at the cost of reduced short scope holding capacity by reducing burying depth.

It seems there is no such thing as a free lunch.

Most anchors combine multiple features in the quest for the ultimate compromise. In the end, the physics of digging may preclude the possibility of a best all-around anchor, just as one cutting tool cannot serve for bread, wood, aluminum, and hardened steel. A wood chisel will never look like a cold chisel. The optimum angles for different soils are known to be different, and thus basic design requirements will forever remain mutually exclusive.

Watch for side-by-side test reports, but review the test conditions carefully and make sure they also report the bad results. Read cruisers' anecdotes with a critical eye—often they don't understand or accurately report the details of the failure. The best we can do is pick a compromise we like, and then strive to understand our choice. I'm also not sure that most of us could tell the difference between a Mantus, Manson Supreme, Rocna, or Spade once it disappeared below the waves. It's more about how you use them than the different compromises each has made.

Chapter 8:

Is an Anchor Ever Really Set?

ANCHOR TESTING always raises as many questions as it settles. There are too many important variables to control, and even if we could control them on test day, cruising will throw something different at you. But testing in soft mud made one thing very clear; it can take a really long distance for an anchor to set in a soft bottom. A full description of the Solomons Island Anchor Test program and the complete data set is available in Appendix III.

In sand most anchors achieve a good set within a few shank lengths and reach full holding capacity within 10 feet, but in very soft mud this took 30-60 feet. When we tested 2-pound mini-anchors in the same soft mud (Chapter 8) we got scaled down results; setting took 8-15 feet and there was never a hard stop. In Chapter 4 we learned that it takes time and very slow pulling to work an anchor to full holding capacity and depth. It is only after the anchor digs several feet below the surface that soil density and strength increases to useful values. This takes distance, and may have taken even more distance in this test protocol based on a slow, steady pull, than it does in the real world of setting, waiting,

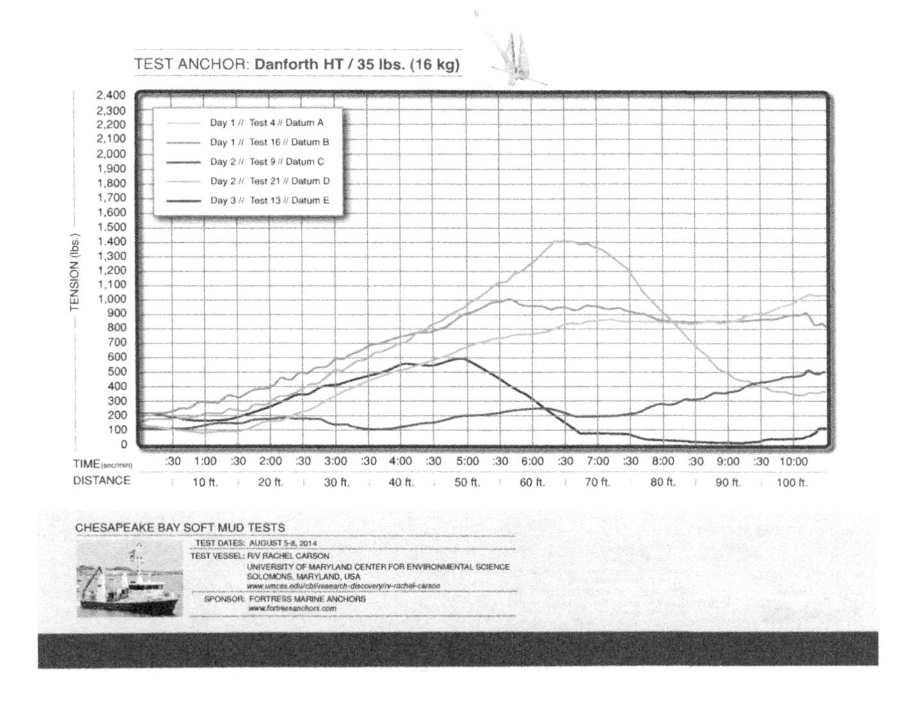

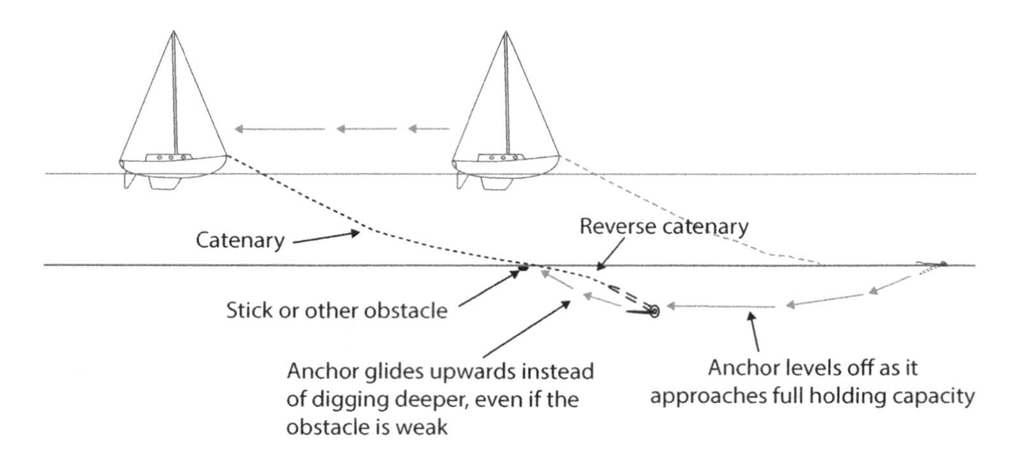

power setting, and then very slowly digging deeper as the storm builds. As the anchor works its way deeper underground, the chain begins to take on a reverse catenary curve and the angle of the fluke to the surface slowly decreases, until it is slicing along horizontally, not going deeper at all. Holding capacity stops increasing with distance pulled.

Why such inconsistent data, and why do so many trip after extended setting distances? There are many possibilities, ranging from impenetrable layers, to piles of shells, to soft spots. The scenario I observed most directly and frequently was debris lifting the chain. Many times I dove on an anchor after it had started to drag and saw a rotten tree limb either snapped in half or pushed to one side of the furrow. Although it was not strong enough to foul the anchor, it was enough to lift the rode and guide the anchor back to the surface. One more reason why even limited dragging is very dangerous and stable dragging is a myth in many areas. Always try to set the anchor carefully and in the shortest distance possible.

Soupy mud is a difficult test, but it is real-world and representative of many estuaries.

What does this mean? Through a series of examples, let's compare this data with actual cruiser experience in the area:

Example 1:

27-foot boat, 14-pound Danforth

Assume 2 1/2 times less holding capacity than 35-pound Danforth HT, based on a 0.92 exponent.

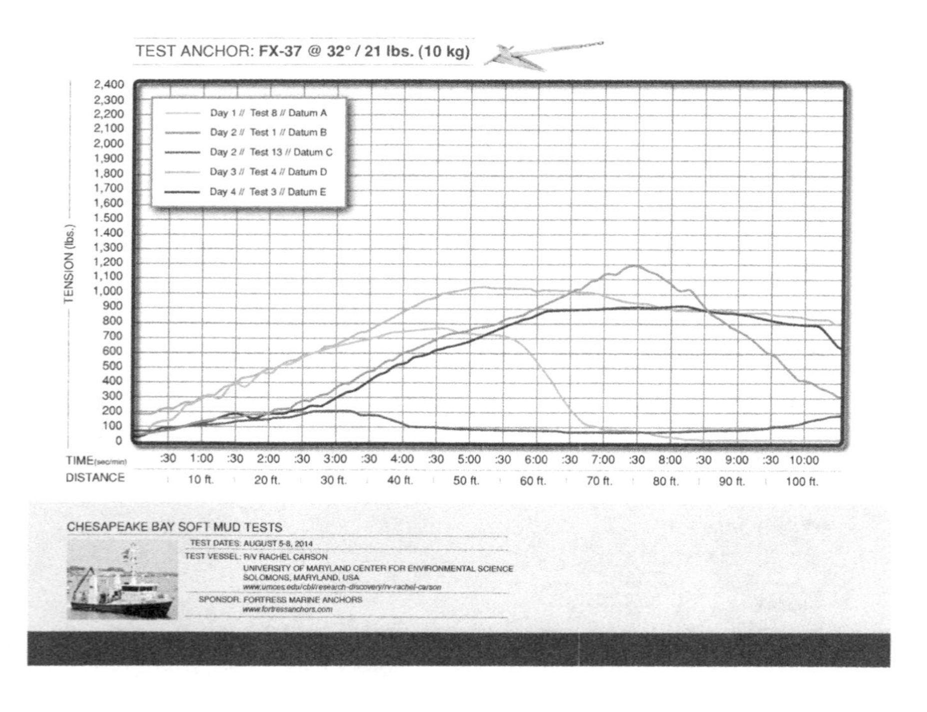

Additionally, the setting distance should be about 1/2 that of the 35-pound Danforth.

The Test 13 curve of the Danforth 35 HT was the weakest trial that would have seemed like a good set.

The following can be calculated for this boat:

- Setting force. 250 pounds (625 equivalent) = 15 feet setting distance.
- Holding capacity. 240 pounds, extrapolated from Test 6 (600 pounds/2.5= 240 pounds).
- Rode Tension. ABYC storm force/3 (allowing for a snubber) = 660 pounds.

Calculation says it will drag. In practice, this boat dragged on several occasions.

- If two anchors are set and some allowance is made for single-leg loading, the anchors will probably move 15-20 feet during extended setting.

The sailor then set a second identical anchor and this held. Assuming some soil consolidation, this also matches the calculations.

Example 2:

50-foot boat, Fortress FX-37 set at 32 degrees

- Setting force. 500 pounds = 40 feet setting distance.
- Holding capacity. 770 pounds from Test 8.
- Rode tension. ABYC storm force/3 = 2,100 pounds.

The boat dragged past me, about 50 feet, and then lifted anchor and departed farther up the creek.

Example 3:

32-foot PDQ catamaran, Delta 25

- Setting force. 280 pounds = no real set, unless I wait an hour and then apply the throttle gently. This matches actual experience.
- Holding capacity. 170 pounds, extrapolated from Test 2 (300 pounds x (25/44)^0.92 = 180 pounds).
- Rode Tension. ABYC storm force/3 suggests about 1,500 pounds. The maximum predicted with an 8 mm bridle is 1,300 pounds, and the maximum I have measured (50- to 60-knot gusts) is 850 pounds.

I dragged slowly in 20-25 knots on several occasions (224 pound rode tension, per Table 1);

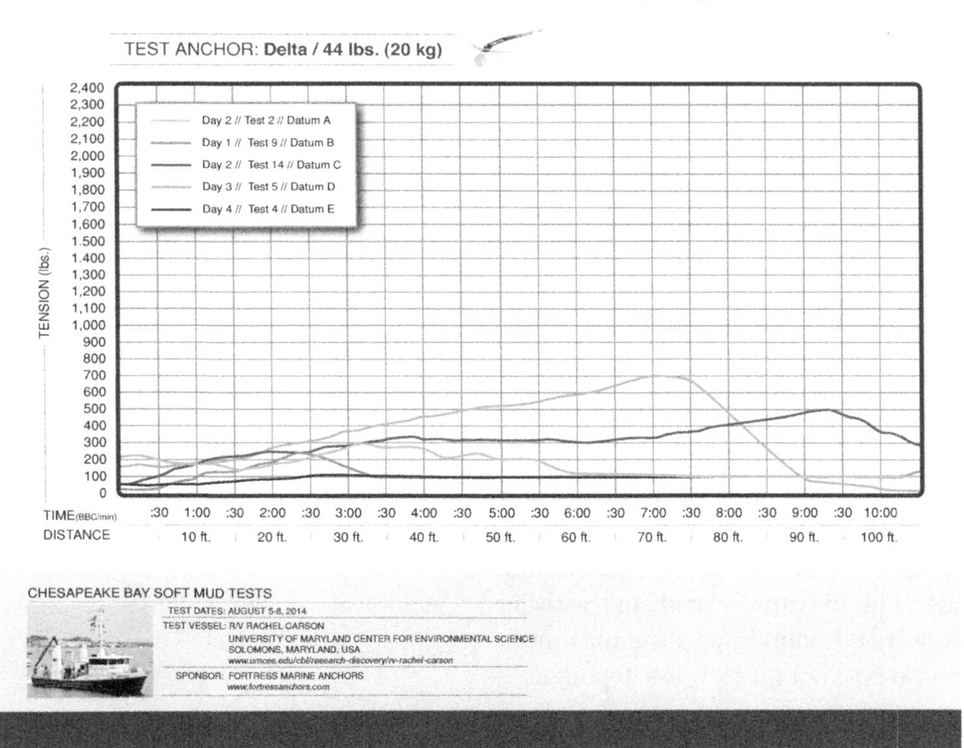

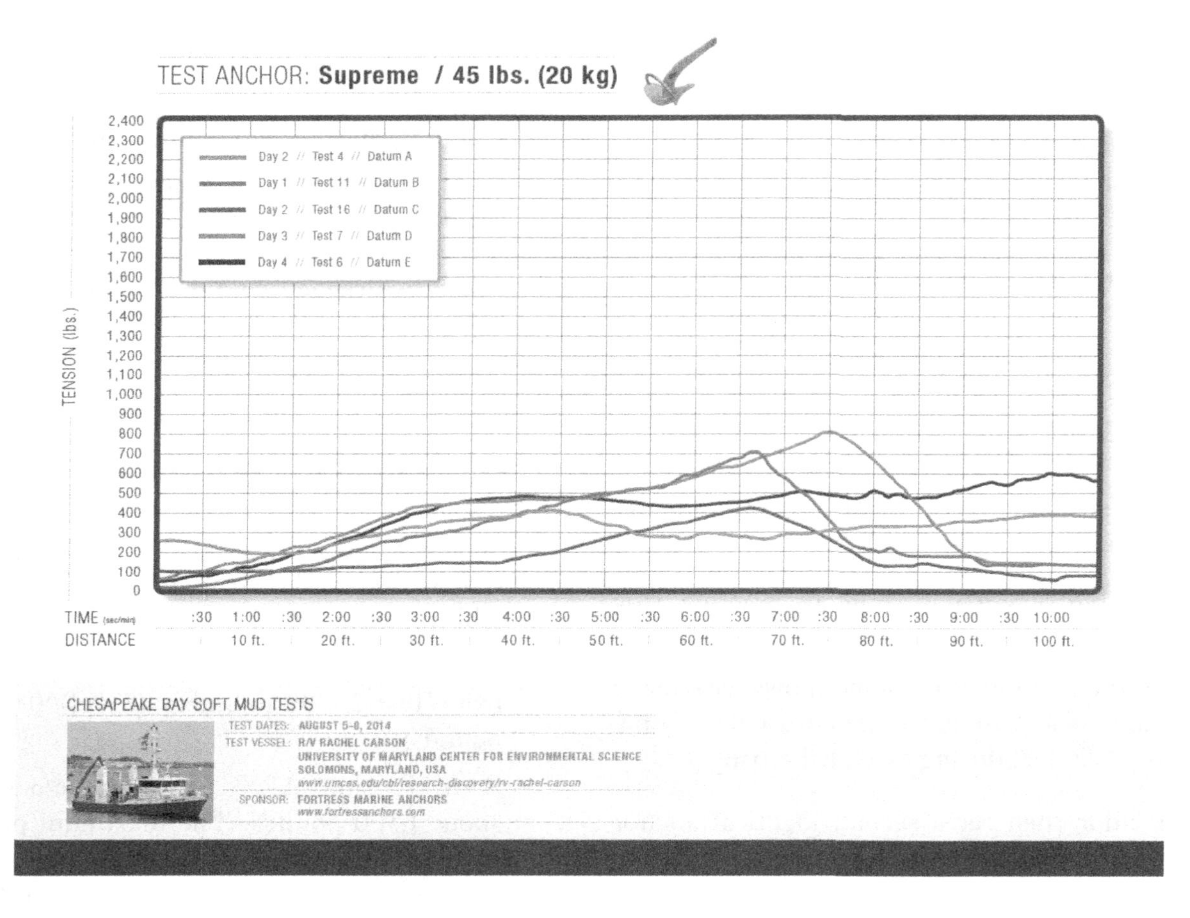

this seemed to be the threshold, which agrees well with the calculation, once improvement due to soil consolidation is considered. The solution was to set a Fortress FX-16 in addition, which easily stopped the dragging each time. In a real storm I would have dragged very quickly. The anchor is clearly undersized for the boat.

Example 4:

32-foot PDQ, FX-16 + Manson Supreme 35

- Setting force. 280 pounds = 15 foot setting distance on each.
- Holding capacity. 330 pounds for the Manson (extrapolated from Test 4) and 350 for the Fortress (extrapolated from Test 8), or 680 pounds total (about 560 pounds after correcting for the V angle).
- Rode tensions. ABYC storm force/3 suggests about 1,500 pounds. The maximum predicted with an 8 mm bridle is 1,300 pounds, and the maximum measured (50- to 60-knot gusts) was 850 pounds.

After dragging too many times with the Delta 25, I upgraded to a Manson Supreme 35. However, in this soft mud I still don't trust it alone when violent weather is predicted. With both anchors set in a shallow V, theory says I might drag, but I don't, most likely because of the substantial increase in holding resulting from soil consolidation (Chapter 4) common in this soil type. I do typically move about 5-10 feet in a very strong thunderstorm (over 60 knots), as measured by GPS, hardly noticeable and consistent with the Solomons Island test data. This is not dragging but rather is extended setting.

In good sand or mud, the 35-pound Manson Supreme is quite secure. Just not in pudding.

Everyone moves in soft mud. Don't let them tell you otherwise. But moving and dragging aren't exactly the same thing.

Chapter 9:
Tandem Anchors: Small-Scale Testing

WITH GOOD BASIC technique you should be able to anchor safely with a single anchor 95% of the time. If your working anchor is not holding in all normal circumstances and through moderate storms over average bottoms, you need to review basic practice and perhaps get a larger or different hook. Ask local sailors with similar boats what is working. Review proper deployment, setting and scope. If the bottom is terrible, the best answer is to move to better holding ground; an anchor will never be better than the ground (Chapter 8). Tandem anchoring is for exceptional situations when you find yourself in a situation you shouldn't be in. Nonetheless, occasionally terrible bottoms or extreme weather will require something more, and so in Chapters 10 through 12 we will explore practical advanced anchoring methods for the other 5%. But before full-scale testing, like any engineering problem, analysis and small-scale testing come first.

Even conservatively-sized modern anchors can't withstand a severe storm in a soupy bottom. Those that can—pivoting fluke anchors—aren't always secure during severe wind shifts. I've anchored in the Solomons Island test area countless times, learning that what one anchor can't accomplish, two can. But hard data on the best way to accomplish this is lacking.

It is also my firm belief that there is no "one-size fits all" answer. Rock, coral, and deep water present different challenges than soupy mud. In Chapter 12 we will explore the use of in-line tandems for difficult bottoms; they are very different in character, and as a result, very different rigging is required. But for the next few chapters we will narrow our focus to sand and mud.

My central premise is that the casual cruiser doesn't carry a monstrous storm anchor or specialized gear for a tandem rig. I wanted to develop a rig that can be assembled from what you do carry. For most of us that is either two plow or scoop type anchors of moderate size, or more often, a working anchor of modern design and a Fortress or Danforth anchor for kedging and storms. My second premise is that you are not interested in hurricane or major storm management; you'll see that coming and retreat to a marina far up a creek. Far more likely, a bad squall is approaching and you're anchored in soup. You've just sat down to dinner, the sky suddenly turns black, and 60-knot winds are reported to the west. Your anchor is well settled into the muck, and raising and re-setting in a different place or different rig would almost certainly reduce its holding capacity. You have neither the time to re-anchor nor a better place to go. You need a 10-minute solution that works using what you have on hand.

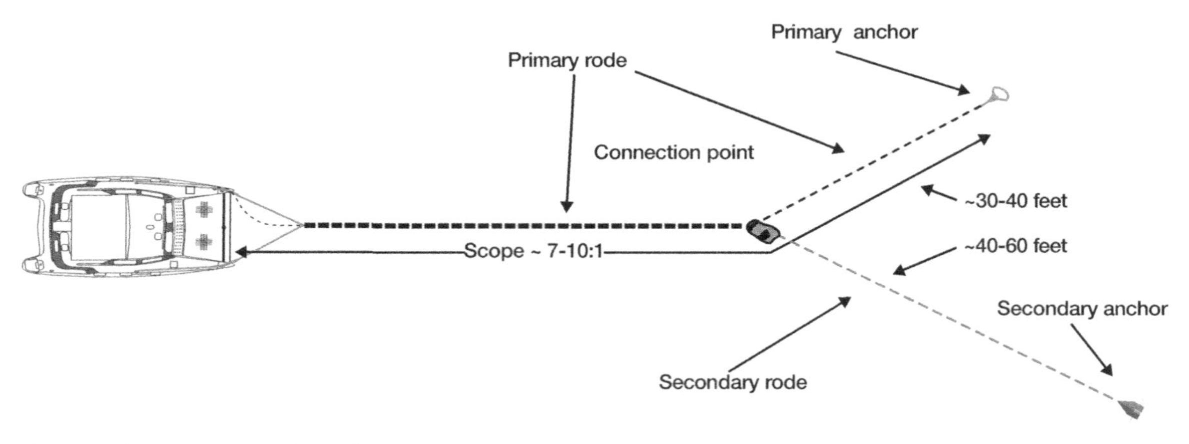

Rigging Arrangement 4: Secondary anchor attached to the main rode via a secondary rode. Anchor combination 3: Mantus primary with Guardian secondary.

My testing odyssey began by using small anchors for practical reasons; pull testing a good two-anchor rig in a good bottom with 20 to 35-pound anchors is beyond any practical pulling power. Deep water would make observing detailed behavior of the anchors difficult, and common sense says a diver shouldn't be anywhere near full scale anchors at peak load. Instead, I selected three anchors that are available in small sizes to serve as analogs for larger anchors. While holding capacity does not accurately scale up to their big brothers in weeds and cobbles, in consistent, clean bottom materials such as sand and soft mud, the differences are minor and scalability is well proven over a very wide range of sizes with many anchor types (Chapter 6). I've used these small anchors on small boats; I've worked with their big brothers for many years; and in the process I've developed a good practical feel for their differences and idiosyncrasies. Differences due to size, it turns out, are few.

How Small Anchors Behave Compare to Their Big Brothers (from Chapter 6)

- Holding power was proportional to weight, within 20%, for all models.
- Guardian. The smaller version is slightly more reluctant to get started on firm bottoms, but reliably digs right out of sight once started. It is also more prone to clogging with debris.
- Claw. Very similar to larger models on all bottoms.
- Mantus. Very similar to larger models on all bottoms.

Instead of focusing on specific anchors, I have focused on trends driven by rigging geometry. Which 2-anchor rig is better, by how much, and why? What is practical to deploy? I used the Claw as an analog for Bruce clones (and by extension, smaller plows and scoops since it is of lesser holding power), the Mantus Dinghy Anchor as an analog for modern scoop anchors (Manson Supreme, Mantus, Rocna, Spade, Super Sarca, Ultra, etc.), and the Guardian G-5 as an analog for pivoting fluke anchors (Fortress, Danforth, and their clones).

Nomenclature. The primary anchor is generally that which is closest to the boat. It is also the anchor attached directly to the main rode. The secondary is typically farther away. The secondary rode may attach the secondary anchor to the main rode, the primary anchor, or directly to the bow of the boat. The tripping eye is located high on the shank on the fluke end of the anchor (occasionally it is on the heel of the fluke) and is intended for extracting stuck anchors only. A tandem eye is located on the fluke end of the shank as close to the level of the fluke as practical, or in the center of the heel of the fluke. A load that is off-axis is one that is not aligned with the original orientation of the shank of the anchor.

Note: I drilled additional tandem attachment points in the Claw, Mantus, and Guardian anchors to allow testing of single-line tandems; while I believe the locations are safe and do not compromise

Initial qualitative testing of Mantus/Guardian V tandem at the Sandbox, Great Falls, MD. Very strong and stable. Most combinations performed worse than a single anchor.

the structural integrity of the anchors, increased corrosion is possible in galvanized anchors. After four years of exposure on full-size anchors, I have not seen accelerated corrosion in these holes. Adjacent zinc coatings provide considerable protection, and when a galvanized shackle is in place, it provides protection for the uncoated steel in the hole.

I tested four rigging arrangements:

1. Secondary anchor rigged to the tripping eye via a secondary rode.
2. Secondary anchor rigged to the tandem eye via a secondary rode.
3. Secondary anchor rigged to the primary shackle.
4. Secondary anchor rigged to the main rode about one boat length (6 feet for 2 pound anchors) from the primary anchor, with a one to two boat length secondary rode. This results in a shallow V angle with asymmetric legs.

We tested with five anchor combinations, although not with every rigging arrangement:

1. Both Claws.
2. Claw primary and Guardian secondary.
3. Mantus primary and Guardian secondary.
4. Mantus primary and Claw secondary.
5. Claw primary and Mantus secondary.

In all cases we initially set the anchors with a 10-pound pull; allowing for scale, this is equivalent to the setting force of a small sailboat engine. Although we have established that a gradually building wind encourages deeper setting, since our focus is squalls, we excluded that variable. In all cases we made certain that each anchor was carefully placed for good setting; this is never certain in the real world. I stopped pulling at 700 pounds to avoid equipment damage; that is a lot

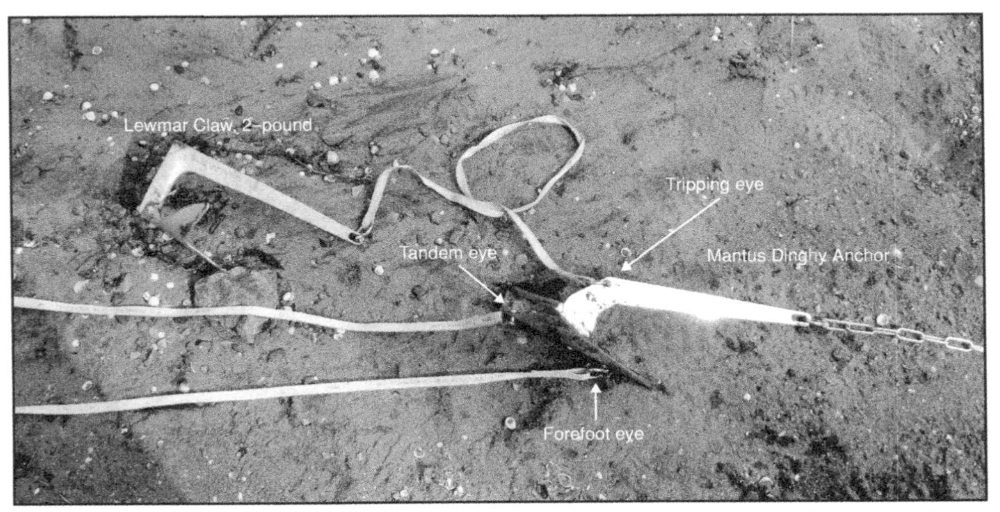

In-line tandem test rig, showing possible secondary rode attachment points. Only one attachment is used at a time, of course. (The forefoot eye is discussed in Chapter 12.)

Typical in-line tandem behavior. One anchor sets deeply and the other is lifted right out of the bottom, even if set first.

for a 2-pound anchor rig, about 12,000 pounds at 35-pound scale! This exceeds the breaking strength of the chain rode.

I then tested the more successful rigs in simulated storm conditions by using 2-pound anchor rigs to hold our 10,000-pound catamaran both for short stops and overnight under a variety of mild to moderate conditions. Rode tension was monitored to ensure it stayed within a realistic range, and the behavior of the anchors was monitored over a period of hours. In the best cases, we left it overnight. Anchors were marked with floats, and I dove on most sets before, during, and after testing. The intention was to observe the effect of dynamic loads from waves, gusts, and yawing under what amounts to a small scale imitation of a severe storm.

Tandem From Tripping Hole

Never do this. The primary anchor was pulled onto its side every time the load was significant and the direction of pull varied by more than 10 degrees. Secondary rode tension would then hold the primary anchor pinned on its back like a turtle, preventing resetting. If the rode lifted off the ground at all, the primary was plucked from the bottom and suspended, like an expensive kellet. Additionally, the tripping hole is not generally designed for anchoring loads; there have been reports of the tripping eye simply tearing out.

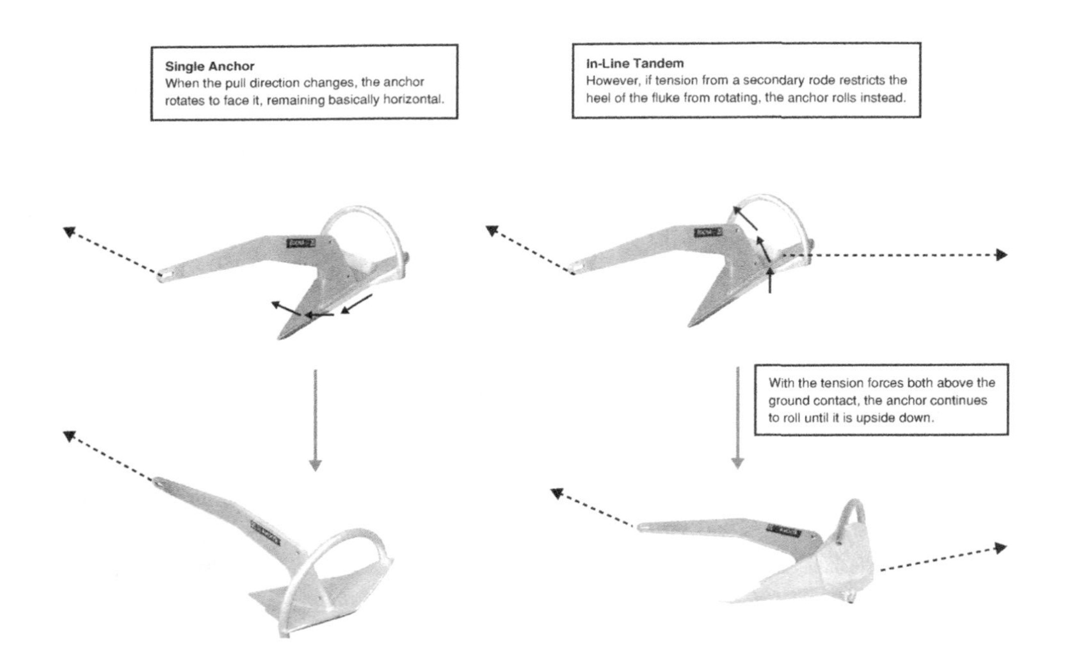

Even with a small secondary anchor (Lewmar Claw), the primary rolls out in a veer and will never reset. This happened in 100% of the tests, at all scales and with all anchor types.

Tandem From Tandem Eye

The U.S. Navy uses pivoting fluke anchors in series to create fleet mooring points and has an extensive research base. Oil platform moorings are sometimes built this way when the soil is too thin for larger anchors to bury to their optimum depth. The secondary rode attaches to an extension (tandem link) behind the flukes of the primary anchor, resulting in a very low lead angle and deep burial of the secondary anchor. The result is great holding power in a straight line—as much as 220% of single anchor holding—but only in a straight line and only with very large pivoting fluke anchors. The Navy uses these in 6-8 leg moorings, so the direction of pull never changes.

However, our testing using anchors that cruisers actually carry, exposed to real-world yawing, painted a very different picture. As soon as the load is as little as 10 degrees off axis, there is a geometrically increasing risk that the primary anchor will simply roll out. Even if the pull remains well aligned, as soon as the rig begins to drag, the primary is nearly always lifted out, losing most or all of its hold. The ability of the primary to dig and to rotate when the direction of the load changes is completely destroyed by the pass through secondary rode tension, which forces the anchor to move sideways and roll rather than pivoting smoothly. In fact, unless the primary is fully set first, the secondary rode tension completely prevents initial setting.

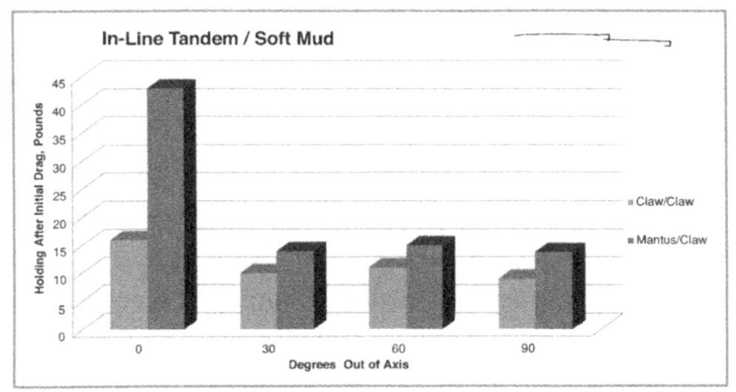

As soon as the wind shifts, the primary anchor might as well not be there.

The in-line tandem only achieved better than 20% reliability in sand or mud when there was no change in the pull direction, and when both anchors were of pivoting fluke design. These bury deeper, and as demonstrated in Chapter 4, are better able to resist uplift once set. Commercially available pivoting fluke anchors are not equipped with a shank extension or tandem link for attachment (U.S. Navy tandem anchors are), and it makes more sense to simply use the correct size, since they are not heavy.

The only situations where in-line tandem rigs excelled were those where normal burying behavior is impossible; cobbles, rocks, heavy weed, hardpan, and patchy sand. In fact, it is the most trouble free and the most effective 2-anchor rig for these bottoms. We will explore this further in Chapter 12.

Easy to foul and no way to know if the anchors are both set.

Although attaching secondary to or near the primary shackle does eliminate the pass through tension from the secondary rode and allows improved setting and rotation, it is still very prone to fouling if setting is not immediate and deep.

The preferred deployment method for tandem anchors for deep sea platforms has evolved away from attaching the secondary rode to the primary anchor, to attaching the secondary rode to the primary shackle. This reduces the influence of the secondary rode tension on the primary anchor. Additionally, the operation manuals for these multi-ton anchors advise that the holding power is still much less than the sum of separate anchors and should only be considered when the soil is too thin for a suitable single anchor. (Vryhof Anchors, Anchor Manual, 2015.)

Tandem From Near Primary Anchor Shackle

Eliminating interference from the pass through secondary rode tension substantially improves the setting of the primary. For the first time, we were consistently able to set both anchors and to keep them set through most changes in pull direction. However, unless the primary is very well buried, the secondary rode can foul the primary anchor as it drags back and forth across the bottom; normal yawing is all that is required. You will not be able to detect this fouling by feel and will not know that it has occurred (this occurred in about 25% of our deployments). Likewise, you cannot independently confirm that both anchors have set, a critical shortcoming; they cannot be power set separately to confirm they are both well set. Like the tandem eye rig, the scope must still be very long (figure 2a, Chapter 12), since the primary must still withstand 100% of the lifting force for both anchors. This rig responds a little better to wind shifts (so long as the shift does not cause fouling) since the primary anchor is free to rotate rather than encouraged to roll-out by secondary rode tension.

V Tandems

There are many variations, starting with the shackle-rigged single-line tandem described above, where the length of main rode between the secondary rode attachment point is zero, and finishing with the Bahamian moor (Chapter 11) where the length of main rode after the connector and the secondary rode are equal. The relative size of the anchors can also vary. The rodes can be led back to the boat or they can be joined closer to the anchors. The focus here is on V tandems with asymmetrical legs of about 1-2 boat lengths; I couldn't test everything without getting lost in the woods.

If the load does not force either anchor to drag, the entire load may be carried by either anchor, without the need to shift to face the wind. However, Chapter 8 taught us that when anchored in soft mud the anchors are going to move around a little. With a Bahamian moor the anchors are too far apart to support each other if the wind changes by more than 45 degrees, and by the time either anchor drags far enough to once again share the strain, it will certainly have tripped or fouled. In the case of a 90 degree shift, the anchor would need to drag over 100 feet, and in some cases nearly twice that; the anchor will surely trip on debris.

An asymmetric V tandem behaves very differently. Because the rodes are shorter, the primary needs to move only a short distance before it can begin buffering the impact of changes in pull direction on the secondary, an inherent characteristic of asymmetric V rigging. In each test, so long as the primary anchor was a scoop or claw-type, it was able to slowly rotate to face the new pull without unsetting, as long as the load was also increasing, just as the rig needs to behave in the face

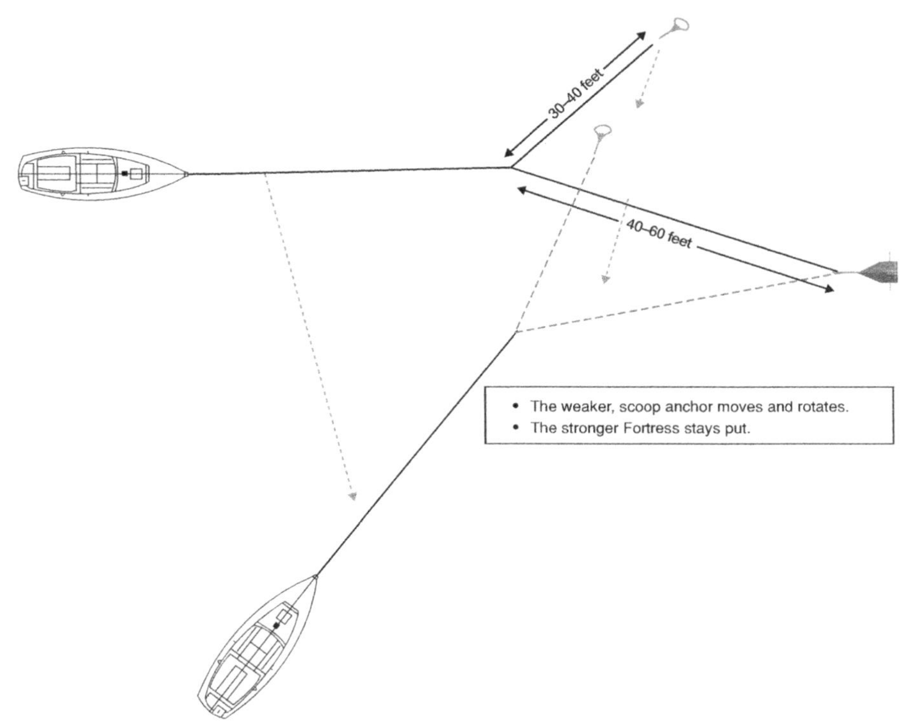

A V tandem with asymmetrical legs is very stable through wind shifts.

of a rising storm. The secondary did not have to rotate as much. This was the most stable rig tested.

Optimum Leg Lengths and Asymmetry

A leg length ratio of between 2:1 and 3:1 was most flexible, and we settled on 2:1 for extended testing. The optimum leg length is a compromise between keeping the anchors safely separated, isolating the primary from the lifting influence of the secondary rode, being able to join the rodes after setting in a given depth of water, and reducing dragging distance. I chose one boat length for the shorter leg, increasing to three times water depth in deeper water as a practical matter; we need to be able to reach the rode connection point, since we want to be able to set and test each anchor independently. In firm sand, full-scale anchors seldom move more than 4-8 feet before reaching full holding power. However, during Solomons Island testing, all of the anchors dragged at 30-45 feet before reaching maximum holding, or about one boat length. This long-setting behavior has serious implications for Bahamian moors; they are unlikely to maintain their original geometry in strong conditions. While they are moving primarily in the direction of the load, it is also important that full scale anchors begin at least 40 feet apart in order to retain a safe spacing of about 20 feet and achieve the intended final geometry (which includes this drag factor). Scaled down, this logic and these relative dimensions formed the basis for our small-scale V tandem testing.

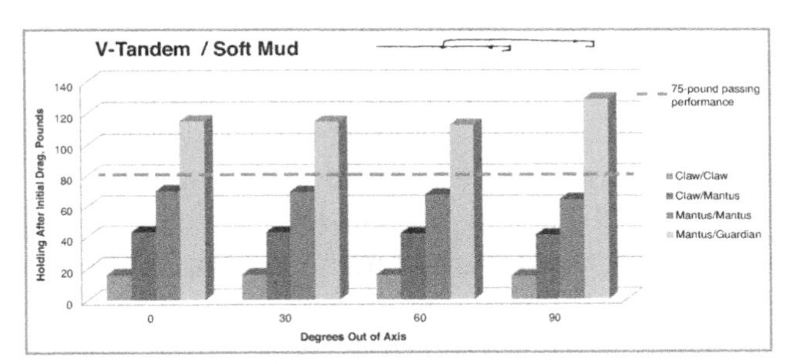

The scoop/pivoting fluke pair was stable over a wide range direction change.

Data Review (please refer to the bar charts in Appendix I). The bottom line is that only the asymmetric V tandem rig could keep both anchors working and stable at high load when the direction of pull changed. In-line tandems tripped. A Bahamian moor collapsed, the secondary anchor fouled or tripped before it could drag far enough to once again share the load.

Our goal was to find a rig that would work with the gear you have on board. If your secondary (actually your main anchor) is a scoop type and the new primary is a pivoting fluke type, this is the best of all worlds, for soft mud at least. Our best results were obtained using the Guardian as secondary and the Mantus as primary. However, all combinations of anchors rigged in an asymmetric V provided holding capacity very close to the sum of the individual capacities through a range of pull directions. They never fouled or tripped.

Adjusted to full scale, the results were very promising. The scale-up factor from test scale to our 32-foot catamaran test boat is 5:1 for the pivoting fluke anchor and 15:1 for the scoop anchor. Windage is roughly equivalent to a 40-foot monohull. The wind plus wave force on this boat (all chain rode, 10:1 scope, snubber) is about 760 pounds with standard snubber at 45 knots (Chapter 2), or about 50-75 pounds at test scale. This was our standard for a "pass" with these small anchors. The chain breaking strength on the test boat is 7,600 pounds, equivalent to 500 pounds at test scale. With this basis, our small anchor tests scale up to standard size anchors as follows:

At Full Scale:

- Soft Mud
    - A single Claw will drag.
    - A single Mantus will drag.
    - A single Fortress will hold.
    - The best in-line rig, the Mantus/Claw combination, will drag as soon as the wind shifts and is weaker than a single Mantus.
    - The Mantus/Mantus V tandem may drag.
    - The Mantus/Guardian (Fortress) V tandem was consistently greater than 120 pounds and should be secure in all conditions.
- Sand
    - A single Claw will drag.
    - A single Mantus will hold.
    - A single Fortress will hold but may be vulnerable to sudden shifts if not well set.
    - The best in-line rig, the Mantus/Claw combination, will drag as soon as the wind shifts because the Mantus will be tripped by the Claw.
    - The Mantus/Mantus V tandem will hold.
    - The Mantus/Guardian (Fortress) V tandem will hold as much as the chain.

Anchoring a 32-foot Catamaran with 2-Pound Anchors

In order to better simulate how a tandem will react to dynamic loadings yawing and wind shifts under storm conditions, we anchored our 10,000-pound catamaran using both in-line and V tandem rigs in moderately strong to breezy conditions in firm sand. We reasoned that anchoring an 10,000 pound catamaran in a moderate breeze with mere 2-pound anchors was equivalent to severe storm testing with full size anchors. Peak loads were recorded.

The single-line tandems were deployed at 20:1 scope. Even so, as the load approached 1/3 of the holding capacity of the primary anchor, typical yawing pulled it out of the bottom and left it hanging above the bottom or flopping uselessly on its side. Since the Claw was too small on its own, uncontrolled dragging followed.

The V tandem anchors rotated to face the force every time. The rig easily withstood the full setting force of the 32-foot catamaran (about 280 pounds). The Mantus plus Guardian pair was stable up to 15-20 knots, with peak loads of up to 450 pounds observed. The surging and yawing had no effect. We never tripped an anchor. When a 15:1 scale-up factor is applied, this equates to holding 4,725 pounds. Since the test boat rode tension is only 1,300 pounds in 60 knots of wind using an appropriate snubber, this is a very secure rig.

Conclusions. Our study has been relatively narrow—uniform sand and soft mud bottoms with just a few anchor types and rigs—but there are a few clear lessons:

- Tandem anchor rigs exhibit the same general trends in mud vs. sand, although the holding in soft mud is far less. Some have suggested that in-line tandems are more stable if deeply buried in soft mud, but that is not what I saw. If a rig is unstable in sand, it will be unstable in mud. An anchor that is buried many feet under the mud would flip over and glide right to the surface, like an airplane.

- In-Line Tandem. Worthwhile for impenetrable or rocky bottoms (see Chapter 12), but not applicable for soft bottoms.
- V Tandem. Make certain the primary is completely buried (they can be set separately); the secondary rode can trip the primary if the wind shifts in that direction and anything more than the roll bar is exposed. Asymmetric leg lengths resulted in more holding power and more stable dragging and load sharing. Place the higher holding power anchor farther from the boat, allowing the primary to buffer the wind shifts and the secondary to provide most of the holding capacity. If you must place the higher holding power anchor nearer to the boat, try to orient it towards the expected wind. Even in very soft mud, a V tandem of appropriately sized anchors should hold in storm winds. Scope requirements are not changed.

There is a synergism gained by using a modern scoop-style anchor in combination with a pivoting fluke anchor such as the Fortress in a V tandem. The Fortress is protected from rapid changes in pull direction, and the extent of the shift in pull direction is also reduced. Thus protected from rapid changes, the Fortress was able to slowly turn to face the load and do what it does best—provide massive holding capacity in a limited range of directions. At the same time, we take advantage of a scoop-style anchor's uncanny ability to track with wind shifts while still providing considerable resistance, buffering the changes the Fortress feels. The result is increased stability and holding power, more than the sum of the parts.

In Chapters 10 through 13 I continue this line of exploration, taking what was learned in the shallows with 2-pound anchors into the field with full-sized anchors, sometimes compromising what is best for what is practical.

Chapter 10:
V Tandems for Soft Mud

Drifting back on my 25-pound Delta, I felt nothing. The chain stretched out, cross sightings and GPS confirmed that I was motionless, but power setting with even minimal throttle started us dragging again. The shore beckoned, but the guidebook reminded me that Harness Creek—a tiny Chesapeake Bay tributary—is notorious for poor holding, and the weather service predicted a sustained 25 knot breeze in the afternoon. As a back-up, I lowered my Fortress FX-16 from the bow, trailed the rode to the transom, and from the lowest step, lightly set the anchor in the ooze at about 5:1 scope. I then led the secondary rode back to the bow (35 feet), connected it to the main rode, and let out 20 feet more scope, for a total of 7:1 based on this new anchor. I would have eased more, but a late arrival was too close to my stern. I should have taken the Fortress out in the tender and set it properly. Sloppy work, but I reasoned sufficient, and I dinghied ashore to stretch my legs and explore. The breeze came up right on schedule, and when I returned two hours later, the boat that was behind me, and the two previously to windward had dragged more than 100 yards and were firmly grounded in harmless mud. I had drifted back about 20 feet and was securely anchored by my hastily rigged V tandem. A few weeks later I upgraded from a 25-pound Delta to a 35-pound Manson Supreme. I don't recommend this sort of learning process—I'm just recounting what happened.

Is it practical to deploy two anchors without breaking our backs, creating horrendous tangles, or adding unreasonable hassle? Can this be accomplished during the approach of a storm, in rough weather, in the dark, and in time? I've made mistakes, tried suggestions that just didn't work, and over many seasons, winnowed our procedures down to those that work dependably and predictably.

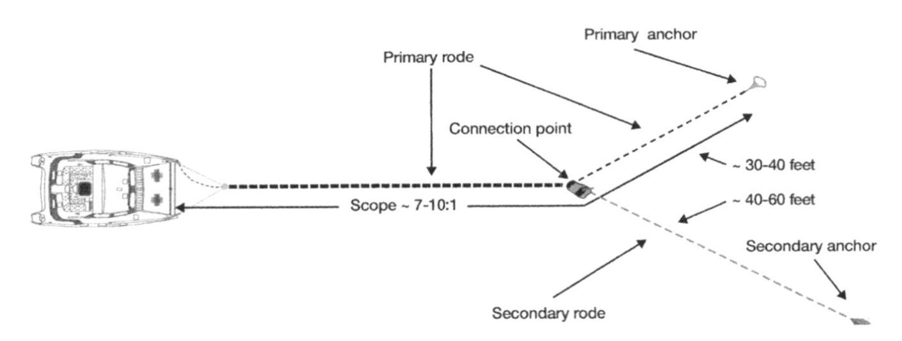

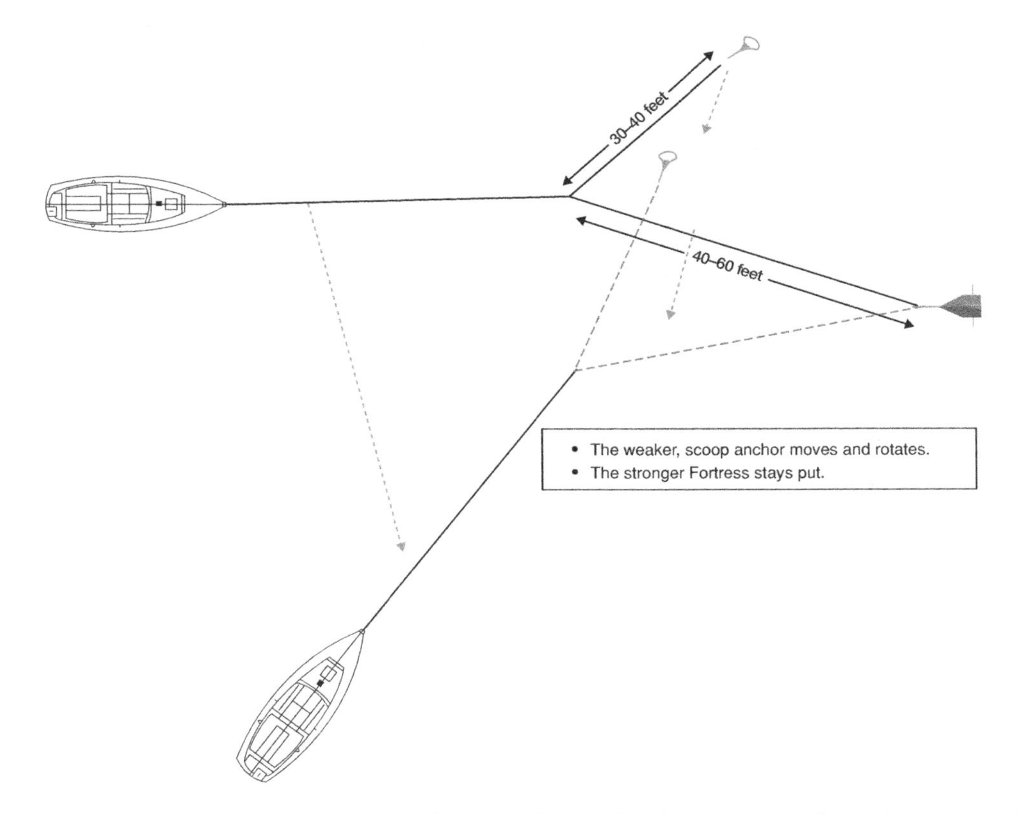

Finally, I reviewed what I learned testing smaller anchors and took those principles into the field, continuing my testing with a 35-pound Manson Supreme, 35-pound Rocna, 25-pound Delta, 12-pound Northill Utility, Fortress FX-16, and Danforth S-160 (16-pounds). Here we go.

The Standard Method

Ideally, the secondary anchor is the stronger anchor, the primary is a scoop-type, and the wind will rotate away from the primary anchor. The primary will set deeper and then drag towards the force until the load is once again shared. The holding capacity is approximately the sum of the single anchors. If the shift rotates back, the secondary rode may pass over the primary anchor, but in sand or soft mud, the primary will be well buried. If the wind continues to rotate in the original direction, the primary will drag farther and farther (set deeper) to achieve balance; the practical advantage of a one-boat length connecting rode is that the dragging distance and risk of fouling is minimized. The stronger secondary anchor sees a change in pull direction, but the change is buffered by slow dragging of the weaker primary anchor. If the secondary is a Fortress, it gets to do what it does best; hold strong with a limited direction change. If the primary is a scoop, it gets to do what it does best; slowly rotate to face the new pull and dig in deep. Instead of interfering with each other, they are complimentary, each playing to its strength. In test after test, this compensation by deeper setting and limited dragging was stable.

Deployment

Although it is possible to set a V tandem rig in one operation from the boat, it never seems to happen that way for me. Sometimes I anchor in the normal manner and only later realize that I'm in for a real blow. Other times it is only after setting the primary, feeling the bottom in terms of setting behavior, that I realize that one anchor is just not enough. Thus the fastest deployment goes something like this:

- Come up to short scope, about 4:1, depending on the depth of the water.
- Take the secondary anchor out to the appointed location using a dinghy or kayak (very practical with Fortress anchors). The rode may be either nylon or polyester double braid and is premeasured to the correct length, typically about 50 feet. The rode will also have a 100-foot extension attached, secured to the boat.

Connecting the secondary rode to the primary rode, before backing away to place the second anchor. The Dyneema leader on the Fortress FX-16 makes this easy work, even from a kayak.

- Go back to the boat and set the secondary anchor using the extension line, either manually or by using the engine.
- Connect the two rodes using one of the connectors described in Chapter 13, either by leaning over the pulpit or from a dinghy. Disconnect the extension line.
- Ease the main rode out to standard scope. Since a storm is coming, that means 7:1, perhaps more.

Heavy Anchor

If the secondary is too heavy to manhandle into a dinghy, you can move the boat instead. I've done this many times when the weather was poor or I simply did not feel like taking the dinghy out. However, I generally find it easier to accurately gauge the spot correctly to get the correct secondary rode length just right when I use the dinghy. Most afternoons I'll be taking the dinghy somewhere anyway.

Backing away to place the secondary anchor. Why a kayak, when I have a tender? Because it's that much easier, even with a large aluminum anchor.

An all-chain secondary rode is often impractical to lay from a dinghy. The weight also makes it very difficult to work out the resulting mess if the rodes twist around each other. In most areas, because a V rig will not allow sawing back and forth across the bottom, only a short chain leader is required for the secondary rode. A bucket is handy for moving chain leaders around on deck and in the dinghy.

Tripping Line

I hate these things for all of the usual reasons: they can tangle around your propeller or rudder, or around someone else's. A foolish boater may think it's a mooring. It's one more thing to fool with. However, I frequently used them during testing because it made it easier to gauge relative anchor positions, and it made locating the anchor for diving inspection much easier. It also provides another recovery possibility; you can simply cast off the rode, perhaps in a storm, and come back for it later. Thus, I believe a tripping line can make a good learning tool until you get the hang of it. You decide. Use a small, brightly painted buoy; it should not have more than a few pounds of buoyancy, since you don't want it lifting the anchor at high tide. See Chapter 12 for a discussion of the best attachment location.

Recovery

Even simpler and hardly any different than recovering a single anchor twice.

- Recover enough main rode to disconnect the snubber.
- Continue recovering main rode until the secondary rode connectors is reached. Attach the extension line to the secondary rode with a carabiner and cleat off. This allows you to remain in contact with the secondary anchor while recovering the primary.
- Detach the secondary rode from the main rode.
- Recover the primary anchor in the normal way. Manage the slack in the secondary rode and

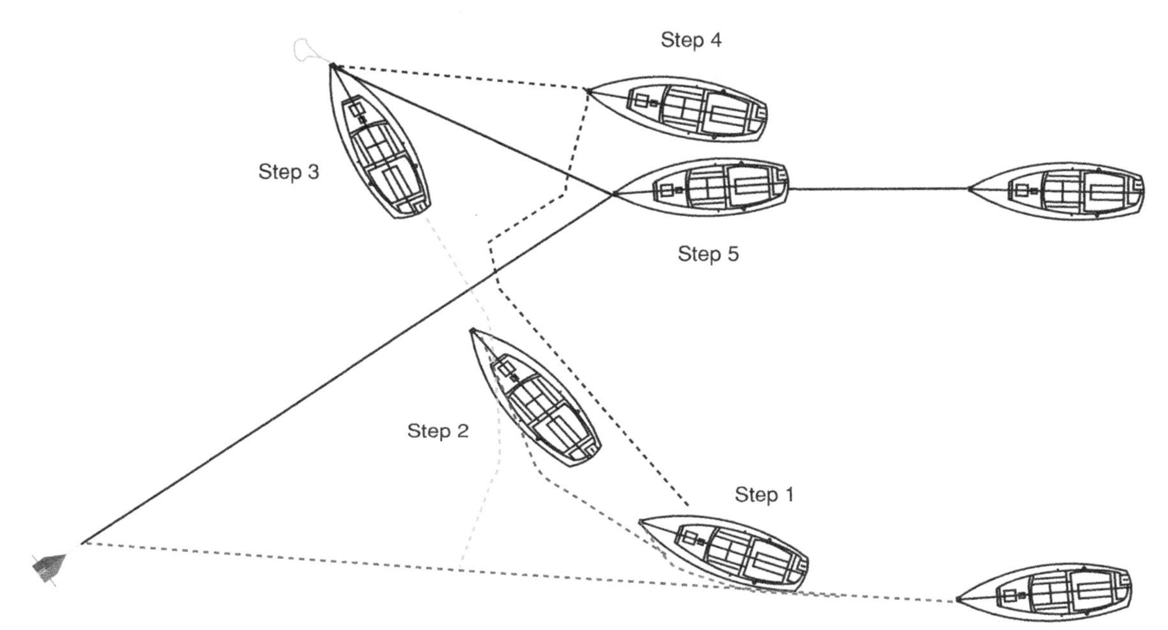

A second anchor can also be placed by moving the boat. However, notice that during steps 2 and 3 the boat basically runs over the rode, creating a serious fouling risk with rope rode, and a scraping risk with chain. If deploying rope, recover the slack while moving to the second drop point.

extension line so that it cannot reach the keel or propeller.

- Recover the secondary anchor in the normal way, using the extension line to pull the boat over to it and to access winches and cleats as necessary to break it out.

Rowing the Strong Anchor Out in the Direction of the Anticipated Shift. Although not as stable, in theory, as the first case, this is often the best we can do. The trick is to add enough slack in the secondary rode, after setting, so that the boat can settle back into the newly formed V when the wind shift arrives.

Deploying from the Deck

While not ideal, the practical advantages are obvious; no one has to go out in a dinghy, the boat does not need to be moved, and the primary anchor is not disturbed. Instead of rowing the second anchor out, it is lowered from the bow and the boat is allowed to drift back. Often the anchor can be hand set by walking the rode back and pulling from the transom. I've done this many times.

Secondary Anchor Positioned to Face Anticipated Wind Shift

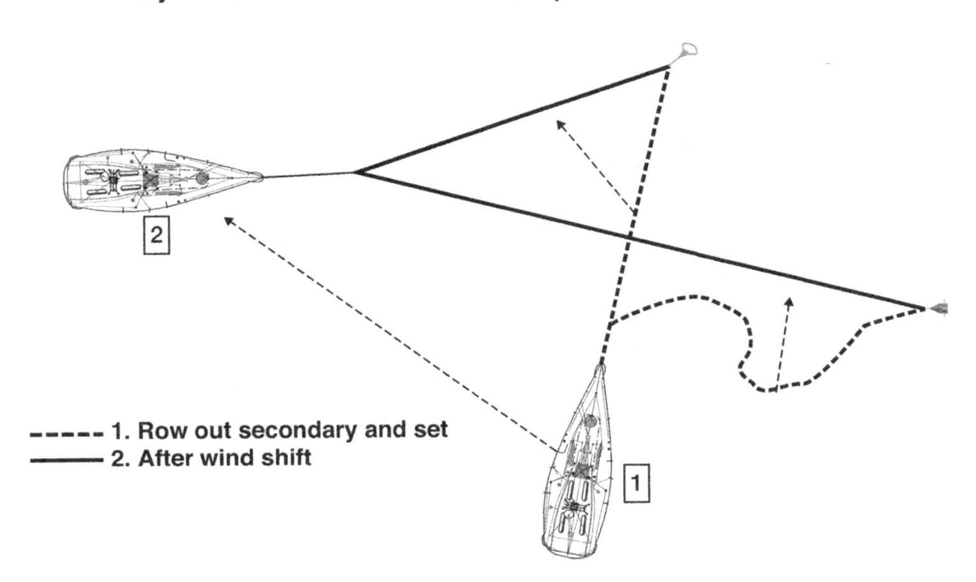

Secondary Anchor Lowered from Bow

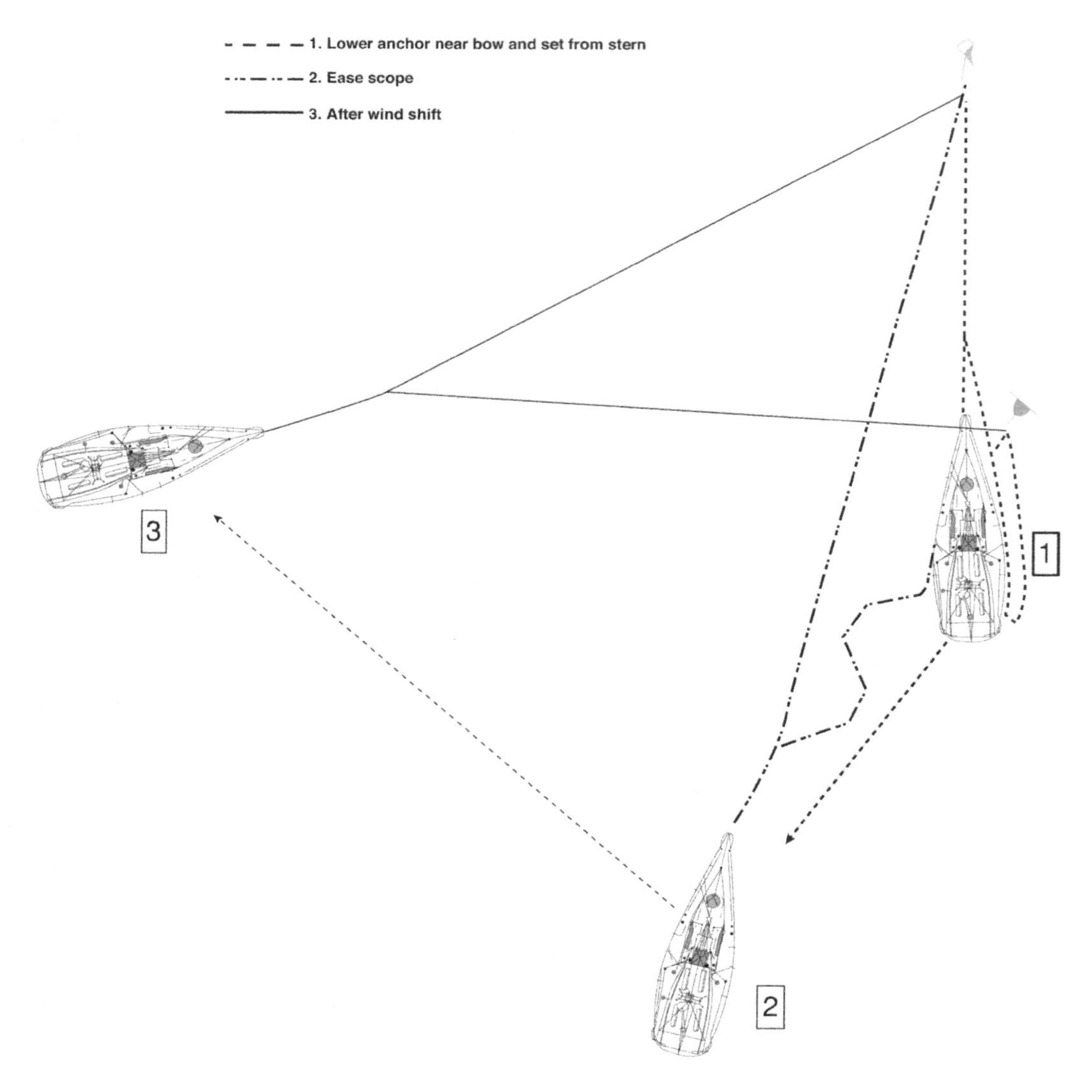

Most often, this secondary anchor is a pivoting fluke type, and the vulnerability of this rig is that the pivoting fluke anchor may see a dramatic shift in direction and carry the lion's share of the load, with the primary anchor doing little to support it. Again, the trick is to add enough slack to the secondary rode so that as the wind shifts, a V is formed. Since the secondary rode is probably nylon, a snubber is not required.

Although I have shown the rodes as connected, in both of these later cases it is perfectly acceptable to bring the secondary rode to the bow, where it can be adjusted as the wind shifts. If the secondary rode is nylon, no snubber is required.

From a Hammerlock Mooring

In this slight variation on deck deployment, the rode of a hammerlock mooring is gradually eased as the wind shifts. The downsides are that the rodes must be led back to the bow, active tending is required during the shift, chafe gear must be repositioned, and it cannot be used with a bridle (no multihulls). Very labor efficient when applicable.

Can V Tandems Drag Together and Foul?

If the legs are asymmetrical, this can only happen if an abrupt shift drags the primary exactly over the secondary. For a Bahamian moor, one anchor must drag one times the original spacing if the load is exactly in line, and at least five times the original spacing if it is at 90 degrees. That means either very bad luck, or that you have dragged 100-500 feet before the anchors become close. Even then,

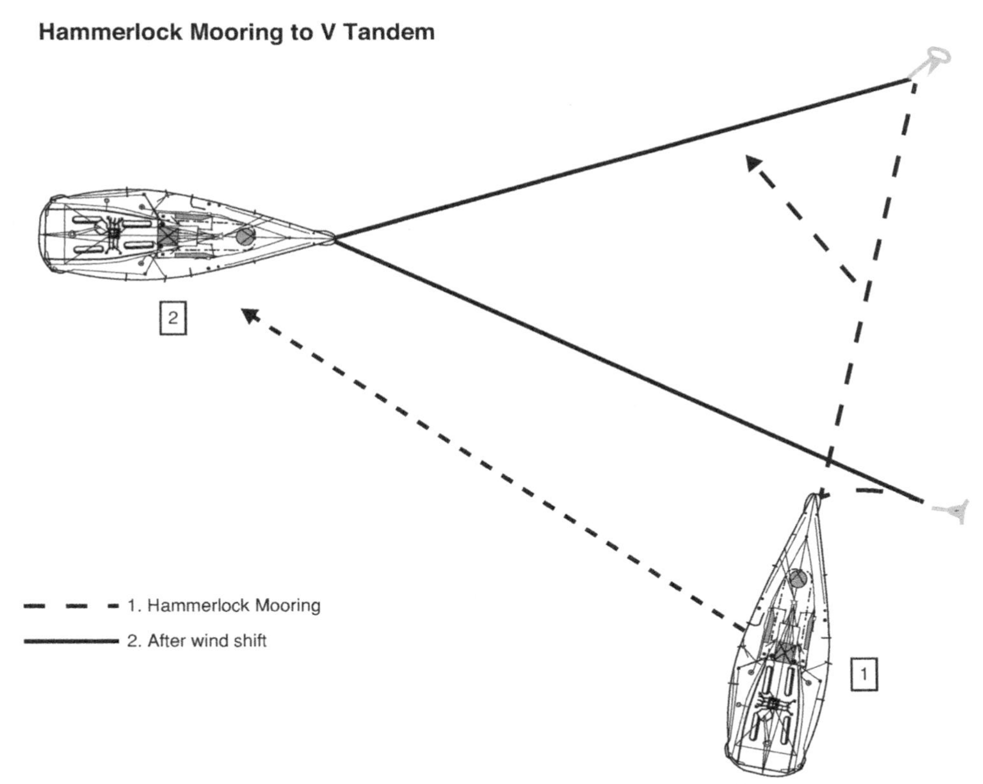

Ease the secondary rode as the wind rises and shifts.

we found that anchors can often drag side-by-side for considerable distances—over 100 feet—without interfering with each other. I suspect they have it backwards when dragging was blamed for fouling; the anchors were off to the races, dragging at high speed, and eventually the lines tangled. Nothing could have saved them, and the tangle was an easy scapegoat. We could only recreate tripping, when the primary was not buried, and even then only the primary was affected.

Secondary Rode Material

Because the connection to the main rodes is a potential weak link (chain grabs, knots, and connectors are investigated in Chapter 13), nylon rope is preferred for its shock absorption capacity, and 3-strand construction is preferred because of superior abrasion resistance and ease of splicing. The risk of cutting is very low because V tandems are normally used over sand and mud bottoms, and because the rodes in a V tandem rig are not subject to constant yawing back and forth, only to very slow migration. If rock or coral are present, the secondary rode should be high-tensile chain, which provides cut resistance with minimal weight. However, unless this is likely, chain may present an unnecessary impediment to use. You won't use what is inconvenient.

Secondary Rode Length

Equalization between the anchors in soft mud depends on limited dragging (or extended setting) by the primary anchor; if the primary has to drag too far it will probably trip by hitting a subsurface irregularly. Because of this, it is important that load sharing begins within 20-30 feet. To accomplish that, the distance from the connection point to the primary anchor should not exceed 40 feet, and the length of the secondary rode should not exceed 40-60 feet. This isn't always practical, but when possible, it provides a considerable benefit.

The most common objection to setting two anchors—aside from the extra work involved in placing the extra anchor—is the miserable labor of untangling rodes after the boat has completed a few spins with the tide and wind. In extreme cases, where boats have been left moored open hawse for weeks or more, the chains twist so badly that the anchors are winched towards each other and fouled. Terminating the secondary rode to the main rode at least 5 feet (generally much more to get proper scope) in front of the snubber attachment avoids this. When the boat

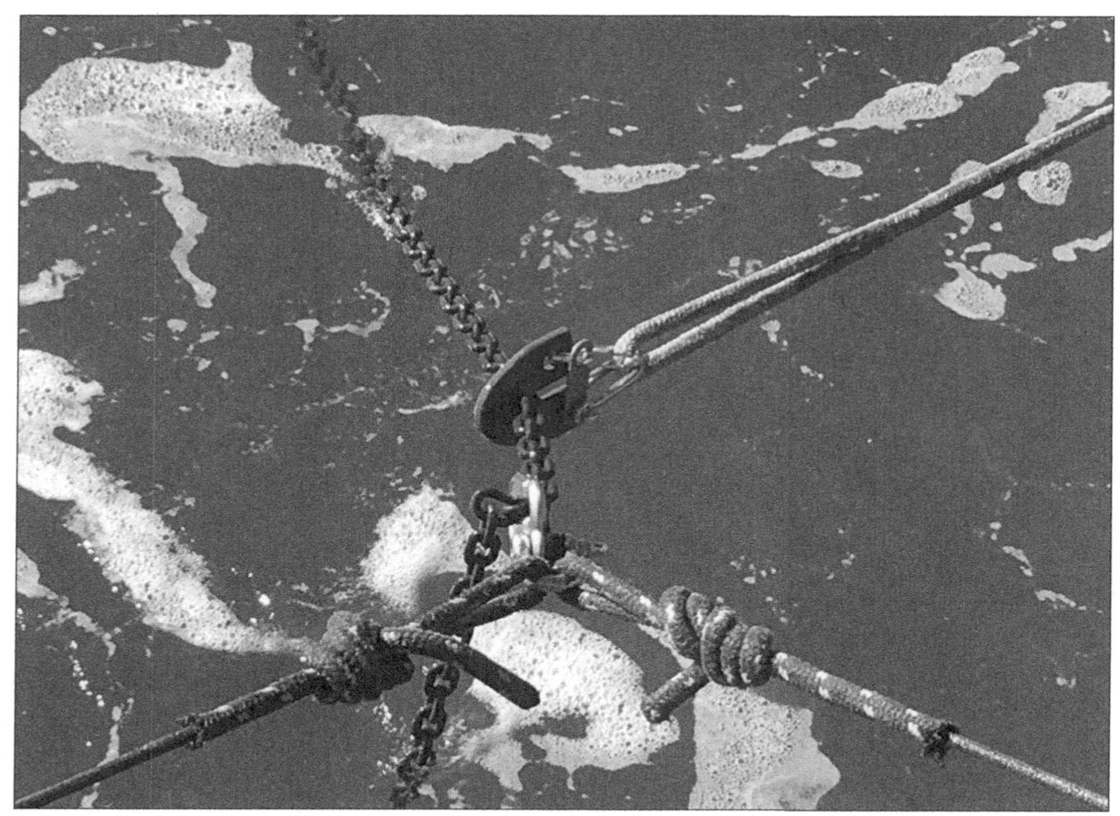

A Mantus Chain Hook connects the bridle to the chain (bottom). A chain bridle plate (Chapter 13) connects the nylon secondary rode to the main rode (top). The ends of the bridle lines wear a second cover for chafe protection. Ordinarily the distance between the snubber hook and rode junction is greater, but we kept it short so that we could photograph it above water.

turns, the chain absorbs the twist without tangling the rodes together. If there is a good load and the V is narrow, there may be a few turns, but these are easy to unwind, since the secondary rode terminates at the juncture and is in your hand. If the V is wider, such as in a Bahamian moor, the rodes are not likely to twist.

Finally, I like the relatively narrow anchor spacing allowed by the asymmetric V attached to the chain. A hidden vulnerability of all V rigs is another boat dragging across your rodes. His dragging anchor will trip one or both of your anchors, and your ground tackle will become tangled together. On the other hand, if you are anchored by a single hook, unless the dragging boat is directly up wind he will drag parallel to your rode and miss you. By combining the rodes some distance from the boat, the width of your rode spread can be reduced from over 150 feet in the case of a Bahamian moor, to no more than 40 feet, dramatically reducing your exposure. Even so, this risk is often enough to disqualify a V tandem rig in congested harbors. As we said in Chapter 1, a single anchor is best.

Expecting tropical storm conditions, with sustained winds over 40 knots for many hours? There is a school of thought that believes two separate rodes leading back to the boat provide additional security through redundancy. Generally the single rode V method is less trouble and provides better equalization. It's better to place your eggs in one basket and confirm the quality of the basket. But if you want something stronger and you are over a good enough seabed for it to work, see Chapter 11 for a redundant rig.

I like keeping the Fortress in a stern locker, rather than on a bow roller. If deployed as a Bahamian moor, we don't have to drop back as far, it's easy to load into the dinghy from there, and in lighter winds we can retrieve it from the stern. But mostly, I don't like having a big Fortress slamming through waves on a bow roller.

After squalls I dove on the anchors (the only way to see anything in murky Chesapeake Bay waters is by feel) to learn what had happened. If the bottom

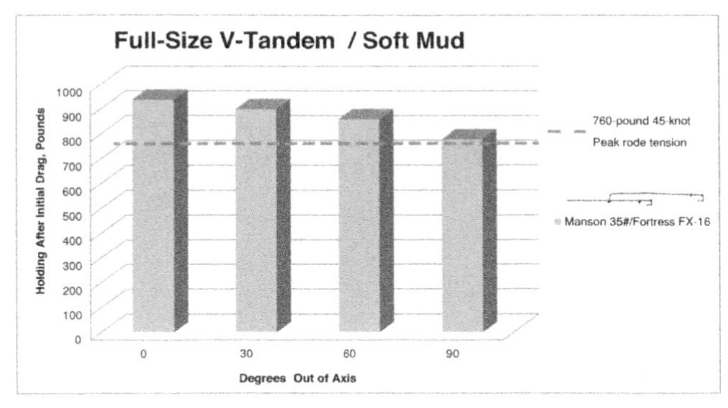

The anchors will have slightly greater holding capacity when in-line in a V, but we must assume the wind direction will change.

was soft, both the Fortress and the Manson had rotated to face the peak gusts; the scoop anchor generally dragged/set a few yards until equalized with the Fortress. Both anchors would bury well out of sight, the Manson just slightly under, and the Fortress much deeper, along with 10 to 20 feet of rode. In sand the Manson would rotate to face the load and the Fortress would rotate nearly as far. The Manson was typically buried half way up the roll bar and the Fortress was buried, along with a few feet of chain. We never fouled, tripped, or tangled.

In sand and mud, full scale anchors and V tandem rigs behaved just as small anchor testing predicted. Because of this, and because of supporting cruising experience, I feel very comfortable extrapolating the small anchor test data to full-size holding power of tandem rigs. (There are differences in weeds, where a larger anchor may penetrate better, but that was not my focus. Additionally, see Chapter 12 for a discussion of in-line tandems and difficult bottoms.)

Holding Capacity

If we scale up the small anchor test results from Chapter 9 (the Mantus plus Guardian asymmetric V tandem held about 140 pounds in soft mud), the estimated holding capacity of a 35-pound scoop and a 16-pound pivoting fluke anchor is 800 pounds. If we average scale the Solomons Island test program data to fit an asymmetric tandem built from a Manson Supreme 35 and a Fortress FX-16, we get 770 pounds at 90 degrees in the same softest ooze, both without benefit of settling time or soil consolidation. A pretty fair match. (In Chapter 9 I calculated 560 pounds with both anchors worst-case, but that is not likely.) During one particularly nasty 60-knot squall (at the mast head) near the test site, we measured a maximum sustained rode tension of 850 pounds. Later examination revealed some dragging/deeper setting of the anchors, exactly as predicted. Thus, the scalability of 2-pound anchor testing in soft bottoms is validated.

Conclusions

It is practical to increase holding power with whatever you have on board, but you need to avoid certain practices and adopt others suited to your gear. In general, the asymmetric V tandem was the most stable rig in sand and soft mud. I did not find these difficult to work with once the procedure was dialed in, and I liked that it could be set independently to confirm holding capacity. The primary always buried sufficiently so that the secondary rode would pass over it without fouling.

In soft mud, Fortress anchors tracked well with the limited direction changes that occur during the extended setting process, common to soft mud. This was aided by the presence of a primary anchor which moderated abrupt shifts. There is a strong synergism between pivoting fluke and scoop-style anchors when deployed as a V tandem.

In very soft mud bottoms in extreme conditions there is no such thing as a "set" anchor. They all move when pushed to their limits, and there is no anchor rig that can prevent this. With each new shift, the pressure becomes greater on one anchor, it adjusts, and the rig moves. At the end of the day, the bottom soil is the most important variable, and it was the variable that caused the most head scratching during testing. If the anchor won't set, get up and move.

Chapter 11: V Tandems for Good Bottoms and Big Wind

THE APPROACH of strong weather makes you question everything. Is the bottom good enough? Is the anchor well set? No matter how staunch the gear, you crave redundancy; the V tandem described in Chapter 10 is simple and well-proven, but it depends on a single rode and snubber.

Bump-Setting. Occasionally, when qualitatively testing small anchors in the shallows, I found I needed more tension than a steady pull would produce, so I would wrap the rope around my hips, reset my feet, and really lean into it, bouncing on the rode. If the rode was chain, the anchor either came loose or simply moved horizontally, going no deeper. If the bottom was mud, the anchor came loose. In both cases, the force was too brief and too great. However, if the rode was nylon and the bottom was sand or firm mud, the anchor dug deeper. The stretch of the rope buffered the force and extended the time, allowing the anchor to break suction and move. Using a load cell, we were able to confirm that small anchors that had been bump set in this manner performed in exactly the same manner as those that had been slowly set with a winch to the same force; the final depth and orientation were the same, and the ratio of setting force to breakout force was the same.

In Chapter 5 we described testing an anchor placement by using the engine; with a sturdy inboard the anchor can be tested in excess of 40 knots, most probably the practical limit of testing with the engine, even when very severe weather is forecast. As the storm builds the anchor will slowly continue to set, and more aggressive setting techniques are more likely to loosen the anchor than to help. However, if the boat is equipped with a weak outboard, the anchor can only be power set and tested to about 20 knots, not enough to fully bury an anchor in a firm bottom and not enough to be sure. However, further setting and testing can be accomplished by using the momentum of the boat and the shock absorbing capability of the rode and snubber to simulate a storm. The key—like using nylon rescue straps to pull a stuck vehicle out of the mud or a snow bank—is to use stretch to apply a good firm pull over a 2-4 second time period, rather than just hitting a solid whack, which won't give the anchor time to overcome viscous friction, and will only break something. We're not driving nails.

By coincidence (supported by both calculations and field testing—see Table 12), the snubber designs presented in Chapter 2 handle both surging in a storm and the stored momentum of backing down against the anchor at up to 2 knots (2.5 knots for multihulls) in equivalent fashion. The amount of kinetic energy gained by the yacht is equal to the energy absorption capacity of the snubber/rode combination, and the peak rode tension is about the working load limit of the snubber. Thus, you

Table 12
Snubber Sizing

	monohull								Catamaran	
Boat Specs	**Pacific Seacraft 34**	**Pearson 53**	**Morgan 41.6**	**not reported**	**not reported**	**Fomosa**	**Cabo Rico 38**	**Van De Stadt**	**Lightwave 38**	**PDQ 32**
length, feet	34	53	41.6	67	55	41	38	47	38	32
weight, pounds	13500	77000	27000	64000	44000	28000	21000	30000	12000	7800
Snubber Specs, calculated										
length, feet	44	69	54	87	72	53	49	61	49	42
diameter, in 1/16th-inch	6	12	8	11	10	8	7	8	NA	NA
if bridle. In 1/16inch						6	6		10	8
Setting Using Momentum										
strength of snubber, pounds	4400	16700	7500	14200	12200	7500	5963	7932	11000	8400
WLL, pounds	418	1587	713	1349	1159	713	566	754	1045	798
stretch at WLL, feet	2.5	3.9	3.1	5.0	4.1	3.0	2.8	3.5	4.7	4.0
stretch at 15% BS, feet	4.0	6.2	4.9	7.8	6.4	4.8	4.4	5.5	7.4	6.2
peak force at 1.5 knots, pounds	667	2485	1113	1858	1576	1142	916	1135		
peak force at 2.5 knots, pounds									1214	932
Estimated 60-Knot Strom Load with snubber, pounds	781	1564	1149	1924	1633	1127	983	1346	1473	1063

*An anchor in sand can be set and tested up to storm force (60 knots) by backing down at 1.5 knots **(monohull)** to 2.5 knots (catamaran). Set properly first.*

can both set and test an anchor to storm loads in good sand and firm mud by setting it in the normal manner, and then back down against it at 1.5 to 2 knots, two to three times. The key is to maintain the peak force on the anchor for several seconds—long enough to get the anchor moving and keep it moving for several inches. Greater speed needlessly increases the risk of over-straining ground tackle or loosening the anchor.

Engineless boats can power set by sailing very slowly downwind when deploying the anchor (described in Chapter 1), but this carries the risk of a missed set. It is also inappropriate for difficult or soft bottoms, which require a light touch to get started digging properly. Instead, repeatedly pull slack in the rode and allow the boat to coast back at the same 1.5 to 2 knots. In light winds, backing the sails can help the boat gain speed, but it is simpler to just wait until the wind reaches about 15 knots. Be prepared to make sail, should the anchor break loose.

This is an adjunct technique to be used only with outboard-powered or engineless boats anchored in good sand or firm mud. It is most effective with a nylon rode, although a long snubber, as described in Chapter 2, is acceptable. It is not appropriate for chain rodes with short snubbers. This method is restricted to pivoting fluke and scoop-type anchors; during testing it was observed that plow and claw anchors require slower setting action. In Chapter 4 we learned that abrupt loading of soft mud reduced rather than increased holding capacity. However, properly executed in fine sand or firm mud, an anchor can be set with a force approximately equal to the probable 60-knot storm load.

Reset vs. Setting Depth

Often strong weather is accompanied by an abrupt change in wind direction. In the best of all worlds, we would set our anchors to meet the strongest expected condition, and they would stay put, without moving. However there may be multiple significant shifts, and there may be no way to set the anchor deeply enough that it won't feel the shift. Are we better off to set the anchor moderately, near the surface, so that it can shuffle around with the wind change without risking an abrupt flip, relying on the design burying deeply when the load comes on, or are we better off to set it deep initially? While the complete truth is unknowable, because of the variability of soils, cruiser experience and testing suggest the following general rules:

1. Consistent Sand. Set with moderate force and allow the anchor to shuffle with the wind shift.
2. Soft Mud. Set it deep. We have no reason to believe the anchor will reset well or at all during wind shifts. Additionally, there is some evidence that an anchor that is set deeply will still shuffle around, without coming to the surface, staying

down in the stiffer deep mud. Consider setting two anchors, as described in Chapter 10.

3. Firm Mud. Generally like consistent sand, but set more firmly. Some risk of the anchor clogging with mud and not resetting, particularly in sticky mud. In that case, consider two anchors.
4. Weeds and Rocks. Resetting is unreliable. Set well and consider in-line anchor strategies described in Chapter 12.

Redundancy for V Tandem Rigs. Leading both of the rodes all the way back to the boat and providing back-up snubbers eliminates any single catastrophic failure point. A complicating factor is that rigging two sets of bridles or snubbers and securing two rodes is simply begging for chafe. A parallel challenge is maintaining simplicity; bringing two rodes, four bridle lines, and all of the associated chain grabs to the bow will make a mess if we are not thoughtful about how we do this. We might need to leave in a hurry—breaking waves could arrive, the boat could start dragging, or another boat could drag down on us—and a complicated mess will make leaving impossible. By using a single point connection and efficient chain connection methods, you can avoid chafe, release quickly if needed, and a centralized mooring plate keeps the rigging visually and mechanically clean, avoiding frustration and simplifying inspection.

Single-Point Connection. This can be accomplished with either large shackles or purpose-built mooring plates. The rodes continue over twin anchor rollers or in whatever manner they would normally be deployed. However, instead of connecting the rodes or attaching snubbers to each rode separately, the snubbers and rodes are all connected to a central point, reducing chafe and further increasing redundancy in the event of a snubber failure. Below are several proven methods. The chain grabs may require a pair of shackles or a short pendant for extension to provide freedom of movement, depending on the grab type. The central hub does not introduce a single failure point because the rodes continue to the bow(s), and because it will be massively strong and immune to failure.

- Bridle Plate with Apex Hole. The primary chain is locked in the slot, bridle legs are attached to the upper shackles (two can be attached to each shackle), and the secondary rode grab is connected to the bottom hole. Not a commercial item, but a description is given in Chapter 13 and specifications to build your own in Appendix IV. This is my favorite big wind method, perhaps because it is my invention.
- Two locking Chain Grabs, Four Shackles, and One Large Bow Shackle. Secure each rode with a chain grab, and secure the bridles or snubbers to the remaining shackles. All four smaller

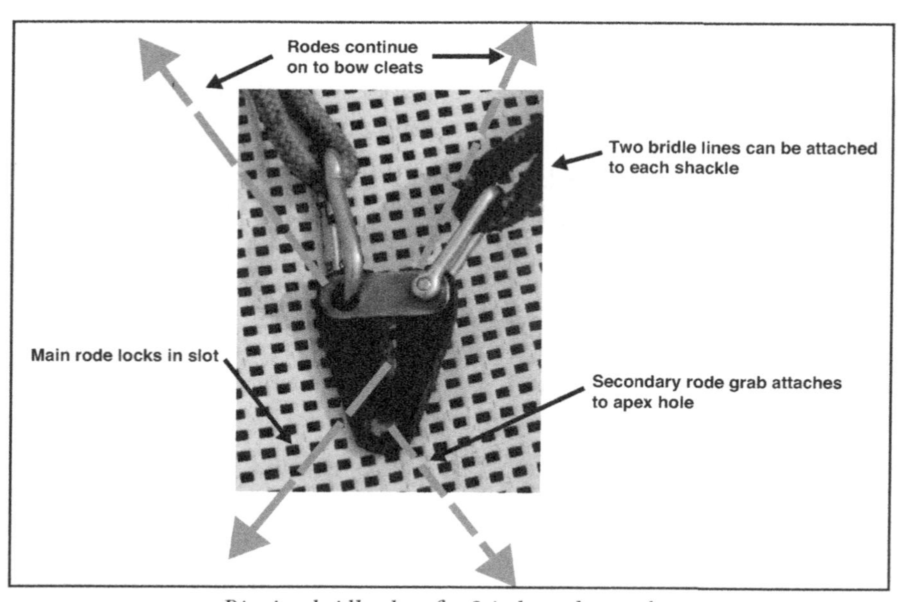

Rigging bridle plate for 2 independent rodes.

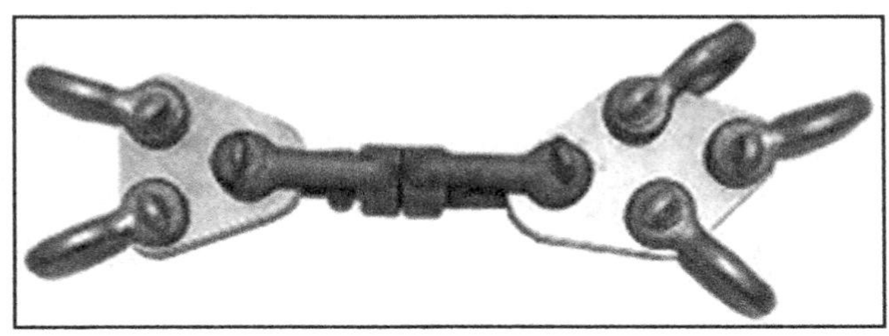

Mooring plate by Taylor Made. The swivel is not needed or helpful in this application.

shackles are then gathered together by a large bow shackle or other strong ring.

- Mooring Plate. A bridle plate with a swivel can be handy if you think you might be there for a while. Attach a chain grab device to each of the bow shackles, and attach both bridles via a large bow shackle to the remaining pin shackle. Very strong, but rather pricey and single purpose.
- A Heavy Plate With Four Holes. Place a shackle in each hole, attaching chain grabs to two of the corners, and bridles or snubbers to the other two. Use a 5/16-inch steel plate for monohulls to 40 feet, 3/8-inch steel plate for boats 40-50 feet, and so forth.

Note: Chain and fiber rode connectors are detailed in Chapter 13.

Redundant Snubber Slack

Snubbers fail from one of four basic causes: chafe (proper routing and chafe gear will prevent this), age (replace every few years), inadequate length (follow Chapter 2 guidance), and fatigue. It is this last cause that is an unavoidable concern in a sustained severe storm because if the secondary snubber is sized to absorb wave impacts, it will be stretching every few seconds. A backup snubber is needed, but proper deployment is critical. The backup should have enough slack so that it is not working, chafing, or decreasing primary snubber stretch as long as the primary snubber remains within its safe working load. However, with just right amount of slack, it can protect the primary snubber from failure due to fatigue by providing backup strength any time the load exceeds the fatigue limit of the primary snubber (about 10% of breaking strength). Since actual overload strikes are relatively rare, even in a severe storm, slightly more strain is acceptable, perhaps as much as 20% on rare occasions. Of course, even as the secondary snubber shares the load, stretch will continue, so slack equivalent to about 15% of breaking strength is a reasonable compromise. A typical 3-strand rope will stretch 10% at 15% of breaking strength. Thus, if the primary snubber is 30 feet long, the backup snubber should be deployed with about 3 feet of slack (30' x 10% = 3 feet). During severe gusts the tension will ease onto the secondary rode, the rate of snubbing will progressively increase, and the primary snubber will not become overloaded nor will it fail.

If the boat is anchored by a single anchor, the secondary snubber should be connected to the chain with a separate chain hook. This adds redundancy and reduces point loading on the chain.

Snubber Design

In Chapter 2 we discussed snubbers for normal weather and common storms. For exceptional storms, a slightly stronger snubber is in order. Since you will have two snubbers deployed, the primary snubber can be your working snubber. The reserve snubber should be increased one line size. In my case, the working bridle is 5/16-inch climbing rope, and the back-up bridle is 1/2-inch 3-strand. Both are 35 feet long.

Deployment

My favorite method uses the bridle plate. The rodes come to a single point, which is also becomes the apex of our redundant bridles.

- Secure the bridle plate with the primary set of snubber arms to the deck cleats. The second set of bridle arms are attached to the plate via the same shackles, but are not cleated at this time.
- Set the primary anchor in the normal fashion. Allow 10:1 scope.
- As with the V tandem described in Chapter 10, attach an extension line to the secondary rode. This extension should be full strength, as it will become the backup rode attached to the boat. Alternatively, a full-length rode can be used.
- Place the secondary anchor either with the tender or by moving the boat, also at 10:1 scope, forming a 60-90 degree V facing in the direction of the anticipated wind. The greater

angle will give better equalization but slightly higher anchor forces. Scope is most easily gauged by taking the anchor out in the dinghy while fixing the rode to the boat at just slightly greater than 10:1 scope, to allow for setting distance and the drop to the bottom.

- Attach the bridle plate to the primary rode by dropping the chain in the slot and locking the latch by clipping with a carabiner or shackle. Attach the secondary rode to the bridle plate at the apex hole. If the secondary rode is chain a soft shackle or locking chain hook are good. Additional chain grabs are described in Chapter 13. If the rode is nylon rope, a prusik sling and carabiner or camel hitch are good. If the rode has been extended, a soft shackle or carabiner between the terminal eye and the apex hole is fast and secure.
- Power set both anchors from the boat. This can be done individually, as they are placed, or after they are combined. If tested after they are combined, they will be tested with only half the force.
- Cleat the second set of bridle arms, allowing about 3 feet of slack.

Recovery

Same as V tandem in Chapter 10. If leaving in a hurry, the bridles can be left rigged (secured on deck), and all that is required is to grind in the anchors, one at a time. If the boat spun, you'll be wishing the secondary rode terminated at the bridle plate.

Bahamian Moor–The Light Duty Case

Many texts and many sailors view a Bahamian moor as a means of increasing anchor-holding power. It is not. It does reduce swing, yawing, and eliminates anchor resetting due to wind shifts and tide changes, which is not quite the same thing.

Absolute holding power is not increased, because sooner or later, the entire load comes onto just one anchor. The weaker anchor then drags until the second anchor can share load, generally much farther than with other V tandem rigs. With each shift of wind or strong gust they continue walking towards each other, neutralizing the initial benefit. Finally, the anchors will have to drag quite far in many cases before the load is shared, and during this dragging, testing and experience show that they will likely snag on a stick, soda can or shell, or simply cross a patch of softer bottom and pop up. The rig then bounces across the bottom, tangles up, and we blame rig fouling, when in fact, the anchors have simply failed.

On the other hand, if radical wind shifts are expected, the wide spacing ensures that the range of pull angles on each anchor is restricted and that neither anchor will need to reset or to

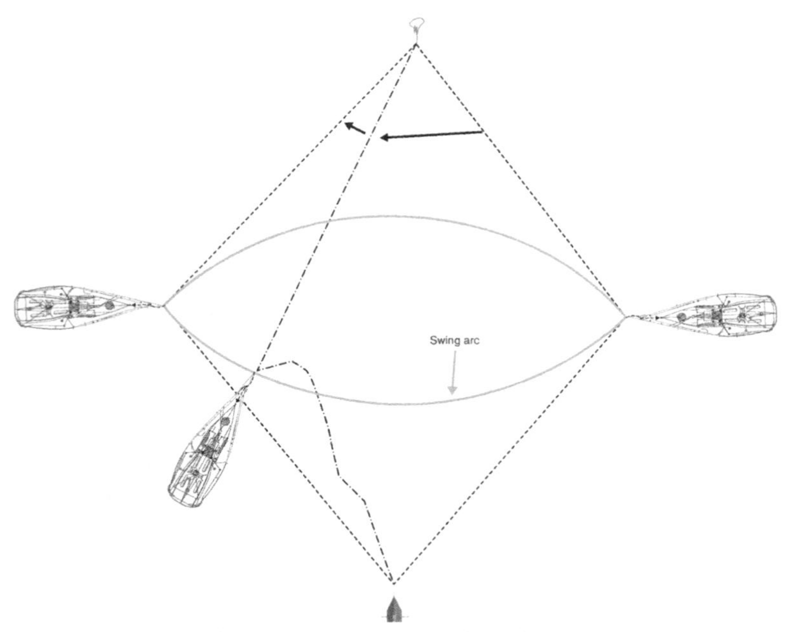

The Bahamian Moor Reduces Swing.

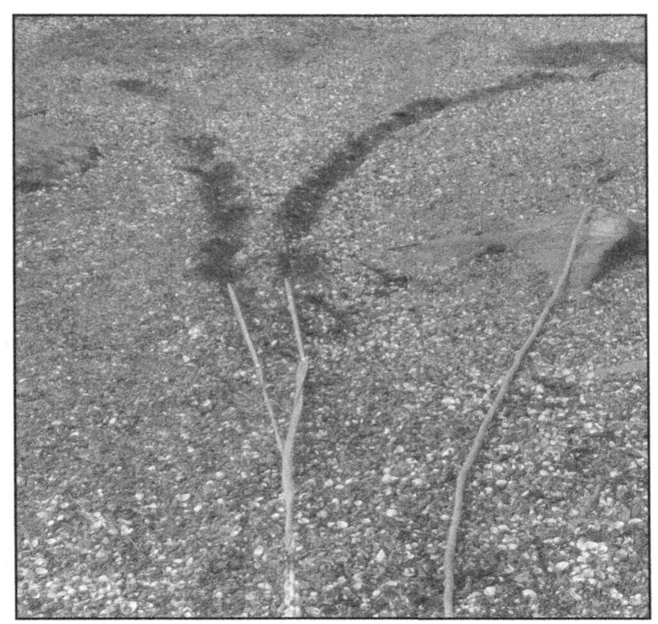

A Bahamian moor will twist together if the tide changes too many times, and the anchors will drag when the side force becomes too great. However, we never actually fouled anchors on each other unless the drag distance was so long that all was lost anyway.

rotate more than a small amount. We've tested many combinations and angles over the years, and learned that the preferred angle between the anchors is nearly always 100-120 degrees. Within this range, the pull on either anchor is never greater than it would be on a single anchor (the tight-rope effect can increase the load dramatically in a crosswind if the angle is too great). The rode will never foul the lazy anchor since the boat never passes over it. In tidal areas the lazy rode can wrap around a fin keel; a kellet (Chapter 2) will keep the rode down. For long-term anchoring, pivoting fluke anchors are perfect, since they shift less than scoop-style anchors and thus will not walk towards each other with each wind or tide change. In fact, this may be the only safe way to deploy a pair of pivoting fluke anchors if the bottom is firm and the available setting power is limited—they will never trip because the direction of pull does not change too much.

If the boat will be moored for significantly more than a week, build a mooring by terminating the chains on the bottom and adding a swivel where they join—otherwise the rodes will twist around each other and the anchors will be dragged towards each other. In this case the anchors should be extra large, preferably a pivoting fluke type.

Included angles greater than 120 degrees actually increase the load above that of a single anchor due the inefficiency of the rode angle. At 90 degrees, depending on the angle of pull, the maximum load on an anchor will be 70-100% of what it would be had only a single anchor been used, and at 30 degrees 57-100% of single anchor load. The load can always be 100% of the single anchor load, because load may fall entirely on one leg.

Deployment is the same as the big-wind V, except the rodes are joined in the manner described in Chapter 10 and only a single snubber or bridle is set. This simplifies deployment and recovery.

Because a Bahamian moor is often used in crowded places, we must consider the effect of restricting our swing on others. Boats on single anchors will swing farther than you, and if there is a crowd, you will bump. If single-anchor mooring is the norm in the harbor, from a certain point of view these collisions are your fault. I only use a Bahamian moor when alone in a tight spot, or at the very edge of the harbor

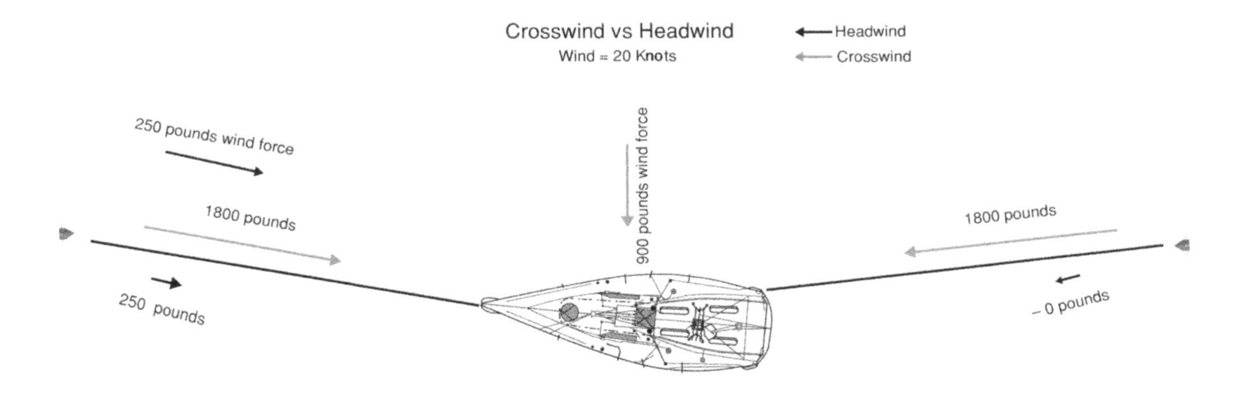

with no one to swing our way and a need to stay off the beach.

A Bahamian moor is only for good bottoms where either anchor can easily hold the full load, on bottoms where resetting may be problematical, and where reduced swing is required. This method is not recommended for very soft bottoms.

Fore and Aft Anchoring–The Weakest Case

In narrow canals and creeks, space can be too limited for even a Bahamian moor. By tying fore and aft, the movement of the boat can be tightly restricted. As long as the tide runs parallel to the boat, there are no waves, and only very light winds, all is well. However, if the wind is on the beam, the picture changes dramatically.

Because the wind force is 3-4 times greater when directed against the beam than on the bow (more area), and because of the inefficient angle of the anchor rodes, the force on the anchors increases 5-10 times. Waves are another factor, hitting the beam, rolling the boat miserably and further increasing forces. If the wind is more than a zephyr and the bottom is less than perfect, the potential for dragging an anchor is extreme. This method should only be used in very narrow waterways and where any crosswind is blocked by trees or buildings.

Shore Ties

Sometimes the available space is tiny. There is no room for swing, fore and aft anchoring isn't secure because of a poor mud bottom and cross wind exposure, and severe weather is predicted. The best anchors may be ashore or pilings. Although I promised this book would not be about major storms, the principles are similar and for a few minutes at the peak of a hail storm, the forces are nearly as severe. The advantages of this method are that shore ties can be very reliable, and it allows you to tuck into the smallest coves and creeks, out of the wind and waves. I've only done this twice, the more memorable involving a tiny island harbor: the available bulkhead was too shallow, and the only alternatives were blocking the only channel or outside in open water. I used two anchors, each with a snubber I could tension independently. Off the starboard quarter, I tied to an abandoned piling using a chain loop slid down to the bottom to minimize leverage, and a bulkhead piling provided a fourth point. The weather turned quite awful, but my cove tie-up remained snug. Working from a dinghy, it didn't take long to rig.

Bringing all of the shore ties to the bow, so that the boat can swing, is problematical. Because they are secured above the water, when the boat swings it will ride over them and tangle. Thus, the boat must be secured in a fixed position, with the

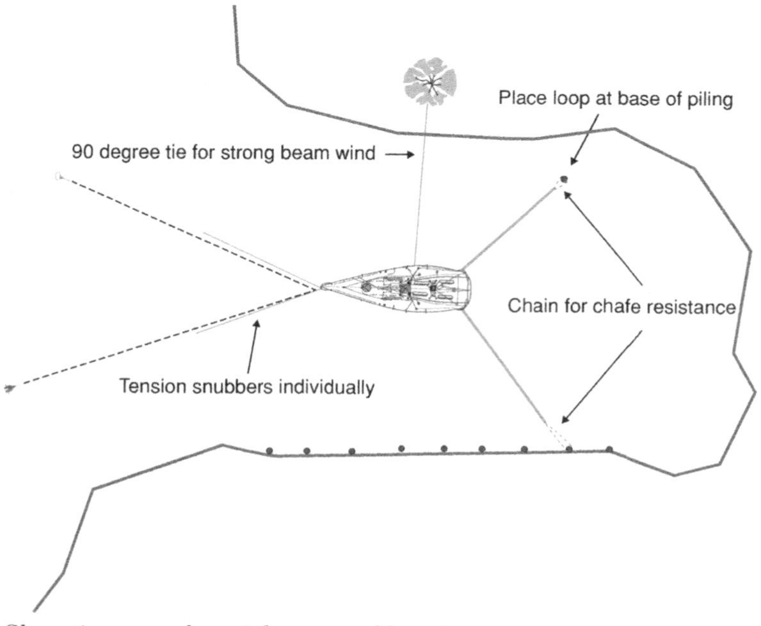

Shore ties can make a tight pace usable and secure.

Over 200 years ago, ring bolts were installed in boulders to moor canal boats awaiting passage up the Patowmack Canal.

shore ties brought to stern or midships cleats. The boat will not rotate to face the wind and will be exposed to beam winds, increasing the anchoring force. This is acceptable in a narrow tree lined creek, since the trees will block much of the surface wind. In a canal or small harbor this may not be true, and adding a 90 degree line is wise.

- If the bow anchors drag even a short distance, the rig will get loose and the boat will dance. Set them vigorously and avoid tying too close to any unforgiving shore or obstacle.
- If the anchor lines can be tended, low-stretch shore lines will limit movement. Be prepared to adjust all lines as the anchors shift. Interestingly, less shock absorption is required for beam wind load, since the keel provides resistance to quick motion. I observed this during extensive testing of dockline forces for a magazine article. Usually only fore/aft gusts result in shock loads, and those can be managed by the ground anchor snubber. However, unless the anchor slack resulting from tide swings is actively managed—impossible if you leave the boat during a storm—the lines will become slack all around and nylon is generally the best choice. If you want less motion, snug them down. A very long scope helps.
- Chafe. A short loop of chain provides chafe protection around pilings and across shoreline rocks. I've found having a few spare 10-foot lengths of chain are handy for rigging shore ties, drogues, and unusual anchoring problems.
- Mark shore ties with fenders if traffic is a possibility; they often run just under the surface and are easily snagged.

Rigged in a crack in the same boulder, a rock climber's wired nuts (Black Diamond Stoppers) can provide over 2 tons of holding power when rigged in tandem like this. The rounded boulders offered no other possibilities for attaching a rope or chain.

With two anchors in firm sand and redundant rigging, I've weathered some vicious squalls in the open, completely confident that I wasn't going anywhere. I've anchored in some tight spots, along canals and in tiny harbors, pulling out old tricks and tying to anything I could reach. So long as you do the math and are not exposed to breaking waves, much is possible. Given the choice, the nice broad creek described in Chapter 1 is better.

Chapter 12:
In-Line Tandem Anchors: A Closer Look

WE'VE SPENT 11 chapters exploring how to stay anchored over sand and mud bottoms, where burying is predictable. We've reduced anchoring, by parts, to an engineered science. But impenetrable bottoms—rocks, coral, weed, hardpan—are a horse of a completely different color, and much of our hard won soft-bottom knowhow just doesn't apply. Unless you do a lot of snorkeling and watch the motion as the wind shifts, you're only guessing about what's going on down there, based on conventional wisdom, dockside talk, and what you feel through the rode. You don't actually know why the anchor held—was it a single tuft of grass, a lucky catch on a rock, or a solid placement? A mountaineer, accustomed to trusting his life to thumb-sized rock anchors, never trusts an anchor he cannot see with his eyes and evaluate through a range of pull directions. He knows that it's not about the absolute ratings of the components in the system, but rather whether the anchors remain in the rock during a bouncing, swinging fall. We've spent the last few years playing with numerous anchor rigs in cobbles, shale, hardpan, weed, oyster rock, and hard clay, looking for patterns. Although these "bad bottoms" don't lend themselves to instrumented testing—they are too irregular for that—we have learned a lot about what works, what doesn't, and why certain things work better for cruisers.

With hard and rocky bottoms, predictable behavior is out the window. Although we learned in Chapters 9 and 10 that in-line rigged tandem anchors stink in good burying bottoms—they interfere fatally with each other's setting behavior—it appeared they might have benefits around rocks and on cobbles, hooking more dependably and resisting tangles. Some adventure cruisers swear by them, and some high-latitude sailors use them every night. These are smart, experienced people, so I reasoned they were onto something, even though they couldn't always explain it. I guess diving in near-freezing water in gale conditions is unappealing. I get that. And yet somehow, that's exactly what I ended up doing.

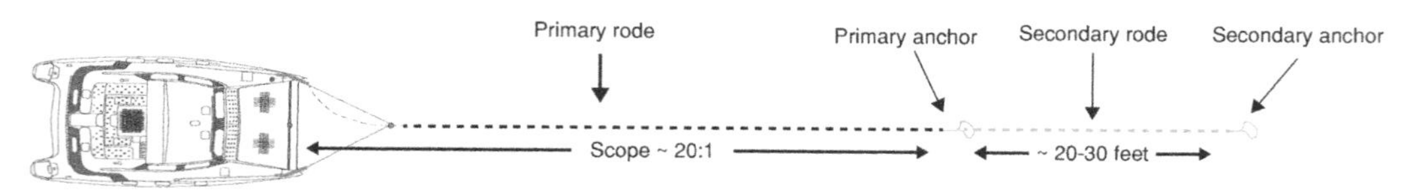

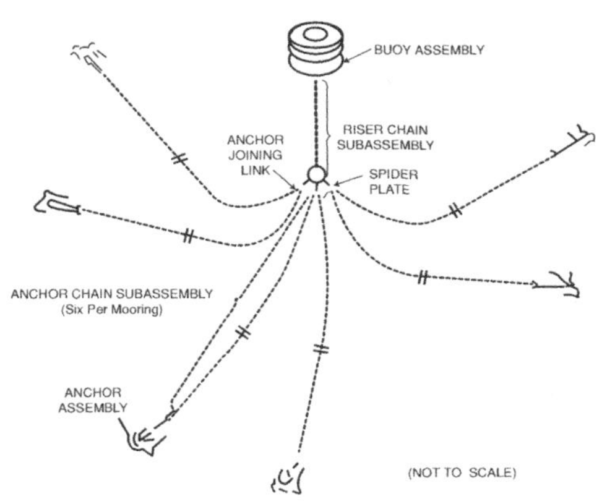

The pull on each anchor always comes from the same direction.

I also became curious about whether scoop-style anchors could somehow be modified or adapted to make them suitable for use as part of an in-line tandem rig. Some vendors, notably Rocna and Bruce, believe in-line tandems can work. Other vendors, notably Spade, are certain that they do not.

Lots more work to do.

In-Line Tandems for Sand and Mud Bottoms

Although small scale work indicated very little promise for sand and mud bottoms, there are proven applications for two or more anchors placed in-line in sand and mud bottoms, and I could not ignore that. Perhaps size makes a difference.

The U.S. Navy has studied in-line tandems for fleet moorings, where six or more anchors are placed in a radial pattern. The anchors are deep-burying pivoting fluke designs similar to Danforth and Fortress, and they are used in tandem only when a single anchor cannot reach full proof holding capacity because of soil conditions (an underlying impenetrable layer such as rock) or because a single anchor of sufficient size is too difficult to handle. Oil platforms also use multi-point moorings, and similarly, only use tandem anchors when the soil is too shallow for proper burying. What these have in common is that deep embedment designs are used and that no veer in direction is possible.

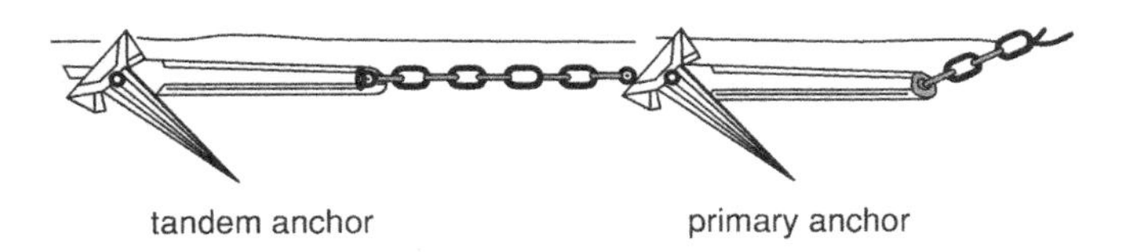

Figure 2. NAVMOOR Anchors shown rigged in tandem.

The NAVMOOR Anchor

Successful for straight-line pulls with pivoting fluke anchors only. The secondary anchor is attached via a special tandem link, a feature no yachting anchor shares. From "Single and Tandem Anchor Performance of the New Navy Mooring Anchor," 1987

My renewed interest in variable attachment points was triggered by the Bruce Booster design. Intended for bottoms where an impenetrable layer (thin soil over rock) limits deep embedment and prevents anchors from reaching full holding capacity, 3-6 small anchors precede the main anchor. These anchors feature an attachment point much farther forward on the fluke than the typical tandem attachments. This apparently works because the main anchor is a stable, deep embedment design, and because the forward attachment points keep the pull in line with the center of effort of each anchor. Additionally, the boosters are so close to the main anchor they behave more as an extension of that anchor than as separate anchors. In conflict, Vyrhof, another maker of platform anchors, specifies that tandem anchors be joined at the shackle (like the shackle eye rig tested in Chapter 9) and never in line.

A few yacht anchor manufacturers have suggested rigging methods or produced anchor

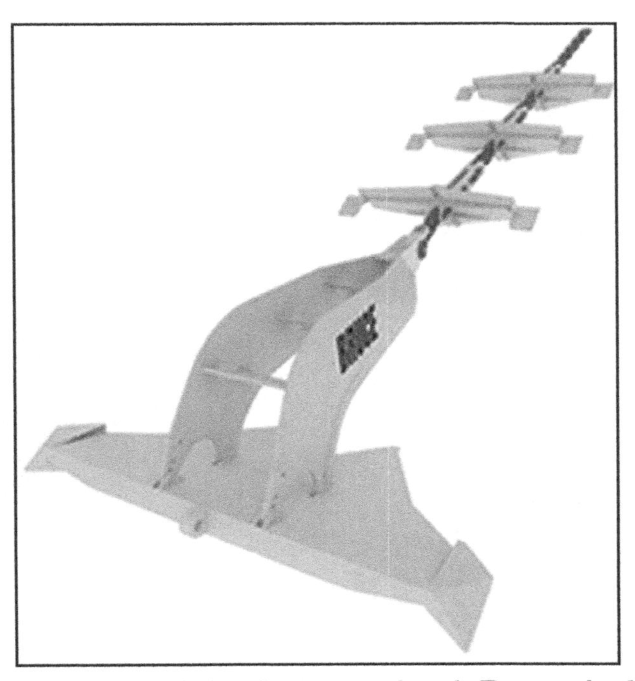
Bruce anchor with three Boosters one the rode.[Bruce anchors]

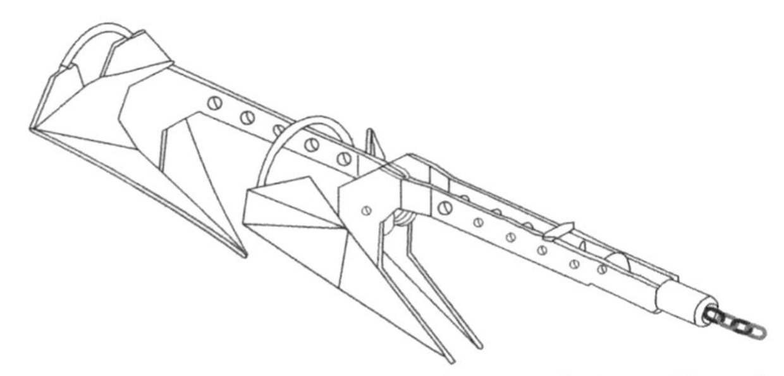

Wemar Tandem Anchor. Even their marketing videos show that one anchor always trips.[Wemar]

systems based on in-line tandems that claim to work in soft bottoms. In the case of the Wemar Tandem Anchor, even vendor footage of a successful deployment shows the primary rolled onto its side after a slight veer. Others have posted instructions and tidal flat demonstrations of in-line tandem rigging, but close examination of the images reveals shallow setting, the onset on instability, and no veer testing.

Multipurpose anchor designs—Rocna, Manson Supreme, Mantus, Delta, CQR, Northill—are not designed purely for deep setting and high holding capacity, but are a careful compromise that includes ease of recovery and resetting ability, something for which pivoting fluke anchors are not particularly well suited. A deeply set Fortress can be very difficult to retrieve, and they don't handle shifts well unless deeply set. On the other hand, a multipurpose anchor like the Rocna has features that allow it to generate holding power without overly deep sets; the kick-up at the back of the fluke and roll bar both provide increased drag and increase holding capacity while remaining near the surface. The Northill anchor has a wide horizontal stock designed to increase resistance when it meets the bottom, which prevents over burying. However, it is the ability to bury very deeply that allows pivoting fluke anchors to resist the instability caused by the tug of the secondary rode on the primary anchor.

Earlier testing (Chapter 9) concluded in-line tandems can work in soft bottoms, but only with deep-embedment designs (Fortress and Danforth) and only when there is no possibility of veer. However, since pivoting fluke anchors capable of holding any required load when used singly are not too heavy for sailors to handle, we didn't see any valid application for sailors in seabeds where anchor burying was possible. And yet I was curious. If the secondary attachment point was changed, like the Bruce Booster, could the performance of in-line tandems built using scoop anchors be improved?

I paired the 2-pound Mantus with a 2-pound Lewmar Claw and tested it with four secondary rode attachment points: tripping eye, base of shank, heel of fluke, and forefoot. I tested in both soft and firm mud and sand, evaluating differences

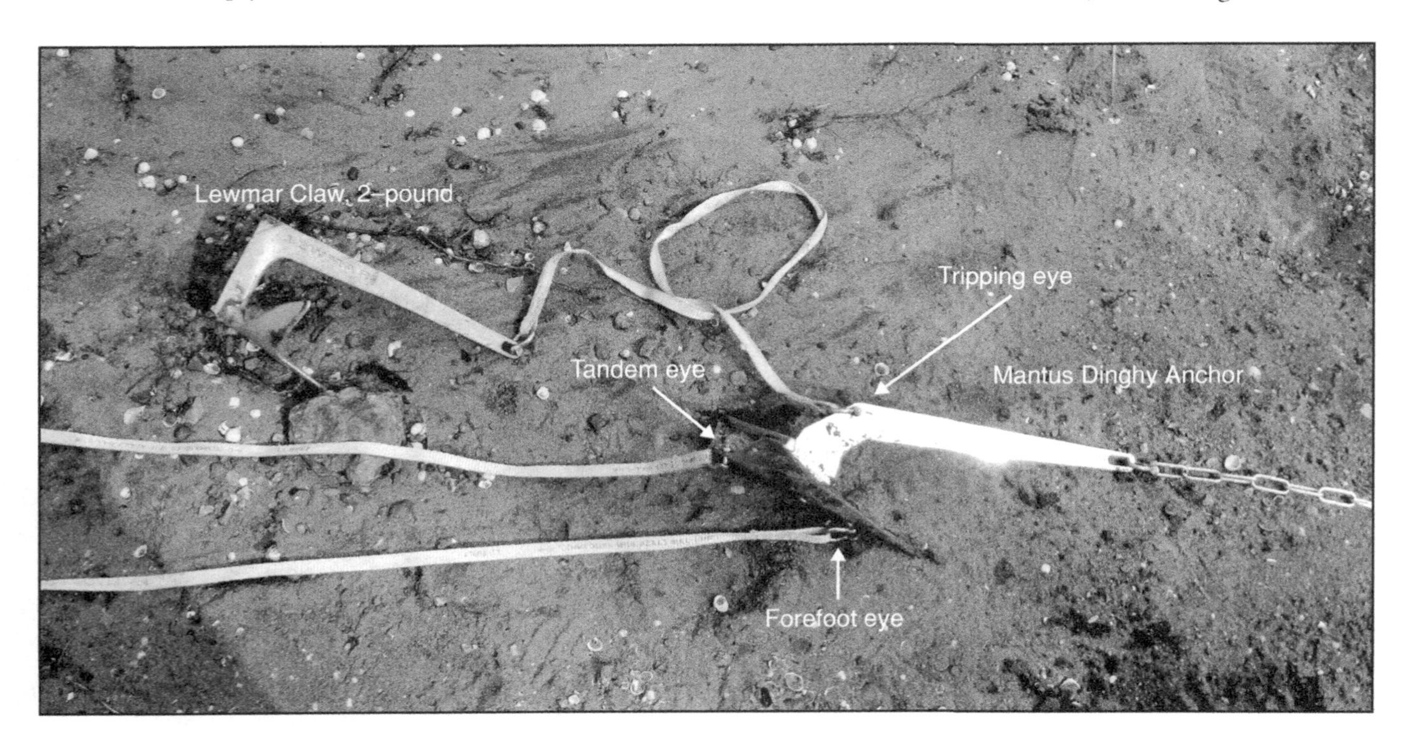

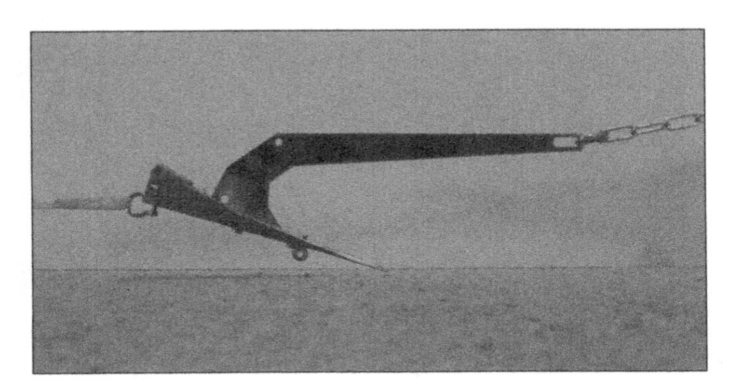

Only the forefoot attachment point promotes a normal digging angle with a secondary anchor attached, but it is not roll-stable.

in digging and stability in minor wind shifts. We then anchored our 32-foot catamaran test boat in light winds over gravel, grass, weeds, shale, and rocks, still using both 2-pound and full scale anchors, judging which rigging resulted in the best anchor stability and reliability in hooking after a shift. Diving, I observed their behavior through gusts and wind shifts, noting both how they held and how they behaved during dragging.

Finally I took the testing to full scale. I tested a Rocna 15 kg with the secondary rode attached to the tandem eye (base of shank). I modified my 35-pound Manson Supreme by drilling a hole near the back of the fluke and in the forefoot, allowing us to attach the secondary rode in other locations. I tested Delta, Claw, and Northill anchors as secondary anchors. These were deployed on a variety of beds, diving and watching the behavior through wind shifts. Our test areas were primarily in the Maryland Chesapeake Bay, around Smith Island (weed), along the Calvert Cliffs and Holland Point (rocks, jointed bottoms, potholes), near Churn Creek (cobbles), and several oyster beds. Scope was held constant at 20:1, which previous testing established to be the minimum for in-line tandems in shallow water.

Note: Extra holes were drilled in the test anchors for attaching secondary rodes. I am not recommending modifying anchors at this time—this is just testing. However, I feel my modifications are safe. I have not compromised the strength of the anchors; the back of the fluke is nonstructural and thick enough to handle the load, and the forefoot location should be acceptable, since any anchor should be able to handle full load on the tip. None of the holes were drilled in welds or in the heat-affected zone near the weld. Corrosion is a concern, but as long as a galvanized bolt or shackle is installed, there is zinc in close contact with the drilled holes, and there has been no significant corrosion in three years.

Attachment Point. Digging angle and balance. First, I stretched the Mantus primary anchor between a trailing Lewmar Claw and rode with long scope to see how the attachment point affected the balance and digging angle. Using the tripping eye, the digging angle becomes very

Wemar Tandem. The primary anchor trips with the slightest veer in pull direction.

shallow, preventing setting. With the bottom of the shank (okay) and back of fluke (slightly better) locations, the digging angle improved, but was still only half that of the single anchor digging angle. Only the forefoot location resulted in an acceptable digging angle, but it also made the anchor unstable, preferring to hang inverted under tension.

We took our test rig to the beach, hopeful that the forefoot attachment might perform in sand and mud. It didn't. When the primary anchor was set first by leaving slack in the secondary rode, the combination would momentarily hold more than either anchor separately. However, as soon as peak load was approached, even without a change in pull direction, the secondary would set more deeply and the primary would gradually begin to rise. Within a short distance, the primary would surface and resistance would drop. In a veer—even a mere 20 degrees a well-behaved boat yaws to meet minor wind shifts—failure was immediate, with the primary rolling out. We repeated this in soft mud and saw the same failure pattern. As far as we're concerned, in-line tandems based on scoop anchors are a complete failure in sand and mud bottoms.

I then tested at full scale, using both the back of heel and forefoot rode attachment points on a modified Manson Supreme. To ensure both anchors

Both are set, but the moment rode tension increases, the Mantus primary lifts out.

set, we deployed the anchors with several feet of slack between them. This allows the primary to dig in before the tension of the secondary inhibits setting. Using a 25-pound Delta as the secondary and the back of fluke attachment point, two out of three times the Manson was only partially set, and the third time it was pulled onto its side by the morning. With the Fortress secondary, twice the Fortress did not set at all (the primary never shifted enough for pressure to come on), and the one time it did, the Manson was lifted from the bottom and was hanging in the air like a kellet. On three out of five Manson/Northill deployments on sand, the smaller Northill set more securely and lifted the Manson clear out of the sand as power was applied, the Manson serving as an expensive kellet. The Northill did not impede the setting of the larger Manson in soft mud (both were well out of sight), but an overnight wind change rolled the Manson and brought it to the surface.

When I switched to a forefoot attachment point the results were similar; initially there might be an outward appearance of setting, but in all cases the primary tripped within 15 minutes of normal yawing. It's possible to take a picture on the beach showing two anchors set. It's even possible to produce good straight line pull results in just the right soil, with perfect setting technique and zero veering. But in no sense is the result useful. An abysmal failure.

Even worse, in every case the tandem gave the false impression of working from above the surface. Again and again, in-line tandem anchors failed in bottoms that permitted burying, providing less holding than our single best anchor. Spade has reported this same behavior.

At this point I abandoned all further investigation of in-line tandems for bottoms where anchors can bury. Except for the very narrowly defined U.S. Navy case, a single larger anchor is more reliable and stronger. We gave it the good fight, we wanted it to work because it would be handy in use, but it failed utterly for general use. However, previous testing and the experience of high-latitude sailors suggested that in-line tandems have merit in non-burying bottoms. We rejoin the investigation there:

In-line Tandems for Rocks, Cobbles and Weeds

Optimum Secondary Rode Attachment Point. There is a compromise between attaching the secondary rode above the primary anchor's center of gravity to keep the anchor from flipping, and keeping the pull low to encourage bite. Both the tripping eye and forefoot locations were failures,

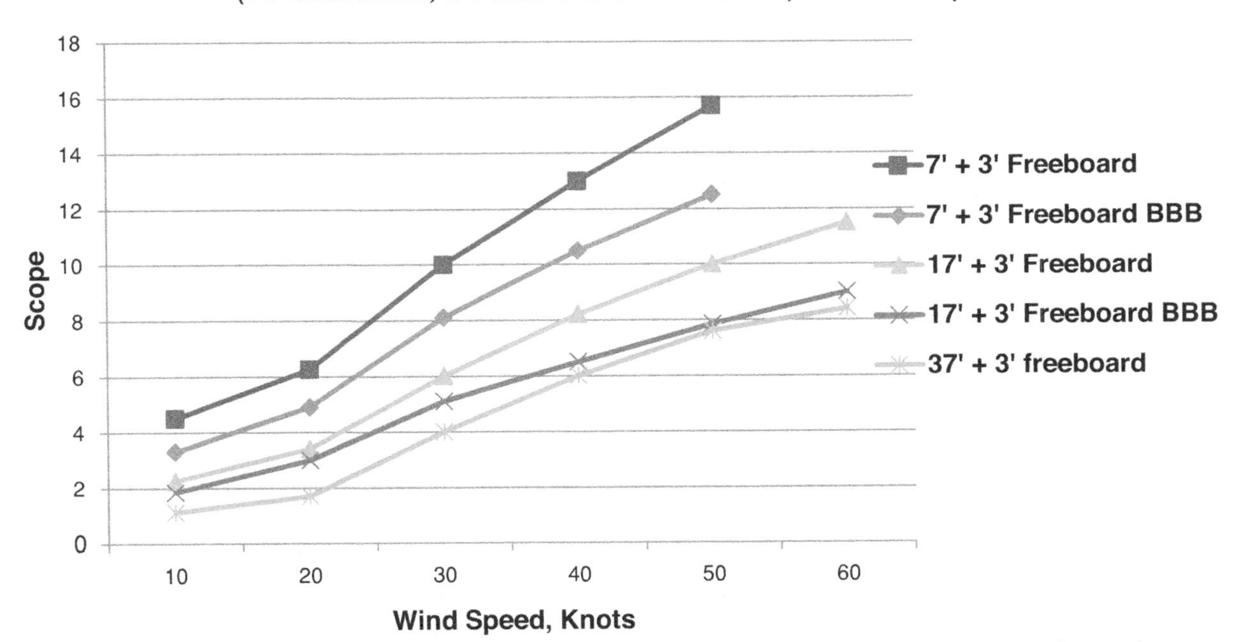

Figure 2a This figure is based on "average" peak loads; those observed every 10 minutes. However, since tandem anchors must never feel uplift (they will move when they do), even longer scope is required to allow for the greatest peak load.

rolling the anchor on its back and pinning it there like a turtle. A compromise location at the back of blade or base of shank (both are quite similar) worked reliably. Structural and geometric details determine where the hole can best be provided; on the Rocna, with its up-turned heel, bottom of the shank is best; while on the Manson Supreme or Mantus, the back of the fluke is better.

Scope and In-Line Tandems

With a single anchor, more scope is better up to about 10:1, after which there is limited improvement (Chapter 4). But in-line tandems follow different rules. Specifically, in-line tandems on rock and other impenetrable bottoms don't require more scope because it is "better" but rather because they aren't buried. Every time we recovered an in-line tandem from a hard bottom we observed the same behavior; the primary would break free at 4:1 or 5:1 scope under very light rode tension, offering no resistance beyond its own weight. Either it was lifted off whatever it had been hooked on, or whatever friction dragging was providing evaporated entirely when it became weightless.

There are two in-line tandem cases. The first case is hooking on rocks. If the secondary catches and scope is not very long, the primary is lifted well clear of the seabed and acts only as a kellet, since even a slight upwards force can lift an anchor out of a crack or off a ridge. In the second case the anchors are scratching for friction on cobbles or coarse gravel, and the weight of the anchor is its only weapon. If there is any up-lift force, the primary anchor becomes progressively weightless and frictionless. It may look okay, but it's holding nothing. Every time the wind gusts, it will lighten-up and float to a new location. In our experience and testing, 20:1 is a good starting point in shallow water, decreasing to 15:1 in 20 feet. The bottom line is that the chain must stay on the bottom, not just in sustained winds and in more regular gusts and waves, but through the worst impact of the entire storm. This is very different from ordinary anchoring. You need a lot of rode, a lot of room, and it only really works with chain rode.

Full-Scale Testing

Two variations were tested at full scale: a 25-pound Delta secured to a tandem eye on a 35-pound Manson Supreme (modified), and a 15-pound Northill secured to the tandem eye of a 35-pound Manson Supreme. 1/4-inch Amsteel was used for the secondary rode to provide ease of handling during testing.

Testing took place along the western shore of Chesapeake Bay in locations known for thin or patchy sand over impenetrable clay (from Holland Point to Chesapeake Beach), or rocks with oysters (from Holland Point to Herrington Harbor South). Again, as soon as the wind shifts, the primary rolls over, sometimes momentarily on its back. However, on these bottoms this behavior is harmless, since the anchor can't bury anyway; the only hope is friction or snagging a rock. In moments they rolled back on their sides, dragging in search of something to grab. A Fortress should not be deployed on these bottoms; it can't dig and it is not a good snagging design. The Delta was also poor; although the toe can hook, the plow-shaped sides would often glide right over rocks and cracks that the Manson, Mantus, or Northill snagged. The Lewmar Claw performed well, grabbing and holding, though it was not as efficient in generating friction on hardpan or thin sand. Other scoop and Bruce/Claw style anchors should also excel based upon what our eyes were telling us. Using a nice long snubber was helpful; the light steady pressure and reduced surging helps prevent lifting and keeps the hooks in place.

Often the first clue that we had that dragging started, before GPS reflected motion, was a plume of algae and other bottom growth floating up around the boat, dislodged as the anchors scraped over the bottom. The chain shuffling with a wind change will also cause this, but to a lesser extent.

On relatively smooth bottoms, governed by friction and scraping, adding a second anchor increased holding power 70-100%, depending on the combined weight of the anchors. This equates to about 5-10 knots more wind. Over rocks and cracked or jointed bottoms, the improvement in performance was far more impressive. Dragging was slowed by 5-10 times or eliminated completely. When both

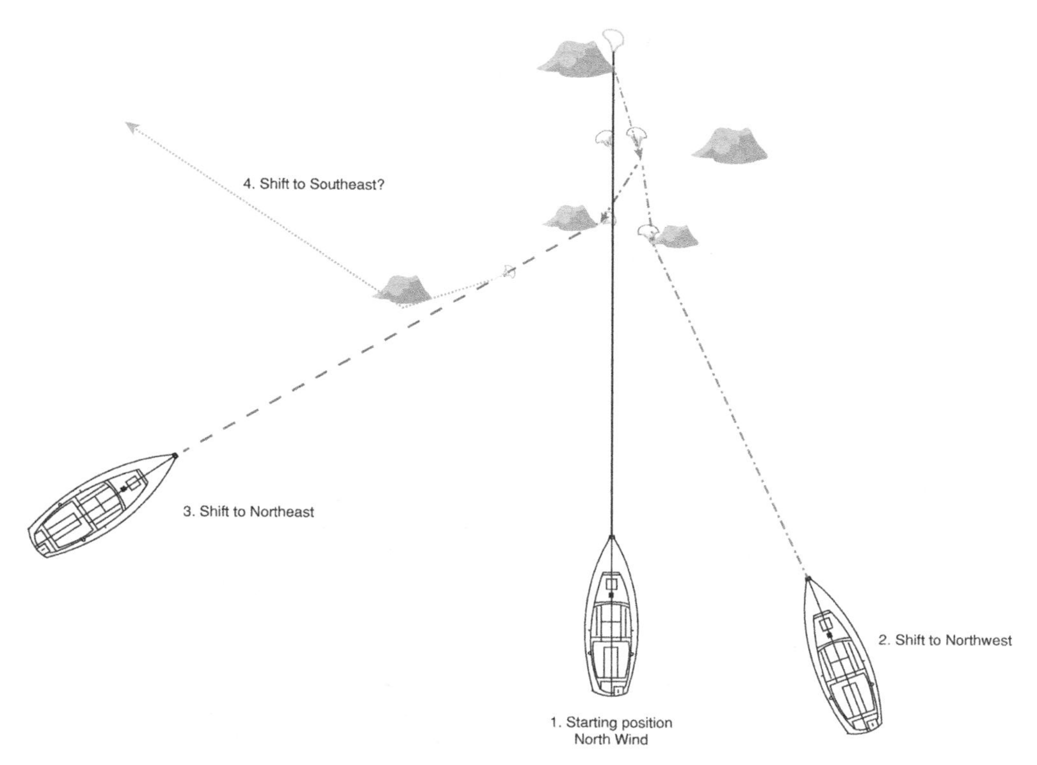

In-line anchors excel at hooking scattered rocks.

anchors hooked, they would stabilize each other, preventing minor shifts from disturbing the other's placement. When a minor wind shift caused one hook to slip, the other hook took over before the boat could gather way, like two hands moving from rung to rung on a ladder. The chain often guided an anchor to its next placement by gliding around the sides of rocks. The V tandem does all of this more poorly, allowing longer skips before re-hooking, resulting in a less controlled drag and more potential for complex fouling of the rodes around rocks.

Secondary Rode Material

Because an in-line tandem is normally used on rocky and other abrasive bottoms, the secondary rode must be chain to prevent chafe and cutting. I experimented with oversized Dyneema—after all, the weight of chain provides no obvious benefit in this position, a floating line could reduce fouling problems during deployment, and it is easier to handle, since the tandem is often hauled by hand or rope winch. However, although the secondary rode never chafed, it did grind cruelly around rocks. Furthermore, the Dyneema secondary rode occasionally floated up, missing good opportunities to guide the secondary anchor to a nice rock, neutralizing a significant benefit of in-line tandems. We also experimented with using 1-inch tubular webbing as a chafe guard over the Dyneema (see Chapter 7). This combination proved very durable when used with V tandems over mud, but it is not appropriate around rocks. Nylon is a poor choice for either the primary or secondary rode in rock and cobble bottoms for two reasons. The first is chafe. The second is that nylon stores energy and the rode will spring forward when the load is released, causing the anchors to skip forward quickly, bypassing good hooking opportunities. For regular use in rocks, chain is the correct choice. High tensile chain saves weight, and heavier chain offers no benefit, since it does not contribute to the catenary.

Secondary Rode Length

Optimum in-line tandem function depends on the reserve hook quickly engaging after the first anchor slips and dragging begins. A 20-foot spacing proved versatile in use, long enough to provide independent movement, while limiting undesirable lateral motion by the primary anchor. Spacing can be adjusted to match the average spacing of good hooking opportunities, to the extent that such an average exists. Recovery is more convenient if the secondary rode length exceeds the depth of the water plus bow roller height.

Specific Difficult Bottoms

The determining factor in anchor holding capacity is always the bottom. You can't make a silk purse from a sow's ear and you can't make a variable bottom perform like consistent sand or mud. We found that variable bottoms fell into five general categories:

Weeds. If the weed is heavy and consistent, the only cure is a heavy anchor with a sharp point and exceptional digging properties. Even then, there is some question as to whether you are hooked deeply or just held by roots. Other than a single larger anchor, the options are:

5. Bahamian moor. The anchors are held more steadily and are protected from veers, but there will be no equalization in most wind directions. The anchors must be carefully placed in clear spots.
6. In-line tandem. If the anchor which is set pulls in constant weed, there is little chance the secondary will catch; they will both accumulate a pile of weed and drag along. On the other hand, if the weeds are patchy, in-line tandems have an advantage in that the other anchor may find a clear patch before the boat gains speed. Additionally, the primary often clears a path for the secondary.

Jointed Rock. Sandstone and limestone bottoms commonly have periodic ridges or cracks between plates where an anchor can catch. An in-line tandem has the advantage of being able to grab ridges with less dragging distance and before the boat gains momentum.

Potholes. Periodic holes filled with good sand. are common in many hardpan bottoms. It is nearly impossible to know whether your anchor is well buried, or near the edge of a pocket, ready to drag out. In-line tandems increase the chance of catching the next pocket.

Northill anchor (12-pound) nicely hooked in a break in the sandstone bottom. But will it hold if the wind shifts clockwise? (The small chain retains a removable cross stock—it is not a rode.)

Rocks. This is where the in-line tandem truly excels. Even well-hooked on a large rock, the anchor can come free in a wind shift. Or perhaps you are hooked on a smaller rock that pries loose when the wind increases. The in-line tandem does two important things to help you stay put:

7. Because there are two hooks, the odds of hooking something before the boat drags far

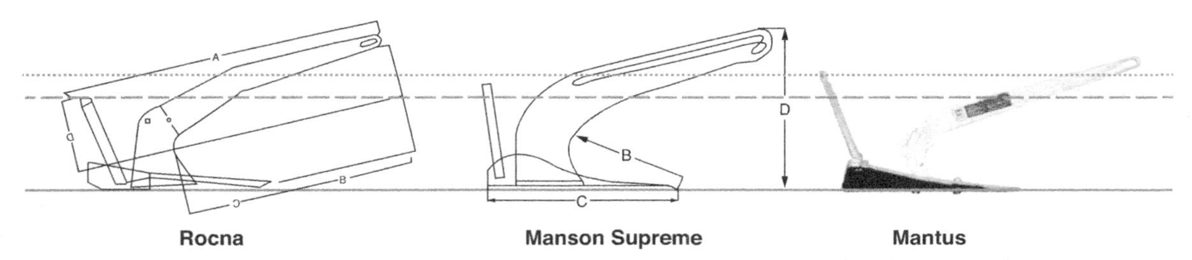

The more vertical Manson roll bar is stronger and superior at snagging on rocks when the anchor is inverted.

enough to gain momentum are more than doubled (two hooks halve the probable distance and double the friction while dragging to the next hook). Since fast dragging is the enemy of effective hooking, the effective holding power is increased 5-10 times.

8. The chain will drag around the sides of rocks, guiding the anchor to a secure hooking location. Rather like untangling barbed wire or unhooking a thrashing fish from a multi-treble hook lure, every time one hook comes loose, the other catches. A big increase in reliability. Yet this causes no increase in terms of recovery, since they are lifted clear one at a time. There is an increased risk of trapping the chain under a rock. I never experienced that because the test area did not have that type of rock.

Cobble and Coarse Gravel. Digging is meaningless and hooking is weak, so holding depends mostly on friction. An individual cobble can be hooked, but it will roll out when the pressure becomes too great. An in-line tandem is the simplest way to rig two anchors and the simplest to recover. If the bottom is rockier than anticipated, the in-line rig becomes the best choice. The primary downside is that scope must be very long—20:1 in shallow water, and 15:1 in relatively deep water. Why? Because the primary anchor feels all of the lifting force but only half of the friction force. If the chain comes off the bottom, the lead anchor becomes increasingly weightless and useless. Of course, holding will be limited even in good conditions.

The Mantus wings help drive the point downwards, but they also hold the edge off the bottom when scraping across hardpan or thin sand.

In-line tandems are not good for tide swings. We fouled the secondary rode several times when the wind rotated through 360 degrees.

Anchor Selection—Hooking. Multipurpose anchors are designed primarily for digging, and less so for hooking. However, in rocks a nice hook presented at a good angle is everything. Our little 12-pound Northill repeatedly outperformed our 25-pound Delta and Rocna, and equaled our 35-pound Manson Supreme. The 2-pound Mantus and 2-pound Claw often outperformed the 25-pound Delta, depending on the shape of the crack or ridge. When choosing an anchor for rocks and hardpan, observe how it lies on the bottom; is the point pressed into the bottom and angled to aggressively hook rather than slide over the top?

Anchor Selection—Scraping. On bare rock, gravel, and hardpan, anchors are sometimes reduced to scraping on their side for friction. Weight helps. I dragged test anchors across a hardpan areas, cobbled bottoms, and bare rock. Although the data were too variable to analyze in depth, a straight, angled side helped, and the Manson Supreme and Rocna generally performed well. Plow anchors such as the Lewmar Delta and picks such as the Northill were weak, and the Lewmar Claw was variable, dependent on whether it could penetrate. (see Chapter 6 for data summary.) This is an aspect of anchor performance that has seen no systematic testing.

After lots of diving and slowly learning how anchors behave on hard bottoms, I discovered I could now anchor the 32-foot test catamaran using a pair of 2-pound anchors in places that had previously been insecure with a 25-pound Delta. A huge improvement.

Handling

Tripping Line. Unpopular with cruisers, they nearly always cause more trouble than they solve. However, in-line tandems are a logical exception, because when there are enough rocks for an in-line tandem to make sense, there is risk of fouling. Only the secondary anchor requires a tripping line, since the secondary rode attachment is a tripping line for the primary. The best attachment point for the tripping eye is not the typical top-of-the shank location found on CQR, Delta, Manson Supreme, and Mantus anchors, but is the back of the fluke or low on the shank, like those on Spade and Rocna

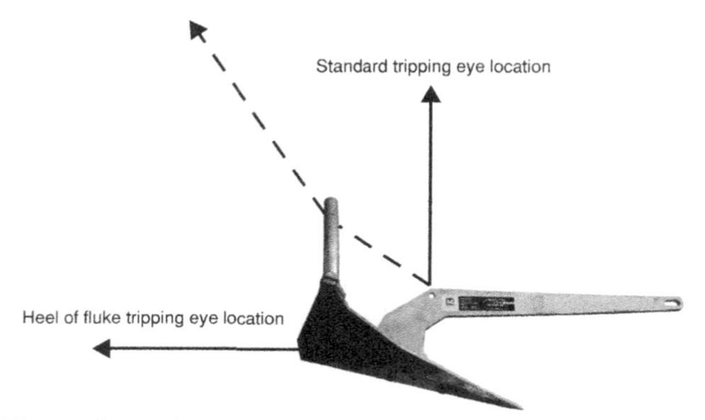

The traditional top-of-shank location is not as effective as a back-of-fluke location. Threading the tripping line through the roll bar helps.

anchors. (Check these later carefully. The tripping line hole in the Rocna is off center, in thinner steel, and is not suitable for use as a tandem rode attachment point—the actual tandem eye is located low on the shank. Spade has a fluke tripping line hole, but it is smaller and is not recommended by Spade for tandem rode attachment.) The roll bar is also commonly used for tripping; if you have to swim down, it is easier to clip. If you choose to use a high tripping hole, thread it through the roll bar from behind to get a better angle. Additionally, the float should not have enough buoyancy to significantly lift the anchor, should it be pulled under at high tide. I like a yellow, fist-sized gill net float—folks around here stay away from nets! I wouldn't use a crab or lobster float; someone might try to check the pot.

There is a popular myth, related to the images above and anchors with rock slots for tripping. "If the anchor snags under a tree or rock, just motor over it in the reverse direction and slide it out backwards." The problem is, if you have been anchored through a change in wind or a shift in tide, do you actually know which direction the anchor is facing and how it is fouled? Has a log or large branch floated down with the tide, ensnaring the rode? This latter has happened to me a half dozen times, and only truly inverting the anchor will unthread it from a tangle of branches.

Recovery Line. The primary anchor is normally recovered onto rollers using a chain windlass, but the secondary is often recovered manually. A recovery line is connected from the secondary anchor shackle to the primary rode (a rolling hitch

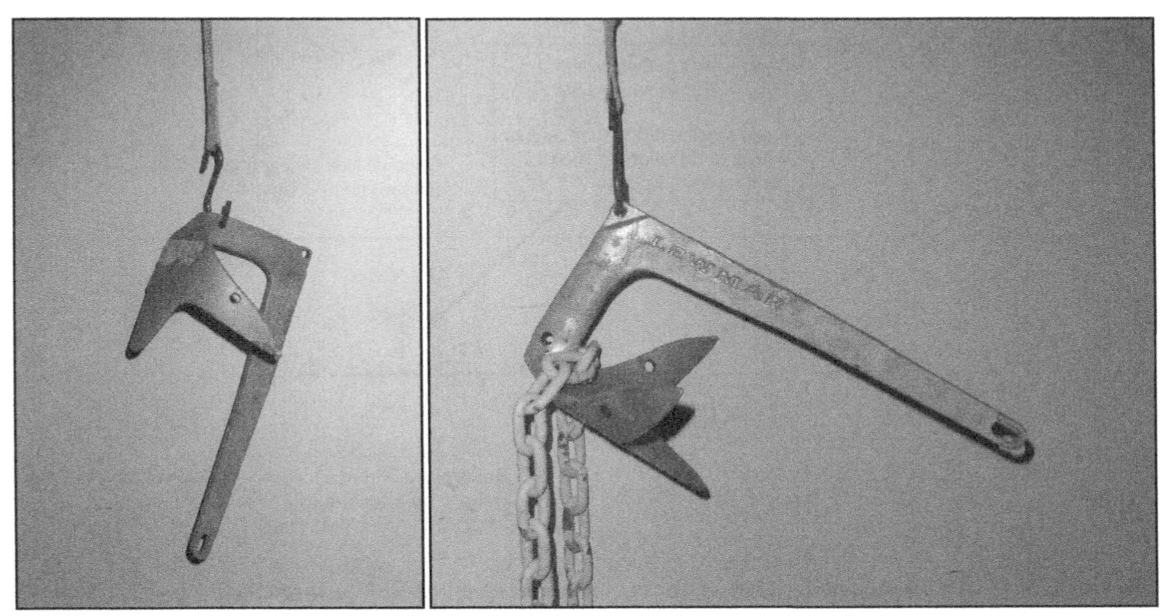

The tripping eye location on the Claw is not effective (the hole near the fluke was drilled for testing—this is not recommended).

works) about 4-6 feet closer to the boat than the primary anchor, with about four feet of slack. This line is also used to deploy the secondary anchor. Floating line prevents fouling on anchors and rocks—it should be a line with good grip, not a thin Dyneema single braid. Alternatively, polyester line works if a small float is threaded onto the line and allowed to seek the midpoint. After the

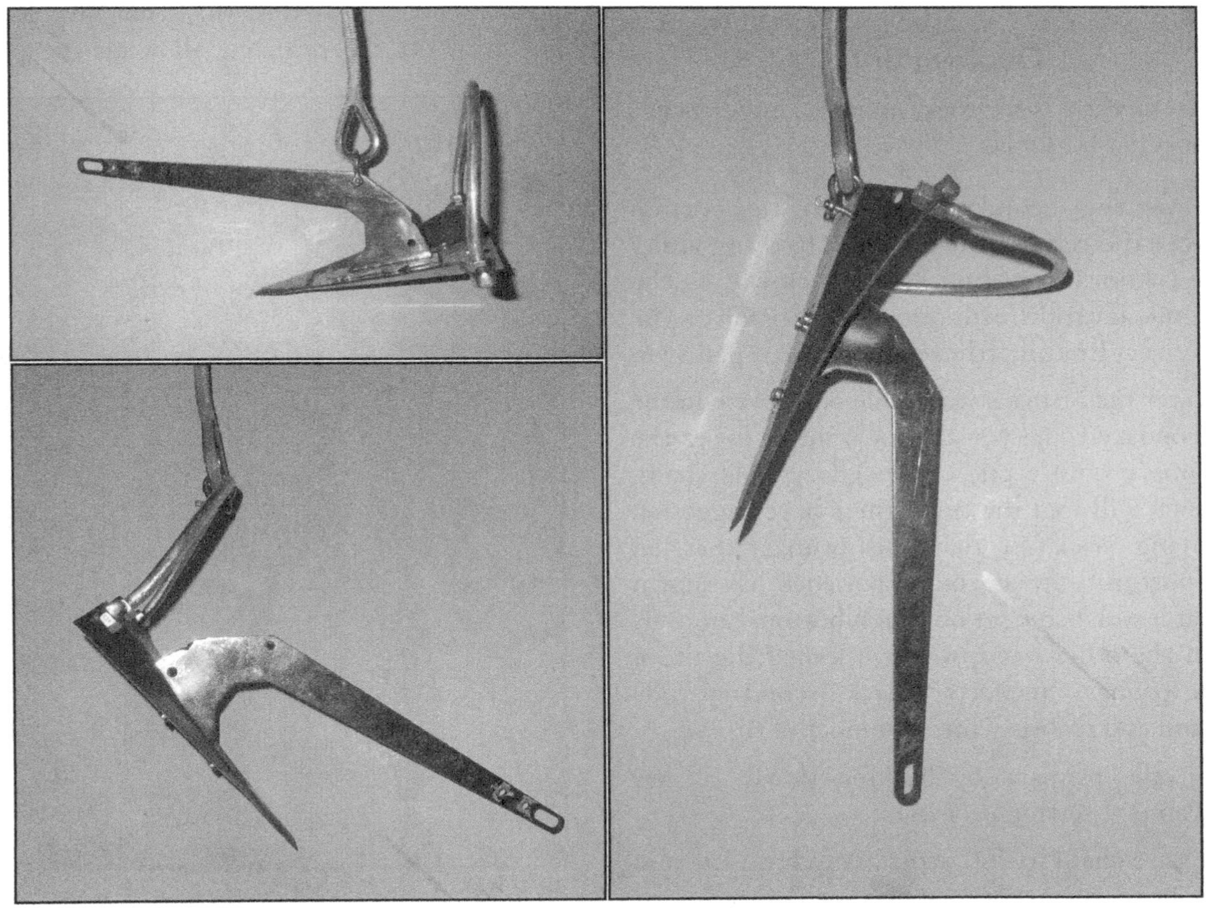

The roll bar is better than the tripping/lashing eye, but the back of the fluke is best.

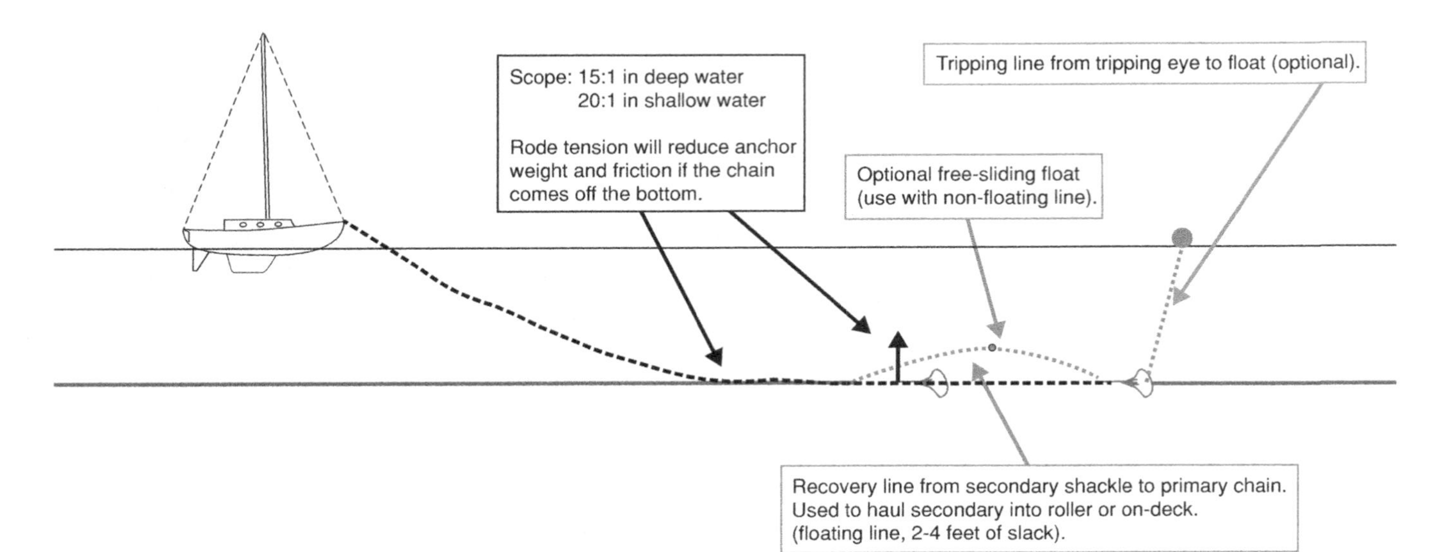

primary is stowed, the secondary is hauled by the recovery line, which can be extended and taken to a winch if needed. It is possible to use the tripping line as a recovery and deployment line, though it does not deliver the anchor to the bottom at an optimum angle and can be more trouble to reach during recovery. After years of testing, we prefer separate lines.

Deployment

This method is for rock, cobbles, and difficult, non-burying bottoms.

- Lower the secondary anchor to the bottom using the recovery line, while backing at 0.5 to 1 knot. Continue backing slowly as the secondary rode feeds out. Keep tension on the recovery line until the secondary is tipped over.
- Lower the primary with little or no slack in the secondary rode; you do not want to lower the primary onto a pile of secondary rode chain, which will foul the tip. Others have suggested leaving slack so that the primary has an opportunity to set, but experience has shown that it won't stay set on tough bottoms anyway. On the other hand, we have fouled the tip of the primary anchor on slack secondary rode chain and recovery line a number of times.
- Tip the primary by backing slowly, as per Chapter 1 setting procedure.
- Release chain to 20:1 scope. Anything less and the primary anchor may lift. See Figure 2a.
- Back down at less than 1 knot. Once the slack is out, increase throttle to test holding.

If there is any side load on the primary anchor from the recovery line or secondary anchor, the primary anchor will jam coming over the roller. To prevent this, attach the recovery line to the primary rode several feet above the primary anchor so that the secondary load can be taken off the primary, allowing the primary

Tension the recovery line while deploying to avoid fouling the primary anchor. We fouled in this manner several times.

anchor to hang straight and come over the rollers straight.

Retrieval

This is the strength of in-line tandems. It is simple, even in a blow.

- Begin recovering the primary anchor in the normal manner.
- When the recovery line is in reach, detach it from the primary rode and secure it to the boat using an extension line if needed. You may need to lift the secondary anchor just clear of the bottom using the recovery line before the primary will feed into the rollers smoothly (side tension will cause the anchor to jam).
- Load the primary anchor onto the rollers.
- Recover the secondary anchor using the recovery line in the normal manner. Place the recovery line on a winch or windlass as needed.
- Recover the secondary rode and secure on deck. It can be detached from the primary anchor later, when it is convenient.

Conclusions

In-line tandems are for very difficult bottoms only. Moving is probably the best solution, but if you must stay, they add considerable security.

The forefoot attachment location for the secondary rode of an in-line tandem has theoretical benefits in burying in soft bottoms, but it was less stable and produced less holding power on troublesome hard bottoms, which is the only place in-line tandems should be used. Thus, the heel of the fluke or base of the shank are the best secondary rode attachment points for in-line tandem anchors on difficult bottoms.

I would like to see more manufacturers supply a tandem eye in the heel of the fluke (preferable) or base of the shank (good) for use on rocky and difficult bottoms only. Understandably, anchor makers shy away from suggesting in-line tandems because of the great potential for misuse; a V tandem is better for sand and mud bottoms, and a larger single anchor is better 95% of the time. They would rather you purchase a larger anchor and seek suitable bottoms. They are correct, and I agree. However, I believe a tandem eye for use ONLY when appropriate is a simple and handy addition for the cruising sailor facing a wide variety of anchoring problems. The heel of the fluke is also a superior tripping eye location.

After all of this, do I recommend drilling a tandem eye in your scoop anchor? A tough call. The hole in my Manson Supreme remains relatively corrosion-free three years later, protection against corrosion provided by nearby galvanizing and the galvanized pin of the shackle. The fluke is strong there, and I left a 1/2" x 5/16" strip of metal behind the hole, more than strong enough for any load. I'm sure this decision depends on the specific anchor, but I'm comfortable with it. However, most of us will never anchor over rocks or cobbles. You must weigh whether this is a feature you will actually use. If yes, drill the hole.

Anchors vary widely in their behavior when dragged sideways across rock, cobbles, and shale, and very little organized testing of this property has been performed. The best anchors present either a long straight edge when dragged sideways (Manson, Rocna, and Spade) or a point directed downwards for hooking (Bruce/Claw-style, Northill, and fisherman anchors in general). Mantus fell somewhere between classes, with the fluke wings keeping the edge off the bottom, but directing the point sharply downwards. Look for a strong roll bar, when applicable; we occasionally hooked the roll bar on a rock, and while not optimum, sometimes it was secure and it was better than dragging. Plow-type anchors, including Delta and CQR often slid over ledges where others would catch. Until better data exists, try to visualize how a new anchor design might behave when dragged across the bottom on its side, scraping and grabbing for purchase.

I was surprised to learn that most of what we've read about in-line tandem anchors is just dead wrong, the result of conventional wisdom and anecdotes repeated over and over, reinforced without systematic testing, comparison, or close observation. They are for difficult bottoms only and simply do not work in sand or mud. Again, I fell farther down the rabbit hole than I expected, but I found a few truths and a few new wrinkles. It was worth it.

Chapter 13: This and That

WHAT FOLLOWS are details and practices that didn't quite fit elsewhere or would have disrupted the narrative. Although anchoring involves big concepts, rigging boils down to details.

- Dragging. What to do when you start moving.
- Marking Chain. Painting the easy way.
- Anchoring Signals. Yelling is bad.
- Rope-to-Chain Splice. The irony splice.
- Swivels. Why you don't need them.
- Connecting the Anchor to the Chain. The weakest link is what matters.
- Connection Snubbers and Rodes. A catalog of hardware.
- Long Bridles Without Chafe. Keeping the chain hook off the bottom.
- Dive Gear. What to do when the water gets cold.
- Mixing Galvanized and Stainless. Better to stay with all galvanized.
- Fatigue. Sizing gear to last and why nylon must be sized conservatively.

All of these are methods I use. Nothing has been regurgitated from other texts.

Dragging

The wind has come up and the GPS shows you aren't where you started. You've confirmed that this isn't simply a change due to swing, and GPS says the drift is a steady few tenths of a knot. The motion of the boat has changed because you are now drifting sideways, beam-on to the waves. Hopefully, you have already considered your options:

More Scope. Do you have room behind you? If you had shortend scope to reduce your swing, you can probably let out a lot more scope now, since in stronger winds boats all lie in the same direction (watch out for nervous boats). If the boat is hobby horsing, increasing scope may break the rhythm, and it will reduce the upward component. Increased scope—up to about 12:1 scope in shallow water—will increase holding capacity. Letting out scope will also momentarily reduce the load, often allowing the anchor to get a fresh bite; however, be careful to snub the rode very gently. In strong conditions you will not be able to recover your snubber; abandon it on the rode and deploy a new snubber (always have a spare). Overall, adding scope is effective only when the increase in wind is modest, the bottom soft but consistent, and you made the mistake of anchoring on tragically short scope in the first place. Any additional holding capacity which had been gained over time (Chapter 4) has been lost, a good reason not to depending on holding capacity improvement due to soil consolidation.

Second Anchor. If you think of it early, and it won't cause trouble with the swing of other boats, deploy a second anchor as described in Chapter 10. If the conditions aren't too bad, take the second anchor out with the dinghy. If the wind is really piping, simply lower the second anchor over the side; there is no need for a V rig, so long as the two anchors are set on rodes of different lengths.

1. Lower the second anchor off to one side of the bow, walking the rode to the stern and setting lightly by hand. Often, the length of the boat provides just enough scope to get a light set, and if you are dragging, the anchor will be moving away from you. This is particularly effective with Fortress anchors, which like an initial set on short scope.
2. Quickly bring the tail of the rode to the bow and connect this secondary rode (50-75 feet long) to the main rode with a connector described later in this chapter.
3. Release the original snubber.
4. Ease enough main rode to provide the anchor you just placed with at least 7:1 scope.
5. Attach and deploy a new snubber, stopping the drift gently.

If you have two anchors on the bow, each with the rode fed into chain locker, this will work without connecting the rodes. However, retrieve the second anchor as soon as the wind subsides, because if the boat spins with the wind or tide, the rodes will tangle together, and this is extremely difficult to unwind with the tails secured in the chain locker.

Re-Anchor. Perhaps you just picked a bad spot in the soil or fouled on trash. If the wind is not too strong, pick up and re-anchor, using the procedures detailed in Chapter 1.

Leave. If the anchorage has become exposed because of a change in wind direction, this is your best choice. Decide early, though, because this will be ugly in the middle of the night when it's as dark as the inside of a cow and pouring rain. Likely as not the exit is into another narrow waterway or through a narrow rock-lined jetty. If the problem is poor holding ground, vow to choose bottoms more carefully in the future, get a larger anchor, and set two anchors the next time you anchor over soupy mud.

Marking Chain

Proper anchoring depends on knowing how much rode is out. Fiber rode can be measured by arm span (fathoms) and chain can be measured by counting time if the windlass powers down (so many feet per second), but a back-up method helps when we lose count or forget. Both chain and rode can be marked by inserting bits of cloth or other materials, but my windlass, a Lewmar V700, hates them all, jamming or shearing them off. It is said the strips can be felt in the dark, but running your hand along the chain in the dark, on a heaving deck, feeling for bits of rag that could entangle my fingers, all in close proximity to a hungry chain gypsy, is fundamentally unsafe; a wave once threw me against a turning gypsy and only a tough leather glove prevented the loss of a finger. Plastic pop-in

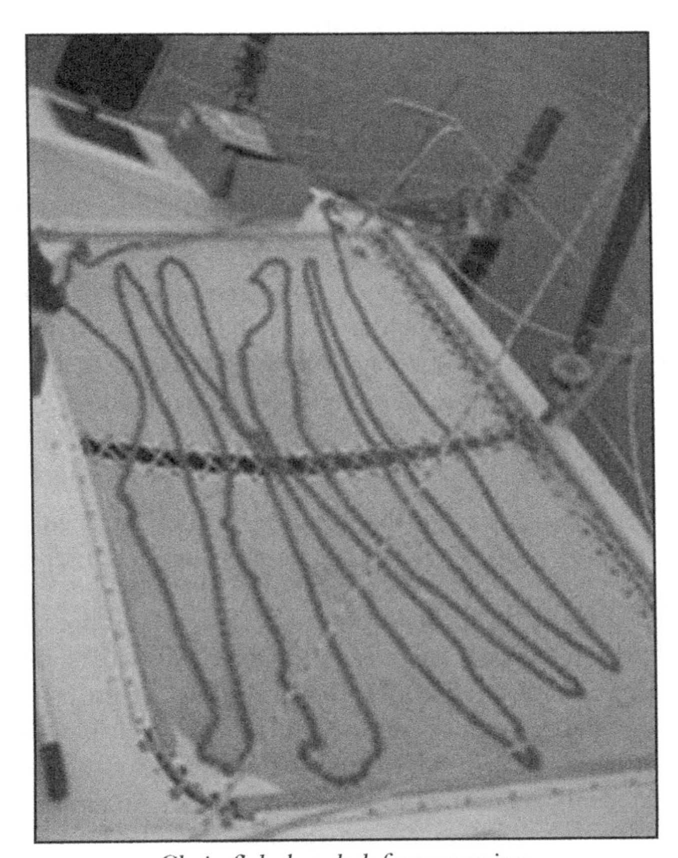

Chain flaked on deck for measuring.

A notched box allows for painting all sides and contains the mess.

markers work, but they also pop-out if enough clay or gravel comes up with the chain. Paint seemed the most obvious choice for me. But how do I mark chain or rope on-deck without making a mess?

- Flake out the chain in even loops. In my case, 10-foot lengths fit neatly across the tramp.
- Pick marking points and mask with tape. I like 6-inch wide bands; 1 for 25 feet, 2 for 50 feet and so worth. Change color at 100 feet.
- Collect a box from the dumpster, notch as needed, and drape the selected locations inside the box. Paint away, flipping the chain to coat the underside. Two coats of Rustoleum Stops Rust hold up nicely on chain. One coat of latex paint will mark nylon rope without weakening it.
- Leave the chain hanging in the box until your next visit to insure the chain is completely dry.

I painted the chain on the deck in a light breeze with little risk of over-spray mess. It wears off the outside of the links within a few dozen uses, but the paint between the links remains visible for at least a few hundred nights (more in mud, fewer in sand), renewal is simple, and it causes no trouble with the windlass. I'm satisfied with the trade-off.

After 100 nights on sand and mud the first mark is well-worn, but still very functional. Other marks receive less wear.

Anchoring the Bitter End of the Chain

The bitter end should be attached to a strong point in the chain locker as insurance against loss if the snubber and chain lock fail, if you back down too far before snubbing the chain, or the anchor somehow comes loose in deep water. This anchoring point has two fundamental requirements. First, it must be releasable in an emergency, hopefully without crawling into the anchor locker in the dark. Second, it must be able to absorb the shock of either the boat laying back on the chain or a run-away chain and anchor deployed in very deep water, falling straight down. A lashing is often suggested, but it accomplishes neither of these objectives. Instead, splice on 20-30 feet of 3-strand rope, as though it were a combination rode. This will run up through the hawse pipe without difficulty and absorb the shock of anchoring or a dropped anchor (an anchor and chain are heavy, but they only fall through water at 5-10 knots).

If you have to abandon the anchor and rode in a hurry—fast changing weather, or more likely, another boat has dragged over your chain—attach a large fender and you can retrieve it later. The line attached to the fender and a rolling hitch will do nicely. Some have suggested a floating line, but the impact absorption properties are not as good.

Anchoring Signals

For the solo sailor smooth anchoring is all about planning. It's the same with crew; there should be no last minute surprises and everyone should know the plan. Poor planning and communication often result in yelling and screaming. My family has moved past this; even when the bottom is uncooperative or the space is tight, we keep it quiet.

- Have a plan. During the approach, we talk about where we are going to put the boat, the approach, and who's doing what.
- Signals. Over the wind and engines little can be heard without yelling, and yelling always sounds like anger or panic, even when it is neither. Better to signal, since the messages are simple. It doesn't matter what the signals are, so long as you agree and post a card at the helm.

When first backing down I usually give simple verbal instruction before heading forward; astern at idle for 2-3 seconds only, just enough to get the boat moving backwards at less than 1-knot. After that I use hand signals to direct power setting. In soft mud I may wait a few minutes, rigging sail covers or straightening running rigging, before backing down hard. (See Chapters 1 and 4.)

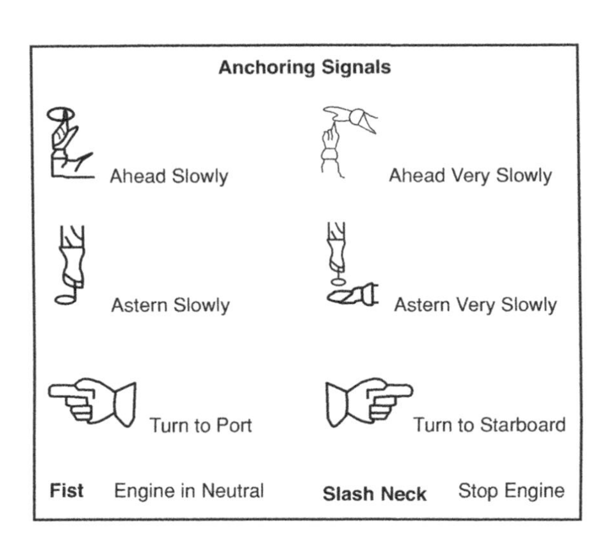

Rope-To-Chain Splice

It has always been something of a challenge to join chain to rope so that it can feed smoothly through a windlass. Back in the day of mild steel chain and hemp rope, a 2-strand splice was developed to allow bulky rope to fit through a link. One strand was unlaid way back, and the remaining two strands were passed through the end link in opposite directions, laying flat and sharing the load evenly. Even with the loss of strength around the link, the four unlaid strands were as strong as the three strands of the rope. One of the strands would be laid back in the empty groove and terminated in the manner of a long splice, and the other back tucked like a three-strand back splice.

With the advent of synthetic fibers, ropes got smaller and a simple three-strand back splice became the standard. The smaller line was still as strong as grade 30 chain and was easily handled by combination rope/chain gypsies. But then grade 43 and grade 70 high tensile chain entered the marketplace, and we find ourselves right back in the stew; if the rope is as strong as the chain, the splice is too fat for the windlass gypsy. And so, we find ourselves ironically returning to 19th century

The irony splice is smaller in diameter (top), more flexible, and much easier to feed through a windlass than the common backsplice (bottom). They got prettier with practice, but this one tested at 85% of rated line strength. I eventually reached nearly 100%.

splicing technology to mate 21st century materials. This old-school splice takes a little more effort, a transplant from the day when seaman took great pride in splicing skills. It takes practice to get the strands to share the tension equally, but if you have modest ability with splices, by the third or fourth attempt you should be in good shape. You're gonna love the way it flies through your windlass. No more jams!

> The name "traditional irony splice" was coined by Brian Toss, and the method is well described in his highly-recommended book, *"The Complete Rigger's Apprentice."*

The following instructions are for half-inch three-strand rope. For larger diameters, increase the spacings proportionately.

The Irony Splice–Instructions

(dimensions for 1/2-inch rope)

- Place a light seizing around the rope about 5 feet from the end.
- Tape the tip of each strand separately and securely.
- Carefully unlay one strand back to the seizing, without disturbing the other two strands.
- Place a light seizing around the two remaining strands, about 3 feet from the end.

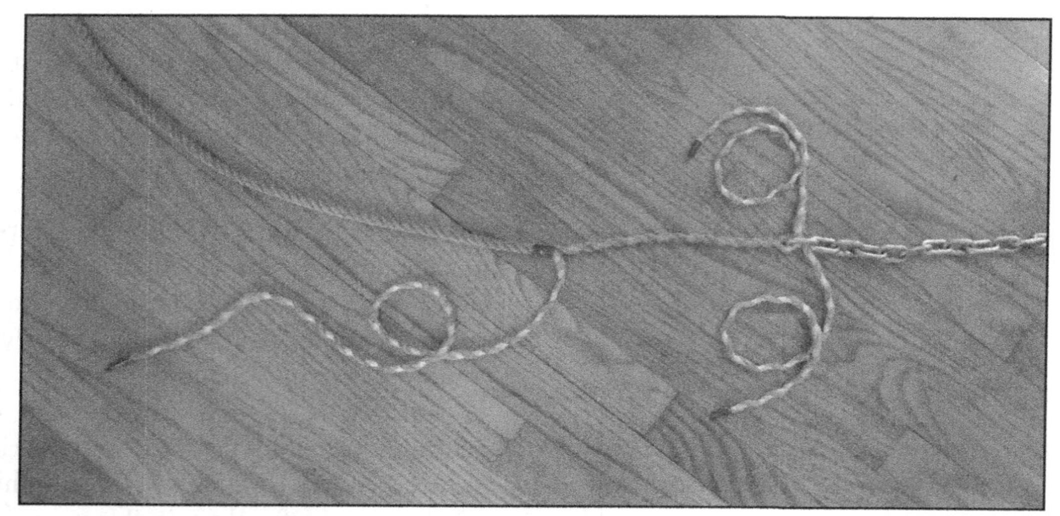

One of the strands to the right will be laid back into the vacant grove. Counter rotate and tension lightly when re-laying so that it matches the other two strands exactly

Where the re-laid strand and unlaid strand cross, lock them together with an overhand knot (must be left over right). Tightened snugly, it will disappear into the lay of the rope. Back tuck the tails 4 times.

- Untwist the two strands and lead them through the last link of chain in opposite directions.
- Lay one of the strands—whichever falls more naturally—into the vacant groove, being careful to restore the original twist and tension to this strand by counter rotating while applying light tension.
- When this strand meets the first seizing and the first strand that was unlaid, join the two strands in the manner of a long splice. This will require a locking overhand knot (left over right), back tucking both strands four times, and tapering.
- Take the remaining loose strand, still hanging idle at the last link of chain, thread it through the last link in the reverse direction, and back tuck it six times. It must bear on the link, not on the other strand. Tension such that it is carrying 50% of the load.

Ditch the Swivel

After fixing this on three boats (mine was the first), I felt I must share something so plainly obvious that it is commonly overlooked. It's embarrassing to even explain it.

The anchor is coming up backwards most of the time, and twisting it around to come over the roller is a battle. The easy, or at least obvious solution, is to add a swivel; it doesn't solve the backwards anchor problem, it only makes rotating the anchor onto the roller easier. There are anchor turners and

The long splice portion, complete, except for trimming the ends. All that remains is to back tuck the remaining strand by the last link.

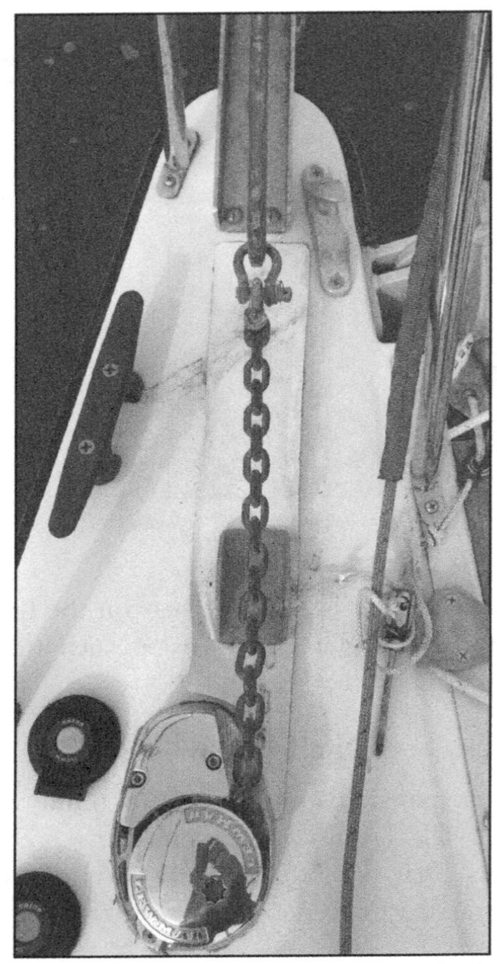

Notice the nice straight chain. No twist. That's why the anchor comes up straight.

flippers—boomerang-shaped links 6-9 inches long that use gravity to rotate the anchor into alignment. But all of these add failure points. The last time I took a swivel apart (to replace my anchor) it was hiding a nice crack inside. Never fear, there is a simple solution.

If the wind or tide created a twist in the anchor chain, it will untwist as soon as it clears the bottom because it can't turn in the windlass gypsy. In fact, the only way a twist can remain between the anchor and the windlass is if you install a swivel and the swivel has allowed the rotation. (The chain can turn in the gypsy if retrieved with zero tension—for example, if a pile accumulated on deck as a result of trying to lower the anchor before the chain lock was removed.)

When connecting the anchor without a swivel there are exactly four rotation options, and unless you considered this at the time, you had only one chance in four of getting it right. If you have a horizontal windlass, lift the chain and rotate as required. If you have a vertical windlass, move the spring load stripper arm to the side, lift the chain out of the gypsy and rotate. Your fingers are in a very dangerous place during these operations—the prudent sailor will turn the windlass breaker off and confirm that the windlass cannot be activated accidentally by pushing the button. This is particularly important if there is a remote switch that could be pressed.

This simple adjustment will bring the anchor up straight greater than 95% of the time. Why add an extra shackle? Because with G43 and higher grade chain, the size shackle that will fit the anchor and the size that will fit the chain are not the same. Place the larger shackle with the bow in the slot (the

The second shackle is pin-up to avoid snagging on the roller. A 3/8-inch bow shackle goes through the anchor, and a 5/16-inch shackle fits 1/4-inch grade 43 chain. The bow goes in the anchor to avoid side loading, which can weaken the shackle by as much as 50%.

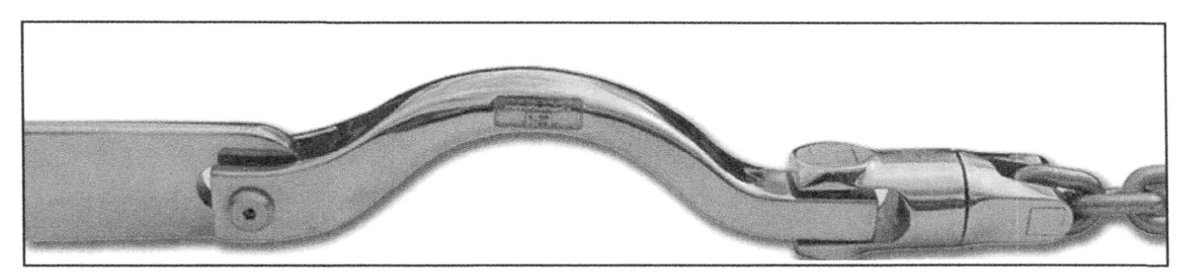

Direct connection increases the side load on the turner and the buried anchor, reducing security. Instead, separate them with shackle or short length of chain.

attachment slot is elongated to clear the pin bosses) and the smaller shackle with the pin (the largest that will fit) through the last link. Nice and flexible, with minimal side loading of shackles. For grade 43 chain, the smaller shackle must be grade B (see Appendix V).

What if it comes up backwards anyway? First, most modern anchors will naturally rotate to face the flow of the water. This is helpful when setting, but if you were motoring forward while raising the anchor to the surface—a common occurrence—the anchor will naturally rotate to face the current and come up backwards every time. The simple solution is to slowly backup while raising the anchor the last few feet, or at least to stop.

It is also possible that a twist snuck over the anchor roller at night and got stuck there. For anchors less than 45 pounds, slowly twist the chain with a gloved hand while slowly lowering the anchor (never while raising—if your hand gets stuck you can easily lose a finger to the windlass). For heavier anchors, either lower until the anchor touches the bottom, which removes most of the tension, or insert a slender tool (Phillips screwdriver) through a link and rotate the chain while lowering.

If you can't resist the urge to install a swivel, at the very least include a shackle between the swivel and the anchor. The same goes with anchor turners; imagine the ridiculous side forces created by this beauty when the wind shifts. It will also wiggle the anchor when the boat yaws, reducing holding capacity.

A simpler and possibly more effective anchor turner is the Boomerang. Developed by an Australian writer, Richard Neeves, it is open-source, with drawings and instructions in Appendix IV. It is also marketed by Anchor Right as the Flip Link, and I believe there is a Canadian distributor.

Connecting the Anchor to the Chain

Connecting the anchor to the chain seems insultingly simple, but since this is a book on modern anchors, and since modern anchors are logically paired with either grade 43 or grade 70 chain, it bears mentioning that nearly all of the shackles available in chandleries—even those selling G70 chain—are only suitable for grade 30 chain. Furthermore, often a bow shackle that is large enough to fit easily through the anchor will not fit the last link of the chain. A common solution is to place a large bow shackle through the anchor,

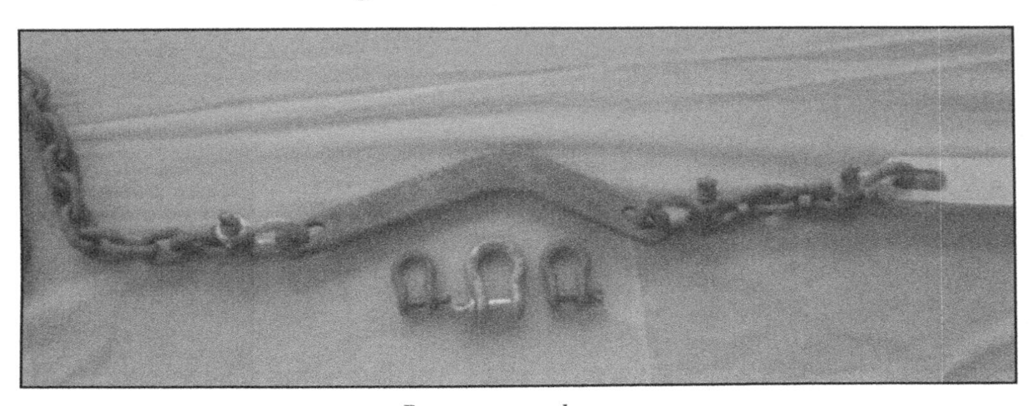

Boomerang anchor turner

and then a smaller, high-strength grade B shackle through the chain. (See also Appendix V.)

Should the bow of the shackle go through the anchor, or the pin? I interviewed a number of anchor vendors, and they all agreed that the bow is better. Loading the shackle to the side will reduce the strength by 50% or more. But when you review vendor websites you'll see there's no standard practice. Additionally, depending on the size of the elongated hole in the anchor shank, a bow shackle can become jammed in a variety of low strength positions. Good setting technique helps. Perhaps the best advice is to use a grade B shackle here too; it will be sufficiently over strength that jamming and off-axis loading won't matter.

Connecting Snubbers, Bridles, and Secondary Rodes

Catamarans universally use a bridle, and all boats should deploy a snubber when anchored by all-chain rodes in water less than about 30 feet deep to reduce shock loading on the anchor and chain. Unfortunately, the most advantageous use of a snubber is in shallow water, where an ordinary chain hook is lifted off by the mud if it rests on the bottom during light winds.

Connecting V tandem rodes presents a slightly different problem, since the pull can come in any direction, not necessarily in-line with the chain. Additionally, because these connections are often slightly weaker than the main chain, this secondary rode should be nylon rope for redundant shock absorption. A few potential solutions are listed below, some commercial products, and some homebuilt:

Chain Rode Connectors

Chain Grab Hook. A common hardware store item, these are placed between the links and hold tenaciously as long as a lazy loop of chain is pulling downwards. However, they will quickly wiggle off if they rest on the bottom during calm winds. They can be suitable for connecting bridles and snubbers if they are meticulously kept off the bottom, which is very difficult to ensure with long snubbers. Recommended for short snubbers only.

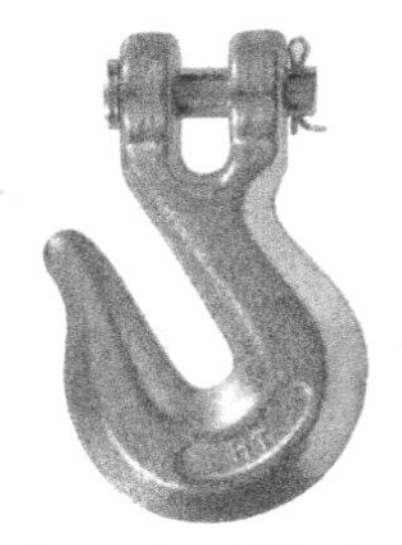

Chain Grab Hook

Mantus Chain Hook. I've used this for about three years and find it very handy. A locking plastic plate keeps the chain in place, even lying on the bottom. The working load limit (WLL) is only slightly greater than grade 30 chain (about 1,430 pounds in the ¼-inch size); however, this is sufficient

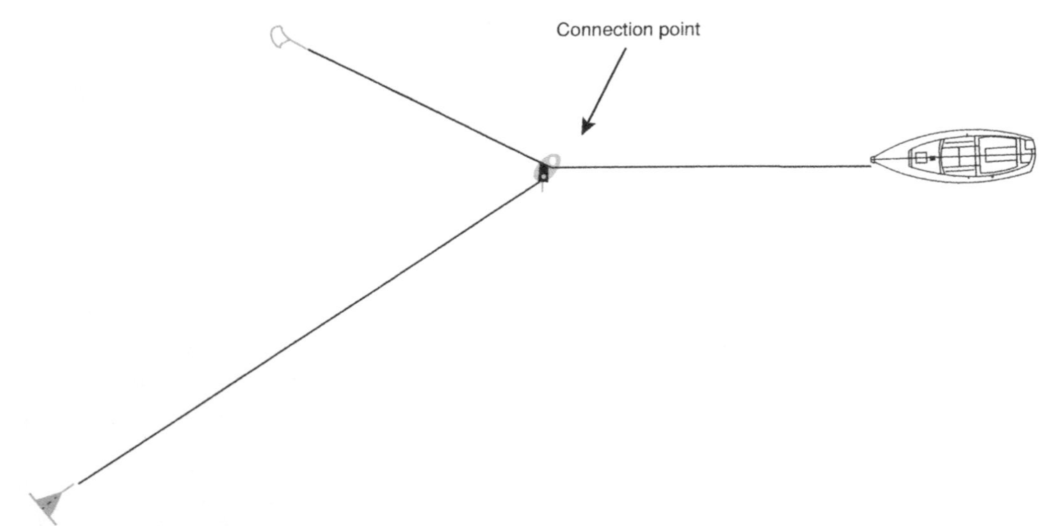

If the boat spins, the chain twist is absorbed by the rode between the connection point and the boat. Even if the two rodes do twist a few times, they are easily unwrapped when the connection is released.

Mantus Chain Hook

for connecting a snubber or bridle even to high tensile chain, since the working load of the snubber is even less. The larger sizes can be difficult to work with, since the plastic lock is stiffer in large sizes. The plastic lock is somewhat prone to breaking, although the manufacture will replace them for free. Recommended for snubbers.

Suncor Chain Hook

Suncor Chain Hook. Another off-set hook, this one does not have a latch, although users report that it stays in place reasonably well. Strength not rated.

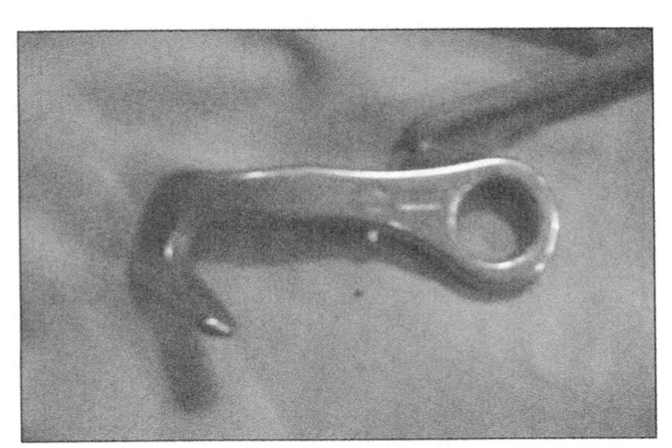

Wichard Locking Chain Grab

Wichard Locking Chain Grab. Also handy, but only 60% of the WLL of grade 30 chain. Distortion is seldom as severe as the photograph, but there have been numerous reports of the locking pin jamming.

Kong Chain Gripper

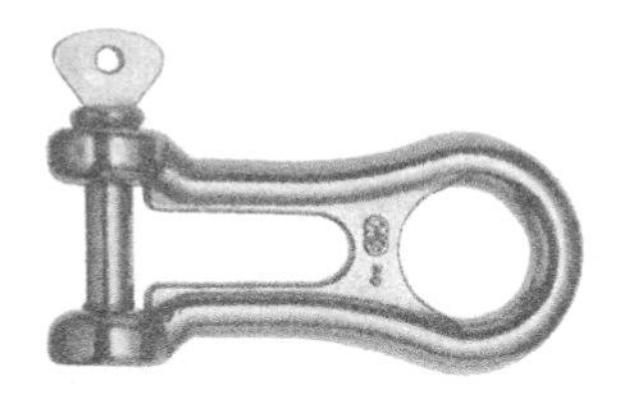

Kong Chain Gripper. Very strong, very near the strength of grade 43 chain. Can be recovered over the roller, though it is a little bumpy. The pin is potentially fiddly; I'm sure I would eventually drop it overboard. Suitable for snubbers and secondary rodes.

Soft Shackle

Soft Shackles. The open, Kohloff style is best, since conventional, closed soft shackles eventually foul with marine growth and lime, becoming difficult to open. As strong as grade 43 chain, they are reasonably abrasion resistant in cruiser experience (they last a few years), easily inspected for wear, and unlike most connectors, do not weaken the chain. Unquestionably their best feature is ease of recovery over the bow roller, making them the

Attaching a secondary rode. I should not have the rope over my lap this way—that was just for pictures.

best overall method for monohulls. For boats that attach the snubber forward of the roller, they are more fiddly than hooks. The shackle should be at least 3 inches long, or it will be fiddly to attach. Recommended for snubbers and secondary rodes.

Prusik Sling. Strong in all directions, it will not slip or damage chain. For best strength, use Dyneema. Recommended for snubbers and secondary rodes.

Rolling Hitch. The links slide around, allowing this hitch to slip at 25-50% of the WLL of the chain. Most sailors will never notice, since this requires serious weather, explaining why there are so many success stories. On the other hand, numerous long-distance cruisers have observed slipping and now use either two rolling hitches or a camel

A carabiner holds the rodes together temporarily while I thread the soft shackle. This makes it much easier in a breeze or waves.

Cow hitch easily holding at 2,500 pounds on 1/4-inch grade 30 chain (WLL 1,900 pounds). A prusik hitch is even better on chain and also holds 800-1600 pounds on wet 1/2-inch rope before sliding, depending on the materials and sizes.

hitch. Additionally, it is not suitable for attaching a secondary rode at an angle. Not recommended.

Rolling hitch slipping through at just 400 pounds. (3/8-inch line on 1/4-inch galvanized grade 30 chain).

Early prototype bridle plate

Camel Hitch. A slight variation on the rolling hitch, where the last turn is reversed, like a prusik hitch. Secure to about 50% of the breaking strength of the line, which is greater than the working load limit of the chain. However, when connecting to chains, the load will come from a range of angles, and camel and rolling hitches are only secure if the load is parallel to the chain. Double rolling hitches or a camel hitch are suitable for snubbers, but not for connecting secondary rodes.

Chain Bridle Plate. Dissatisfied with the existing gear, I developed a stronger, more versatile chain grab, which I call a bridle plate. Though originally conceived to work with two separate bridle lines (catamaran), it can as easily be used with a single line snubber by attaching both connectors to a single eye.

The chain rode drops into the slot and can't escape once the latch plate is lowered and the second bridle line is attached. The apex hole is for attaching a secondary rode for when it is desired to bring the rode back to the boat in heavy weather (Chapter 11). Fabrication is detailed in Appendix IV. Very simple and idiot-proof in

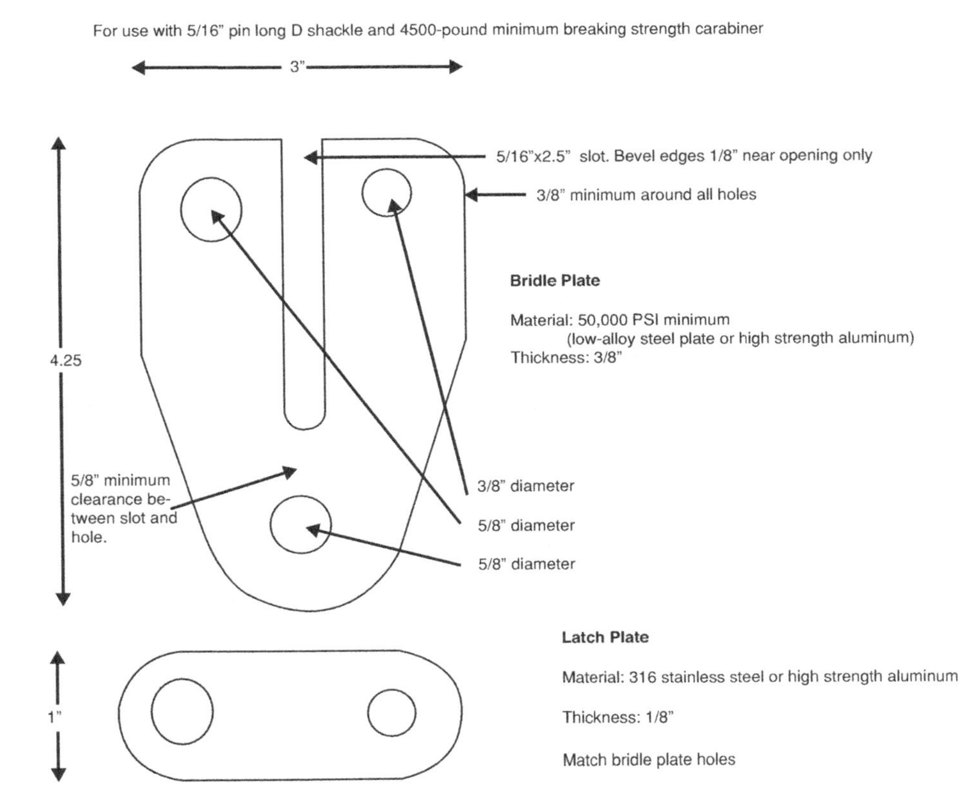

years of testing. Recommended for snubbers and secondary rodes.

Rope Rode Connectors

Rolling Hitch. A simple knot, easily tied and not too prone to jamming. It is not secure unless the snubber line is smaller than the rode. Slipping begins at about 30% of line strength (about 1,500 pounds for 3/8-inch line tied on 1/2-inch line). However, this exceeds the storm load on a rope rode. It is not secure if the load comes from an angle, such as a secondary rode.

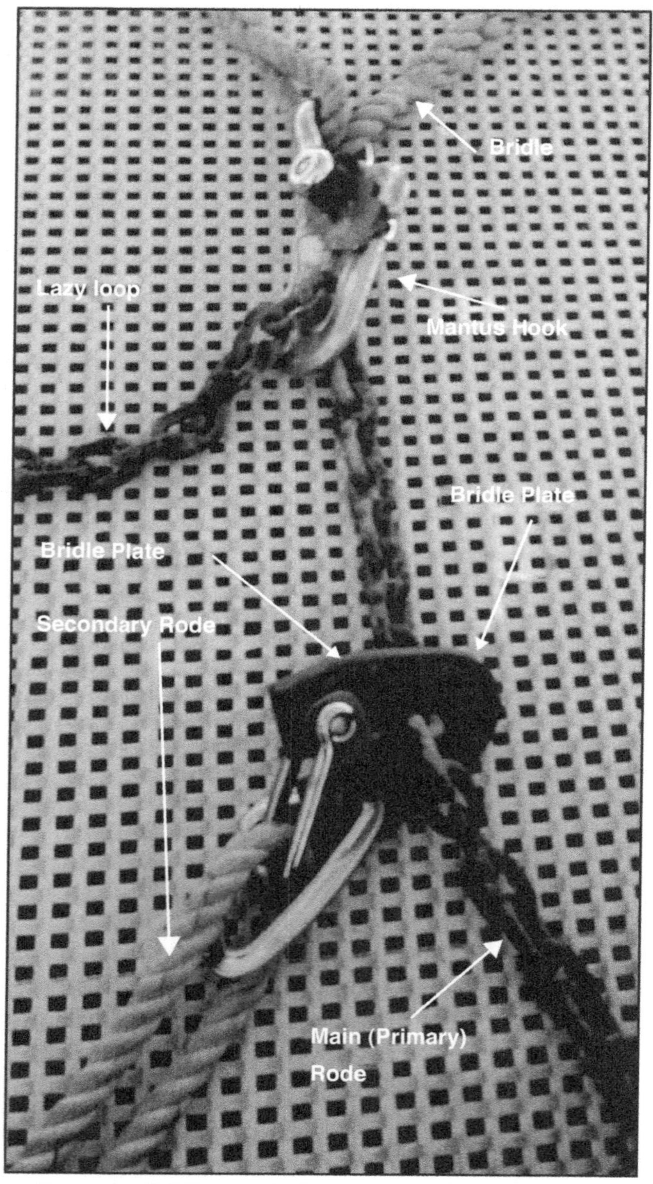

Example: Bridle attached to chain with Mantus hook at top; chain bridle plates used to attach secondary rode at bottom. The bridle plate is full strength with only one shackle, but the carabiner keeps the gate closed, adding security and strength.

A Dyneema prusik sling is a fast and secure way to attach a bridle to a rope rode.

Prusik Hitch. Wrap a sling (sewn climbing sling or spliced from Amsteel) around the rode twice. The sling is then attached directly to the bridle plate using a carabiner or shackle, or to the primary rode via one of the chain connectors described above. Used on rope it will slip at 1,200-2,400 pounds, depending on rope and sling materials; smaller sling diameter and polyester/Dyneema fiber blends perform best. Prusik slings can also be rigged in tandem, one a few inches above the other, reaching strengths approaching line strength. Convenient, secure, impossible to tie wrong, and non-damaging to the line, this is one of my favorite rope rode attachment methods. Recommended for snubbers and secondary rodes.

Terminal Eye. If a fixed length rode is used—a common occurrence with V tandems—splice an eye in the end of the secondary rode and connect it to either the bridle plate or to the primary rode using one of the chain connectors described above. Although this sounds inflexible, many of us anchor in a limited range of depths. The simplest method. Recommended.

Cow hitch, slipping and unlaying at only 250 pounds (1/2-inch line).

Cow Hitch on Ring. Double the rode and push it through the center. Bring the loop around the back of the shackle so that a cow hitch/larks head knot is formed. Attach the ring or large bow shackle to a bridle plate or a chain connector described above. Simple, but there are fatal downsides. First, the knot begins to slip at 350-800 pounds, depending on the line type and ring size; however, with even the slightest tension applied to the standing end (secure it to a bow cleat), the knot locks securely. However, the second downside is that if the knot is prevented from slipping, it becomes difficult to untie when strained above 250 pounds (30-knot breeze). If strained to 650 pounds (45-knot storm), five minutes of wrestling with pliers is required. Additionally, the line may be unlaid and damaged. Finally, the knot weakens the rope about 60%. Not recommended.

I have used both the terminal eye and prusik hitch methods for many years. Neither has failed in storm conditions.

Long Bridles (or Snubbers) Without Snagging or Chafe

Even with a secure chain hook, allowing the snubber connection to drag back and forth on the bottom is a recipe for snags (if there are rocks) and abrasion. Thus, in lighter weather it is common to rig the snubber bridle short. Unfortunately, if the wind comes up during the night, this leaves

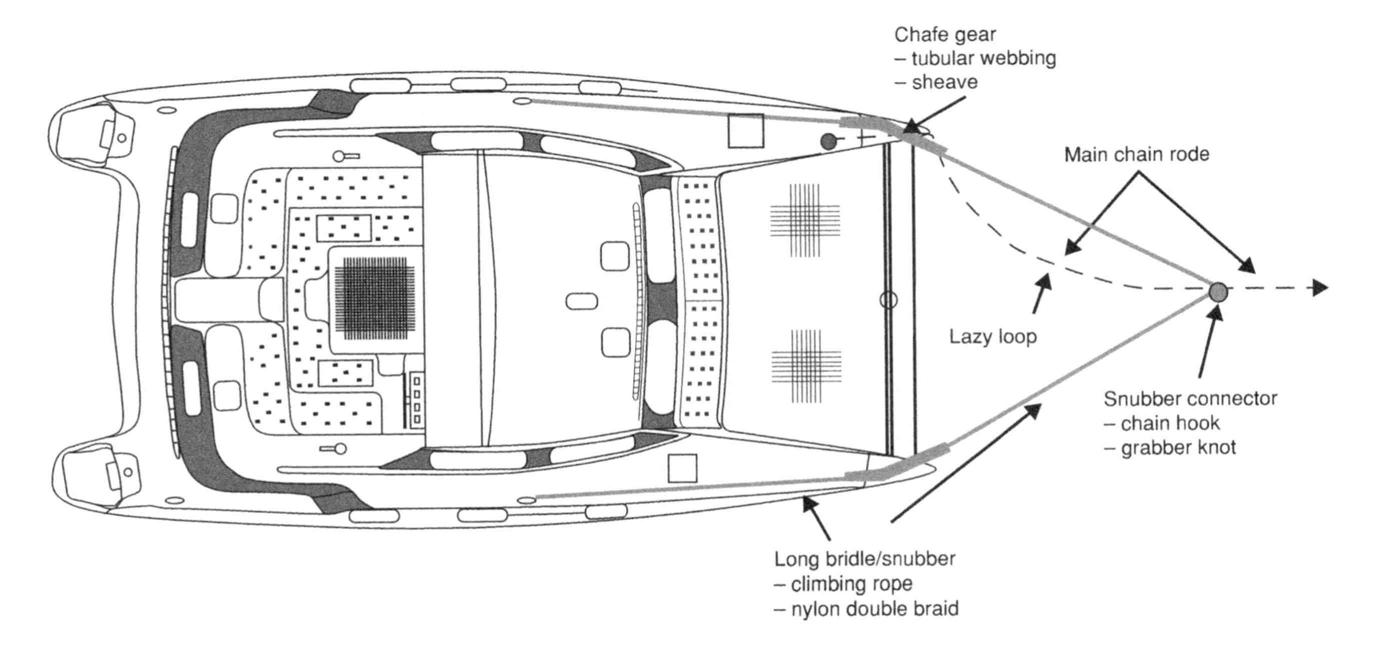

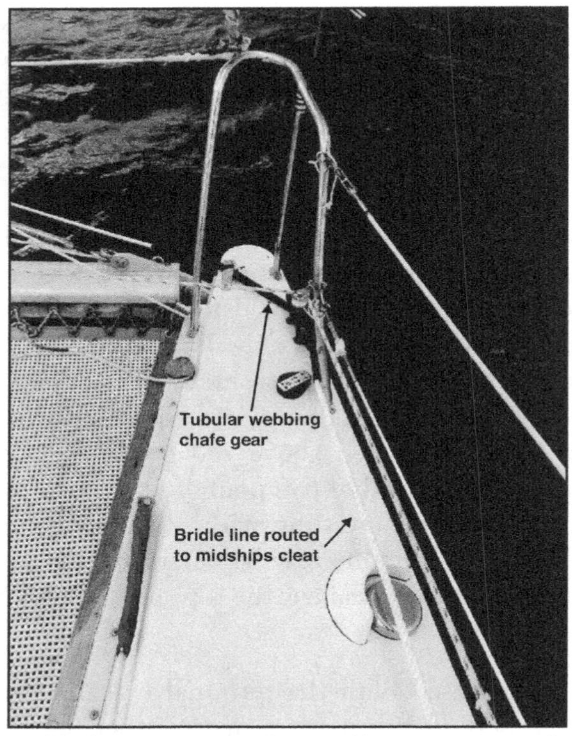

Chafe gear protects a long snubber on its way to the midships cleat.

the snubber far too short for optimum shock absorption.

One solution is to secure the ends of the bridle farther back. I place the spliced eyes over my midship cleats and lead the bridle around the bow cleats and through the chocks by means of low-friction chafing gear (tubular nylon webbing). Other sailors take the bridle ends clear to the stern cleats. In gusty winds and chop, you can watch the rope easily glide through the webbing providing full shock absorption while extending only about 10 feet forward of the bows. Some sailors have placed ball bearing sheaves in this location to completely eliminate heating and chafe.

When the wind comes up, it is a simple matter to move the eyes to the bow cleats and release another 20-40 feet of chain, increasing scope when it is most needed. There is enough stretch in the snubber that snatching the eyes off the midship cleats during a lull is practical if done before the wind becomes too strong. Alternatively, the tails can simply cleated.

Another solution is to attach a very small fender (3"x12") to the snubber near the connection point. It need only be large enough to float the snubber, connector, and a short portion of chain; anything more diminishes the catenary by lifting too much chain. A small carabiner and a few feet of light line work well.

Which is simpler? It comes down to the boat. I've used both, and they are reliable.

Dive Gear

The means to safely enter the water, regardless of temperature, is a cruising safety essential. Perhaps the anchor has fouled. More likely, a lobster or crab pot line has wrapped around the prop or rudder. In warm climates, a snorkel, mask, and fins may be enough, though anywhere other than the tropics, a light wetsuit is better for winter and shoulder seasons. In cold climates a full wetsuit or drysuit should be on board once the mercury drops. I started with a wetsuit and eventually graduated to a drysuit, which is warmer, more comfortable, and also makes excellent foul weather gear. A wet suit is more agile in the water.

If the water is more than 12 feet deep you won't be diving all the way to the anchor. In muddy water,

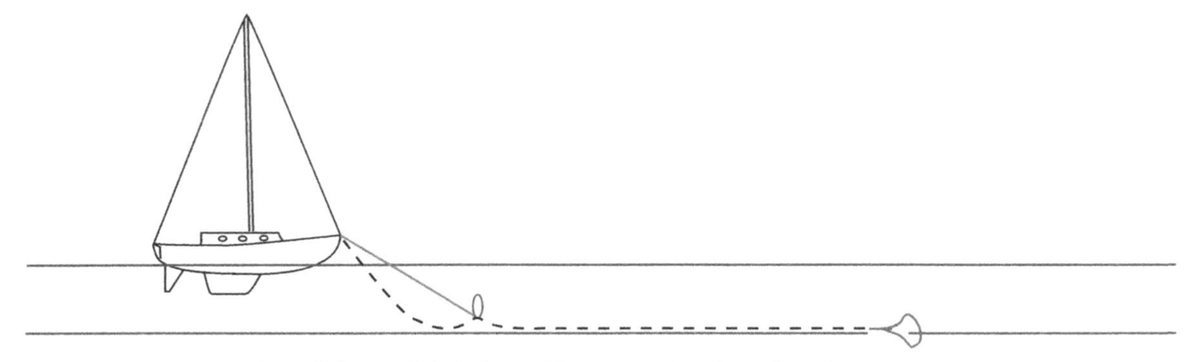

A small float will lift the snubber connection clear of the bottom.

Corrosion of the last few links is accelerated by proximity to the stainless steel swivel.

you may not dive that far, since the only practical way to find the anchor is to follow the chain. On the other hand, some sailors have taken using an 8-12 feet length of yellow Dyneema as a short floating tripping line. It is far enough below the surface to avoid the rudder, keel, and passing boats, but it is close enough to the surface for easy recovery. If I frequented rock and coral strewn waters, I might adopt this practice.

Mixing Stainless and Galvanized

Notice how the first few feet of chain are more rusted than the rest of the chain? I see this all the time with big stainless swivels. If nothing else, remember to trim the first few feet off every few years, since the first link wears first. While we're at it, notice the how the swivel will bear a side load; many have been broken this way. Always isolate the swivel from the shank with a pair of shackles or a few links of chain.

Fatigue

Gear seldom fails because the minimum breaking strength was exceeded. It normally fails after thousands of lesser cycles cause gradual weakening.

Steel. Moderate alloy steels can tolerate a nearly infinite number of cycles below what is known as the fatigue limit. This is about one half of the breaking strength and is the primary reason the working load limit is typically specified as 1/3 to 1/5 of the minimum breaking strength, depending on the grade of steel, quality control, allowance for corrosion, and the consequences of failure. As long as steel gear is not overloaded or corroded, it has an infinite working life. Stainless steel is subject to crevice corrosion and accelerated fatigue cracking if frequently loaded to near its fatigue limit in a corrosive environment, making it less desirable for cyclically loaded equipment such as anchor chains.

Aluminum. Although aluminum does not have a fatigue limit in the strict sense that steel does, at about 1/5 minimum breaking strength the allowable number of cycles exceeds that any anchor—or most boat gear for that matter—will ever see. I am not aware of any aluminum anchor component failing due to fatigue.

Rope. Conventional wisdom is to use nylon for dock and anchor lines, polyester for most running rigging, high modulus line for genoa sheets, and wire rope or Dyneema for standing rigging and soft shackles or lashings. Each has the right properties for the task at hand. But this may be an oversimplification.

Dyneema. Several times more resistant to fatigue than steel and eight times more resistant than nylon rope, Dyneema can survive more than 1,000,000 cycles to 70% of breaking strength. Samson Ropes rates the working load of fabricated Amsteel slings as 20% of breaking strength—the same as steel components—quoting industry norms as the reason rather than fatigue. Five to eight years in full sun will reduce strength 20-40%, depending on line size, but snubber shackles are either underwater or stowed. It will outlast steel cable where fatigue and repeated bending cause failure, but it is not as resistant to abrasion against sharp edges. Perfect for soft shackles, running rigging, and even standing rigging, it does not have enough stretch to serve as anchor rode.

Polyester. Considerably more resistant to fatigue than nylon, polyester lines can work at 30% of breaking strength for over 1,000,000 cycles. This is three times more than nylon can carry for a similar number of cycles. Unlike nylon, it is not weakened or made more vulnerable to abrasion by water. There's a lot to like for running rigging, but it does not stretch enough to serve as anchor rode, except as a deep water extension (after 300 feet of chain has been deployed).

Nylon. Nylon gets occasional bad press for failure well below its rated strength. The reason, of course, is that nylon has a limited fatigue life. If cycled beyond about 10% of its breaking strength, it will fail within 10,000 to 30,000 cycles. At 20% of breaking strength, adjusting for chafe and age, it will fail within 1,000 cycles—not enough for a single prolonged storm. In part because of superior fatigue endurance, polyester and Dyneema are preferred for deepwater moorings. But these lack the necessary elasticity and energy absorption capacity to serve as docklines for yachts or for single point anchor rodes in the relatively shallow depths in which most yachtsmen anchor.

Nylon is sometimes indicted for heating under heavy loads, and that melting contributes to failure. This is a false observation. First, even brand-new nylon rope, when pulled very slowly to failure during testing, will exhibit melting at the ends, the result of the enormous energy release at the instant of rupture. Second, simple engineering calculations show that for nylon rope less than 1-inch in diameter to increase in temperature enough to appreciably affect strength, it must be repeatedly and rapidly cycled to over 25% breaking strength, in which case its predicted life expectancy is only a few hundred cycles. At this point it has been seriously overloaded and it will fail during a storm. Research by rope and off-shore oil platform companies shows minor heating begins at 15% of breaking strength, and this only with much larger ropes, where heat dissipation is much slower. Impermeable, insulating coverings can theoretically contribute to heating in smaller ropes, although testing has confirmed that the heating is negligible. Failures have been noted under such chafe gear, and blamed on heating, but the real causes were locally high flexation, overload, and frictional heating.

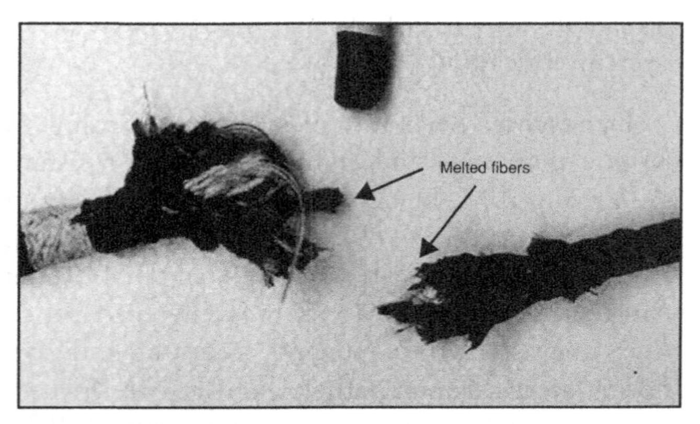

Brand new nylon double braid dockline, broken at low strain rate at ambient temperature. Heating and cycling were not involved, and yet the ends melted anyway.

Storm melted dockline with the same melting pattern. Heat was probably not a factor, only overload.

Depending on the application, traditional engineering design procedures suggest 8-10% of breaking strength for nylon rope, and the ABYC anchoring standard specifies 9.5% of breaking strength (ABYC H-40 AP Table 1). Operating in

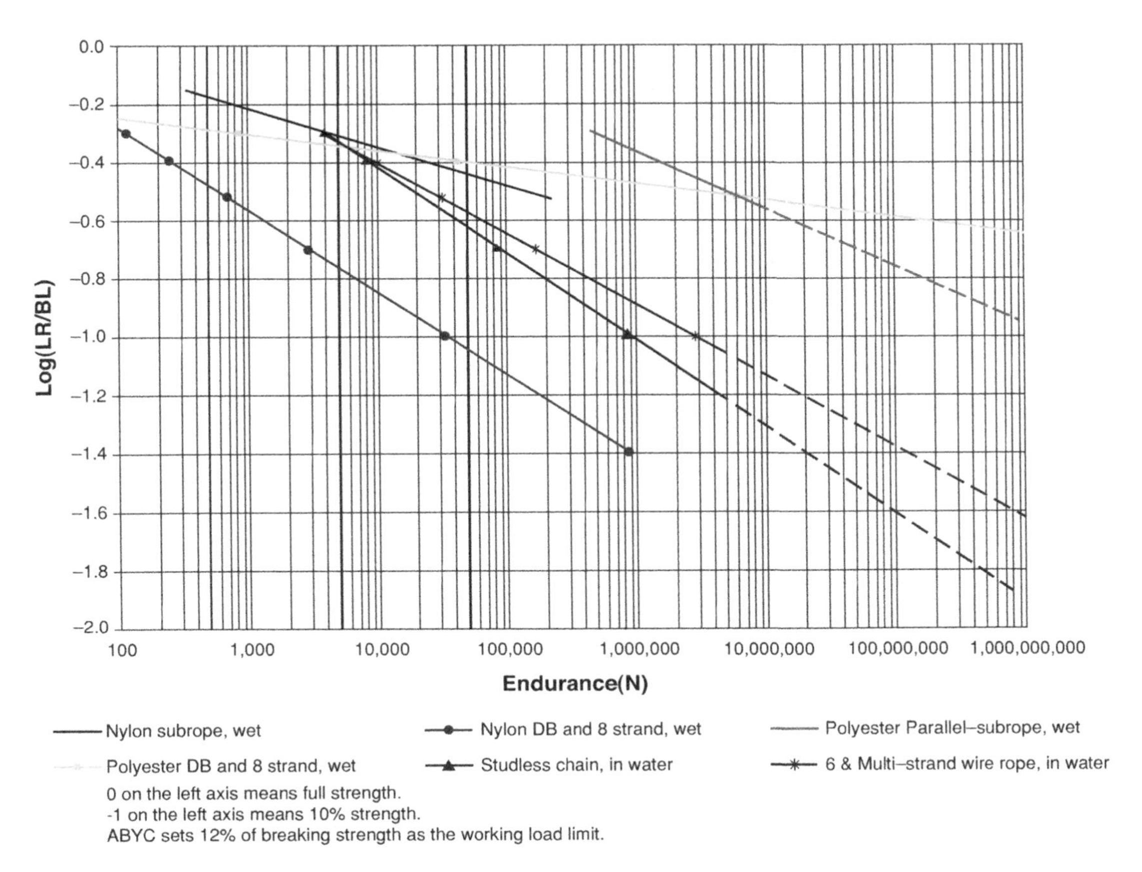

the range of 15-25% of breaking strength is wholly unacceptable.

Nylon as Drogue and Sea Anchor Rode

Although slightly off-topic, the following is related from an engineering viewpoint, and a few paragraphs might be beneficial.

Three-strand rope is not recommended. Because only one end is restrained, under pulsating loads this construction will rotate when loaded, and then hockle when the load is abruptly released. Double braid is acceptable, and single braid is preferred by some vendors.

A sea anchor (parachute type, generally 12 to 24 feet in diameter) requires a very elastic rode for the same reason a ground anchor requires elasticity. In storm conditions the boat will be struck by mountainous waves and something must give. Additionally, an elastic rode provides consistent tension on the parachute, helping to maintain its stability; if slack develops, the ball of water within the sea anchor, even though drifting at only 1-knot, still has considerable momentum. If the load is suddenly released, the anchor will continue forward, inverting the parachute and tangling the lines. I have seen this happen during load testing with power boats, time and again, and it has been reported by cruisers. A long, elastic rode helps by maintaining constant strain.

The rode must also be conservatively sized. I believe the cause of failure is not some mysterious heating of nylon rope, for which there is no calculation basis, but rather something much simpler; the manufacturers have underspecified the rode. For example, a Beneteau 40 displaces 19,000 pounds and anchor attachments were specified as 16,000 pounds by Don Jordan (Jordan Series Drogue, or JSD). This is similar to the ABYC permanent mooring guidance (4,800 pounds working load, or about 19,000 pounds breaking strength), which assumes some wave protection, at least as compared to a major storm on the open ocean) of. A nylon rode with the same working load limit would have a breaking strength of about 50,500 pounds—at least 1 1/4-inch nylon rope. Calculated another way, a 40-foot boat would have a wind load of 1,960 pounds at 90 knots, and at least 2-3 times that in large waves, or about 4,000-6,000 pounds. In contrast, the instructions for this size anchor (15-foot diameter) typically specify 3/4-inch rope, which has a breaking strength of 16,700 pounds and a working load limit of 1,670 pounds, less than the wind load alone. As a result, the sea anchor rode will be cycling to 20-30% of breaking strength, resulting in a fatigue life of 500-1,000 cycles. Assuming a storm period of 20-30 seconds, this is only 3-5 hours, and there are going to be failures, before chafe and or heating assumptions are considered. The rode is simply over loaded.

The obvious answer is to double or triple the strength of the rode. That's a lot of rope, considering you will need 300-500 feet of it, and I can understand the reluctance of the manufacturer to specify it and the customer to buy it, but this is what conservative engineering design calls for. Either buy bigger rope or avoid the worst storms; it's that simple.

Speed-limiting drogues can be served by either elastic or inelastic rodes. Vendors are split between specifying nylon because of its shock absorption, and polyester or Dyneema, which ensure that the drogue feels the acceleration of the boat as soon as it begins to surf, without having to wait for the nylon to stretch. A few vendors specify nylon/polyester blend lines. Based on my testing up to 12 knots (Seabrake, Galerider, Delta Drogue, Paradrogue, and several cone-types) for a series of magazine articles, elasticity is not required in a speed-limiting drogue rode because the drogue itself limits the force. As speed increases, they simply rip through the water that much faster, the load seldom exceeding 1 ton for a 40-foot boat, depending on the size and design. This is 2-3 times less than the loads imposed by a parachute sea anchor; not surprising, because speed-limiting drogues give with the wind and waves, rather than standing rigid. Polyester is the logical material for most boats, providing a good compromise between handling, low stretch, good abrasion resistance even when wet, and excellent fatigue life. Because polyester is less affected by fatigue, the rode can be sized at 20% of breaking strength. Based on a maximum drogue load at about 12 knots this will result in a rode of about the same size and strength as the main anchor rode, which is in line with manufacturer guidance. In my case, ½-inch polyester double braid is a good match for a Seabrake GP24.

Chapter 14
Summary

BY THIS TIME you should have a good understanding of the forces involved, what anchors can and cannot do, and how to get the most out of the tackle you have through proper rigging. Anchoring is deviously complex, to be sure, but a methodical approach can keep it practical.

- *One Anchor (Chapter 1). Over good bottoms and in reasonable weather, a single anchor is nearly always the right answer. Multiple anchors are more time-consuming, more prone to failure if rigged carelessly, and they take up more room in the harbor. Choose a primary anchor that will hold your boat 95% of the time.*
- *The Proper Anchor (Chapters 6-8 and Appendix VI). All of the new generation anchors (Manson Supreme, Mantus, Rocna, Sarca, Spade) are excellent and I doubt you could tell which was at the end of the rode. Fortress is very good in soft seabeds and unmatched as a secondary or kedge. The anchor must be big enough.*
- *Chain and Snubbers (Chapter 2). A rode and snubber combination suitable for your boat will minimize peak rode tension and not fatigue in any weather.*
- *Scope (Chapter 4). The "answer" depends on so many variables—water depth, anticipated wind, chain type, anchor type, and seabed—it's small wonder people disagree. 10:1 may not be enough in shallow water for an all-rope rode attached to a poor short scope anchor in soft mud with a thunderstorm approaching. On the other hand, 4:1 is plenty in 30 feet of water with a grade 30 chain rode over good bottom in settled weather.*
- *Grade 43 or Grade 70 Chain (Chapter 6 and Chapter 12). These are well-proven in industry to be both tougher and more reliable than grade 30 chain. However, in anchorages between 15 and 30 feet, the extra weight of grade 30 chain can reduce jerking and the need for long snubbers. The best choice may come down to your local cruising grounds, habits, and your sensitivity to weight. The anchor shackle should match the chain strength.*
- *Rode Selection and Anchor Selection Are Separate Issues (Chapter 2 and Chapter 4). The rode should be designed to prevent snatch load and overloads, protecting all of the gear from bowsprit to anchor shackle. Even an over-sized anchor can fail if the scope is too short and wave and gust impacts are jiggling it around. The anchor should be conservatively sized based on wind load and poor conditions. That said, if you adventure cruise and expect to anchor over bad bottoms, going up one size never hurt.*
- *Understand the Bottom (Chapter 5). Closely observe setting behavior and all that you can infer from it. An anchor can never be better than the substrate. Power setting can give some indication of the probable security.*

- *Anchor Holding Capacity Improves With Time (Chapter 4). But it does not always happen that way; short scope, shallow anchor setting, and excessive yawing or hobby horsing can prevent soil consolidation. Don't expect miracles, and use a conservatively sized anchor and scope.*
- *Using Two Anchors Can Help (Chapters 9-12). When a second anchor is needed, select the correct rig and learn to deploy and recover without frustration.*
- *V Tandems are for Soft Mud and Tight Spaces (Chapters 10-11). For soft mud, use an asymmetrical tandem with a Fortress or other high-capacity anchor as the secondary. Combine the rodes before the roller so that only one rode comes onto the boat.*
- *In-Line Tandems are for Rocks, Hardpan and Cobbles Only (Chapter 12). Don't use in-line tandems for mud or sand bottoms, no matter how strongly common sense suggests they are better. They are worse.*
- *Get the Details Right. A rig is only as strong as its weakest part; minimize strain, set well, and be on the watch for chafe and fatigue. Dial-in your techniques until you can easily do it the best way, every time.*

This book has taken an engineering approach, and the reading benefits from an engineering mindset. You don't build a bridge based on gut feel; you calculate, measure, test materials, and check against well-established standards. When you are finished, you know the bridge will stand. Rock climbers must know with complete certainty that their anchors are sound. I don't believe anchoring is an art; it is a learned skill.

By practicing the same discipline as the bridge engineer or rock climber, you can sleep like a baby, without dragging around hundreds of meters of oversize chain, and 50% more new-generation anchor than you need. If you like the idea of oversize gear, I hope I've helped you figure out how to best accomplish that.

A chain is never stronger than its weakest link, and anchoring will always be about the details.

Glossary Terms

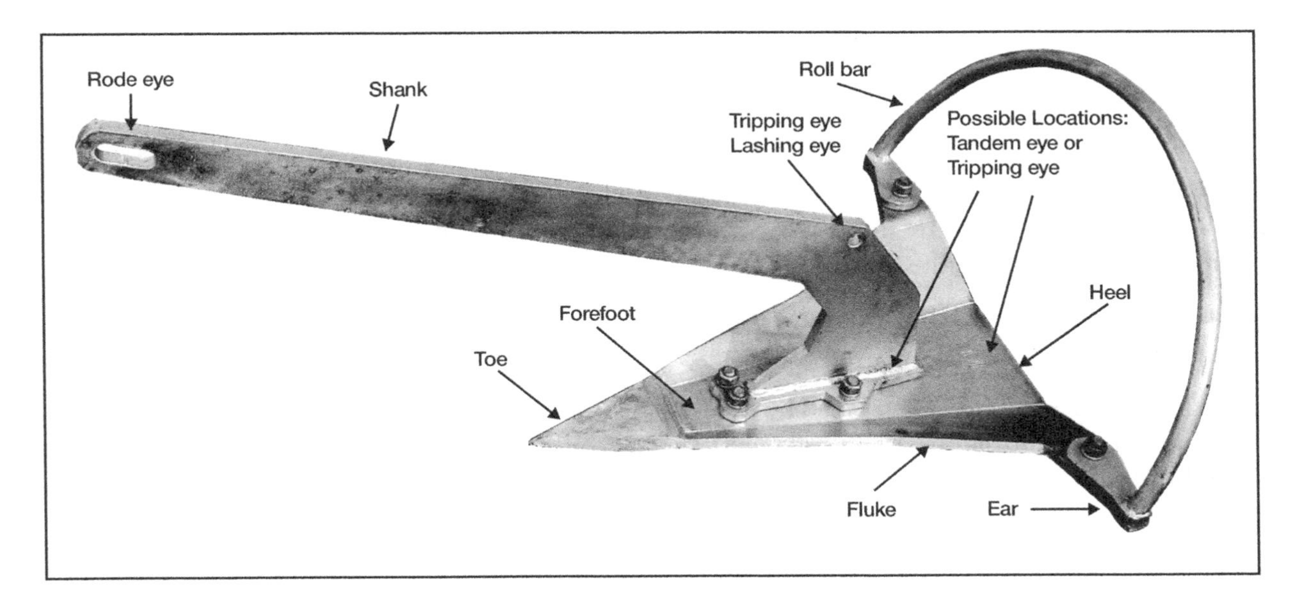

ABYC (American Boat and Yacht Council): The primary U.S. recreational boat trade standards association, responsible for developing voluntary constructions standards for boat builders and providing training and certification for marine technicians.

Actual Scope: Scope as measure where the rode enters the bottom. See Chapter 4.

Bahamian moor: A special case of the V tandem rig. Two anchors are rigged to the bow of the boat via separate rodes of approximately equal length. The angle formed between the rodes is large, typically 110-160 degrees. It is not employed to increased holding, but rather to limit swing and control the angle of pull on the anchors.

Bridle plate: A metal plate which allows the connection of bridle legs and multiple rodes to a single point. See Appendix VI for construction details.

BS (breaking strength): Refers to the minimum breaking strength unless otherwise noted. For climbing gear, this is six standard deviations below the average breaking strength—only 3.4 parts per million should fail below this value. The statistical basis for other gear is not generally provided.

Catenary: The curve taken by any rope or chain hanging between two fixed points under the influence of gravity, as illustrated by suspension bridge cables or the curve of an anchor rode underwater.

Catenary stretch: The difference between the straight length of chain and the end-to-end length when hanging in a catenary.

Combination rode: A rode including a chain leader (typically 10-100 feet), connected to several hundred feet of rope. The chain leader functions to protect the rope from abrasion near the anchor and to dampen motion.

Cyclical loading: The process of repeatedly stressing an anchor to a significant percentage of its ultimate holding capacity. Short period cycles (less than 15 minutes), such as waves and yawing, reduce soil consolidation around the anchor and reduce holding capacity. Slow period cycles (greater than 15 minutes), such as periodic wind gusts, generally increase holding capacity by encouraging deeper setting, although the critical time period, force, and the magnitude of the resulting changes depend on the specific soil.

Fetch: The distance the wind has blown over the water; the longer the fetch, the larger the waves.

Figure 8 coil: The simplest possible coil, where the rope is looped in a circular motion over one hand, without applying a twist with each turn. The result is an irregular figure 8.

Ground tackle: Collectively, the anchor rode, anchor, and all components.

Gypsy: The toothed wheel that grips the chain on a windlass. Also referred to as a wildcat.

Hockle: Of laid rope (3-strand). To acquire a knob in a bight of cordage, caused by twisting the line against the lay. Such damage, caused by improper coiling, rough handling, or quick release of tension combined with slight twisting, weakens the line and causes it to jam in blocks.

Horsing: The tendency of a boat to move forwards and backwards at anchor when the rode stretches with wind gusts. Also known as surging.

Jordan Series Drogue (JSD): Developed by the Donald Jordan of the U.S. Coast Guard, the JSD is a storm management drogue consisting of 50-200 small conical drogues. Curiously, while in-line ground anchors fail miserably, multiple in-line drogues function more like an in-line tandem scraping for friction. The great number of elements provides redundancy and averages out the effects of waves.

Kedge: As a noun, a large anchor used to move the boat through use of the windlass or winches. As a verb, the action of moving the boat using ground tackle and winches or windlass.

Lashing eye: An eye located on the top of the shank near the fluke. Often identified as a tripping eye, although anchor tripping is more effective if a hole at the base of the shank or on the heel of the fluke is used.

Leader: Also known as the forerunner. The section of the rode nearest to the anchor. Typically chain is used as a leader for nylon rodes because it resists cutting and its weight increases catenary. May also be steel cable or Dyneema with a chafe guard. See also "combination rode."

Lee shore: The shore that is downwind. Where you will end up if the anchor drags too far.

Leeward: In the downwind direction.

Mooring: Generally a fixed point anchor, either deadweight or screw pile. Also used to describe permanent multi-anchor rigs.

Mooring ball: Also mooring buoy. A float marking a fixed mooring. You attach to these to an eye at the top using either an attached pendant or your own. These are either private property or available for rent. Regulations specific that these are white with a blue stripe; never use a tripping line float that looks like this!

Open hawse: The practice of mooring using two anchors set in a V, including Bahamian moors.

Primary anchor: The anchor that is on the primary (main) rode. Also typically the anchor that is closer to the boat. It is not necessarily the larger anchor.

Primary rode: The rode going from the boat to the primary anchor.

Rode: The rope, chain, or combination, connecting the anchor to the boat or connecting two anchors.

Roll bar: A hoop designed to self-right a scoop-type anchor.

Scope: The ratio of rode length to the depth of the water plus height of bow anchor point above the water.

Mooring ball. Never use a float with a blue stripe as a tripping line float!

If 100 feet of rode are deployed, the water is 7 feet deep, and the anchor roller is 3 feet above the water, the scope is 10:1.

Secondary anchor: A second anchor set either farther from the boat on a rode attached to the primary anchor or rode, or set on a second, independent rode.

Secondary rode: The rode connecting the secondary anchor. It may connect either to the primary anchor via the tandem eye, the primary rode via a connector, or directly to the boat.

Snub or snubbing: To take tension on the rode by securing it to a cleat or locking mechanism.

Snubber: A length of nylon rope that is attached to a chain rode near the bow, led over the bow roller or bow chocks, and secured to the boat. It is used to take tension off the windlass and, by virtue of its elasticity, reduce shock loading on the ground tackle and boat caused by wind and waves.

Soil consolidation: The tendency of disturbed soil to settle, pack around an anchor, dewater, and increase in strength with the passage of time. Improvements in density and strength are measurable within 20 minutes and continue for about 90 days. See *Cyclical loading*.

Surge: A periodic motion of water in and out of a harbor at 10-30 second intervals, the result of long period waves from distant storms. Also surging, the fore-aft motion of a boat at anchor in response to wind gusts (see *Horsing*).

Tandem eye: An eye located on the heel of the fluke or the base of the shank, used to attach the rode of a Secondary Anchor. Not all anchors have this feature. Also used as a tripping eye.

Tandem anchors, in-line: A two-anchor rig where the primary anchor is attached to the main rode, and the secondary anchor is attached to the primary anchor via a length of chain (tandem rode) to the tandem eye of the primary anchor. For use in rocks and weed only. Use with twice the normal scope.

Tandem anchors, V tandem: A two anchor rig where the anchors and rodes form a V, with an included angle most often between 20 and 90 degrees. Both rodes may reach back to the bow, or one may be terminated on the main rode. A Bahamian moor is a type of V tandem.

Tripping eye: An eye located on the top of the shank near the fluke end. Used to extract the anchor when fouled under a rock, cable, or tree. Also used to lash the anchor to the roller. A more effective location is either the heel of the fluke or the base of the shank, where a tandem eye might be (Rocna and Spade).

Tripping line: A line attached to the tripping eye used to retrieve an anchor with the toe trapped under a solid object. Either floating line or rigged with a float.

Ultimate holding capacity (UHC): The maximum sustained force an anchor can sustain without moving appreciably. This changes with the bottom material, rode, and time. Often shortened to holding capacity.

Veer: A change in wind direction. Sailors sometimes refine this to mean a wind change in the clockwise direction (a counter clockwise change is backing), but it is not used in that sense in this book.

Working Load Limit (WLL): The maximum stress to a rope, chain, or other component should be subjected to if a long, safe lifespan is expected. Typically this is 3-5 times less than minimum breaking strength for metal components, 4-8 times less than minimum breaking strength for polyester and high modulus fibers, and 10-12 times less than minimum breaking strength for nylon rope.

Warp: As a noun, a long, heavy rope. As a verb (to warp or warping), to move the boat using ropes. Kedging is a subset of warping.

Wildcat: The toothed wheel that grips the chain on a windlass. Also referred to as a gypsy.

Winch: A geared mechanism with a drum used for pulling on ropes, to adjust sails and raise halyards.

Windlass: A geared mechanism fitted with a gypsy, drum, or sometimes both, used primarily on sailboats for recovering ground tackle.

Yawing: The tendency of a boat to swing from side-to-side in an arc at anchor, the result of windage forward of the center of lateral resistance.

Appendix I
Data Tables for Chapter 10

Based on the static holding capacity of 2-pound anchors. Soaking followed by slow cyclical loading (Chapter 4) will typically increase ultimate holding capacity holding capacity in soft mud by 65-200%, and in fine sand or firm mud by 20-50%.

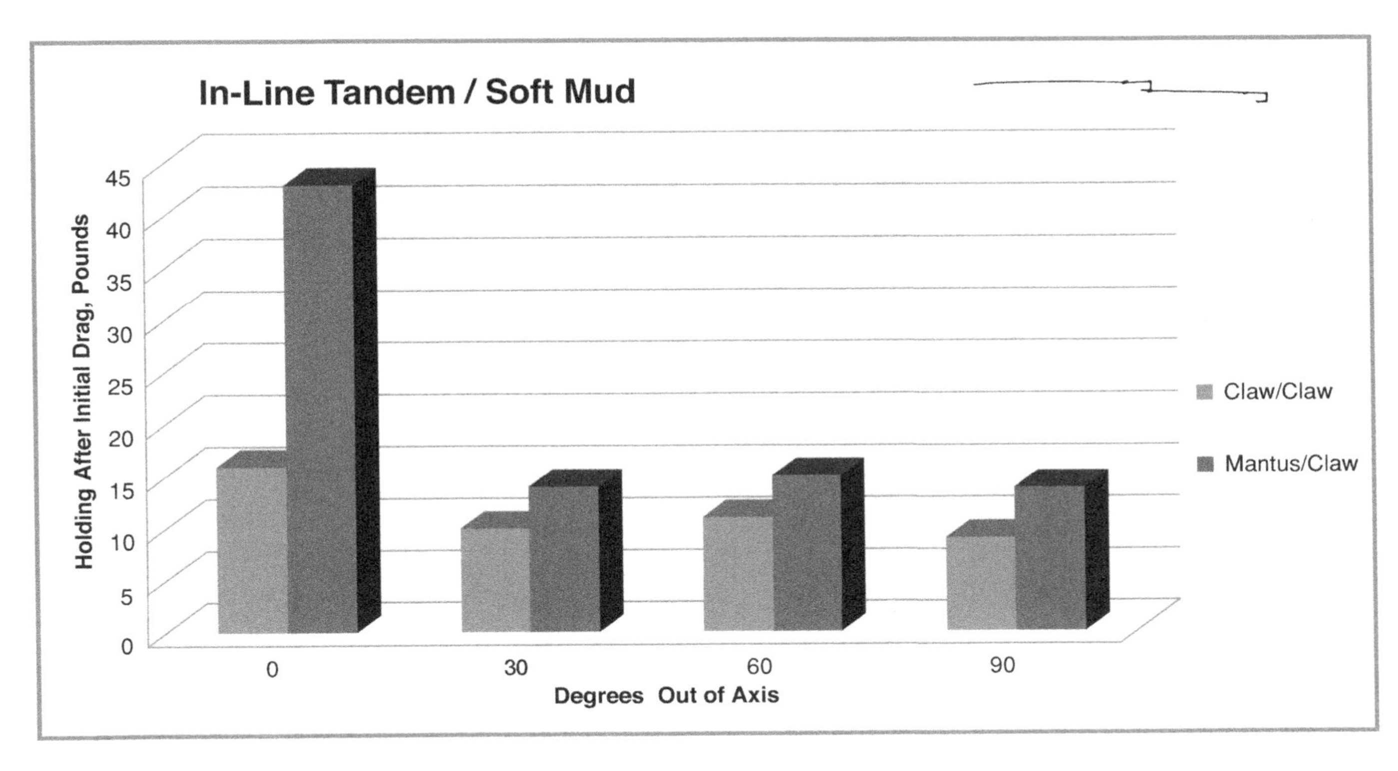

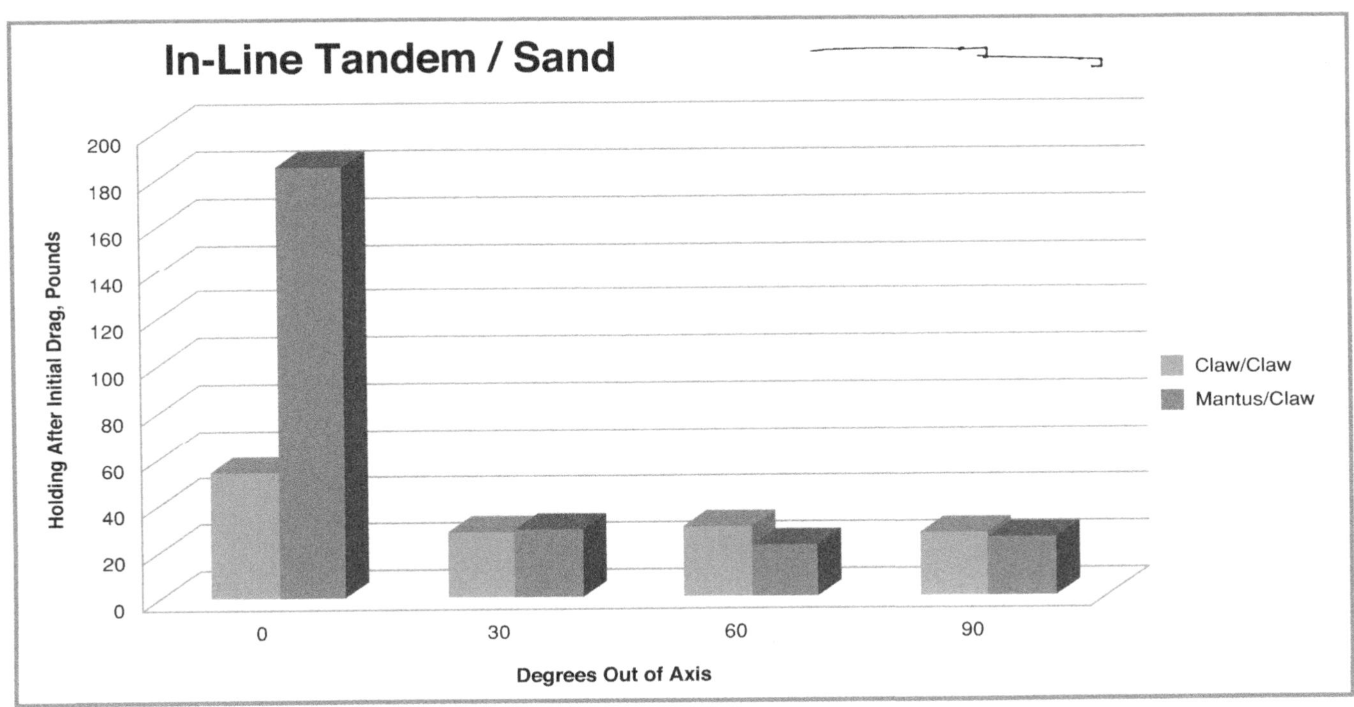

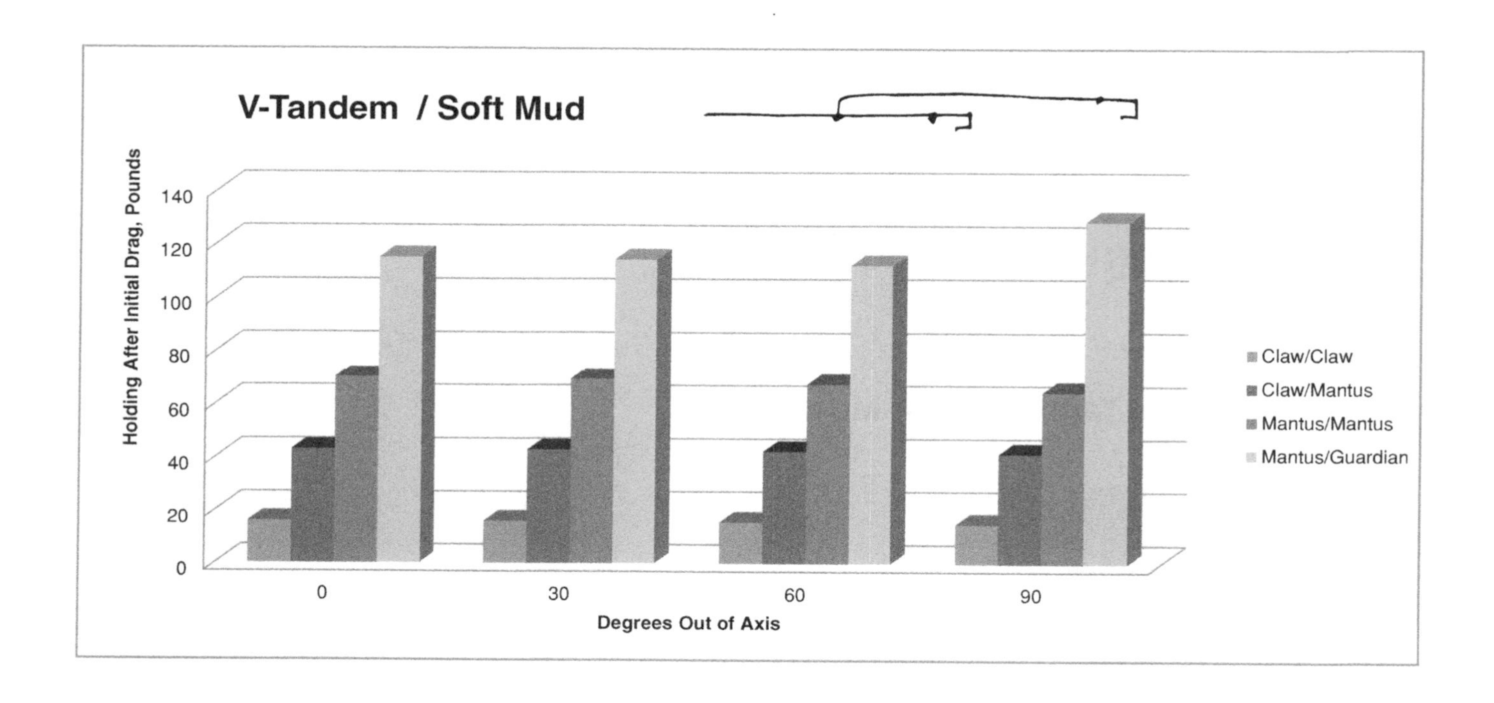
V-Tandem / Soft Mud
Holding After Initial Drag, Pounds
140
120
100
80
60
40
20
0
0
30
60
90
Degrees Out of Axis
Claw/Claw
Claw/Mantus
Mantus/Mantus
Mantus/Guardian

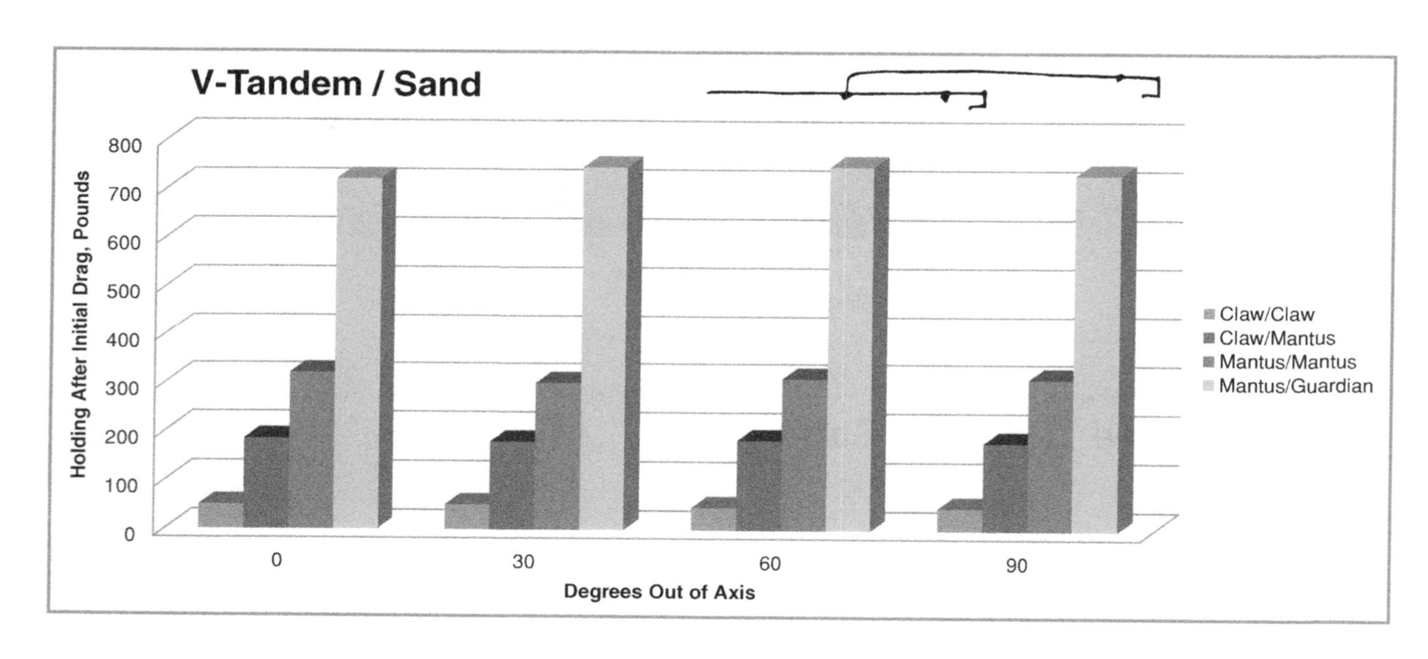
V-Tandem / Sand
Holding After Initial Drag, Pounds
800
700
600
500
400
300
200
100
0
0
30
60
90
Degrees Out of Axis
Claw/Claw
Claw/Mantus
Mantus/Mantus
Mantus/Guardian

Appendix II
Data Tables for Chapter 11

Based on the static holding capacity of full-scale anchors. Soaking followed by slow cyclical loading (Chapter 4) will typically increase ultimate holding capacity holding capacity in soft mud by 40-100%. In fine sand and firm mud the increase will be about 25%.

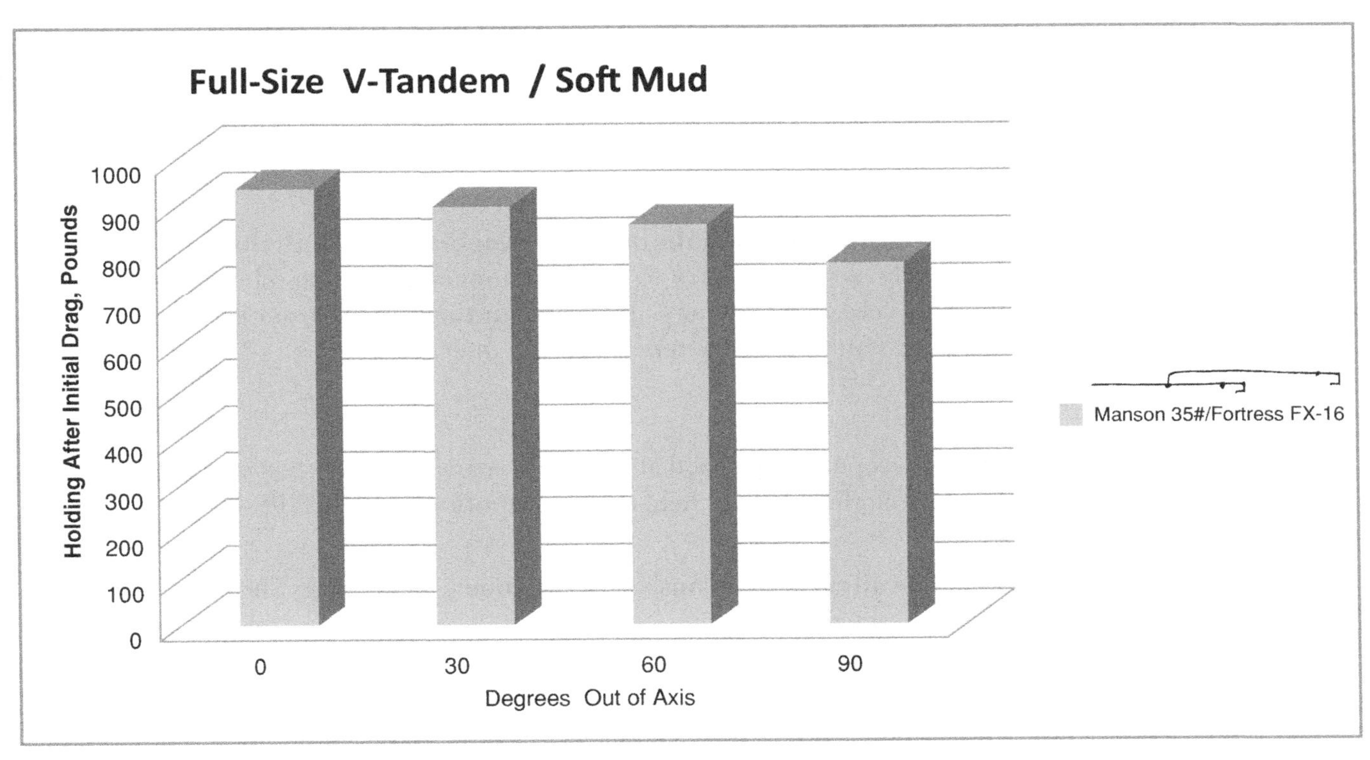

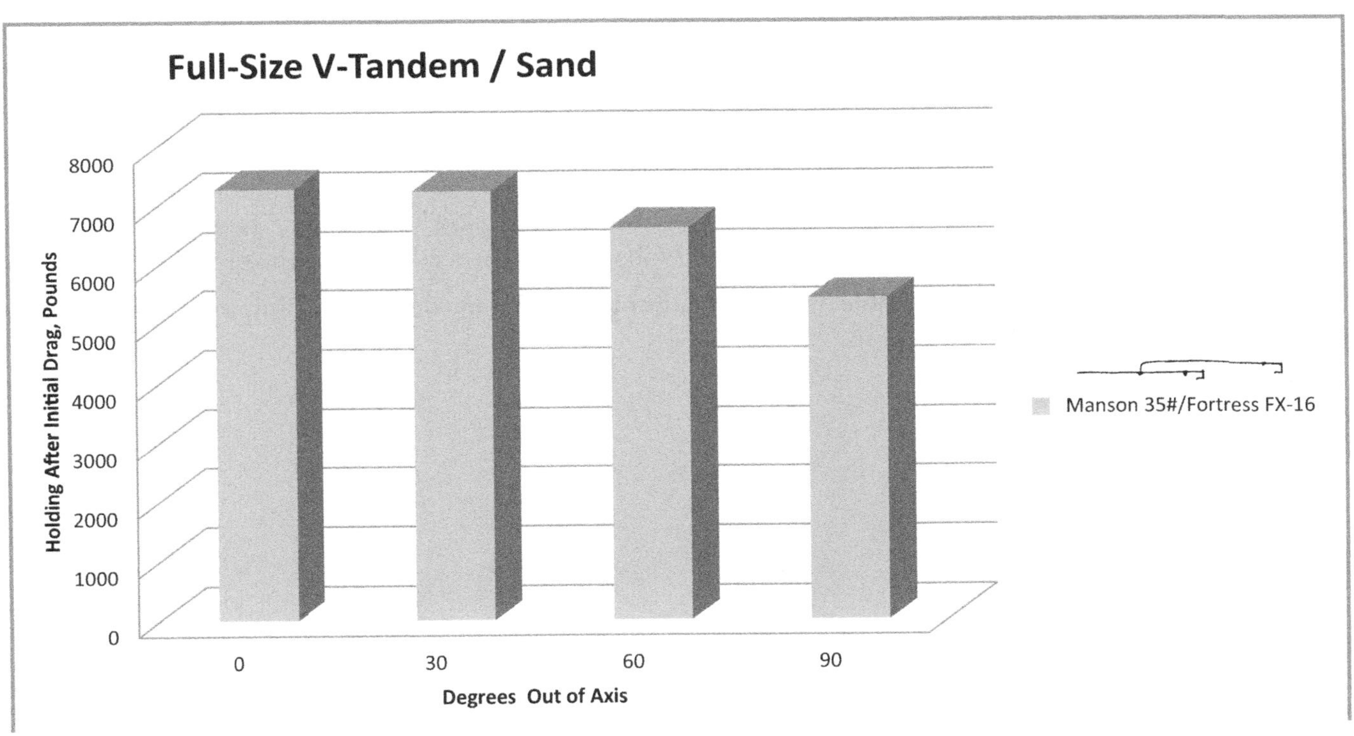

Appendix III
Solomons Island Test Program Data
Chesapeake Bay Anchor Test

In early August 2014, Fortress sponsored an extensive anchor holding power test that was conducted aboard the Rachel Carson, an 81-foot research vessel that is owned by the University of Maryland Center for Environmental Science and located near the Chesapeake Bay in Solomons, Maryland. Chuck Hawley, formerly the VP of Product Testing at West Marine, was aboard for all four days of this test, and he served as the independent reviewer. Additionally, Robert Taylor, a 45+ year U.S. Navy anchor design and soil mechanics expert, consulted on this project as well. The bottom condition was soft mud, which is common in the Chesapeake Bay and in other bays, lakes, and rivers throughout the USA and the world.

Anchor testing in mud is always like herding cats; the data is all over the place. With this much variability, it is best not to read too much into the details or to try to declare winners. Better, search the data for macro trends relating to the bottom and to classes of anchors. The value in this test program is the transparency of the data. There are multiple videos and summary reports on the internet.

Summary:

- Each pull started at about 8.3:1 scope and finished at about 5:1 scope. Each anchor was pulled 100 feet at about 2 inches per second, while the boat was held relatively motionless by a GPS-linked positioning system.
- Bottom variation. They used five different locations, all in the same general area. The range of variation is typical of soft mud in the Chesapeake Bay.
- Different anchors are optimized for different bottoms. Changing the fluke angle on the Fortress made this clear. While it is stronger in soft mud with the 45 degree setting, testing has shown that on firm sand bottoms performance is better at 32 degrees, and it will not engage at the 45 degree setting. Horses for courses.
- Many different behaviors. Theories explaining odd or poor performance included the anchor rolling onto its side, striking debris, reaction to layers in the bottom, and steadily declining scope. They are probably all correct and only diving and watching can determine which is happening. The corollary is that all of these things happen (except declining scope) and you won't see it, you will only feel it.
- Setting practices matter. Anchors were simply lowered and slowly dragged. Testing with setting procedures like those described in Chapter 1 and Chapter 7 improved performance in most cases.
- Complete setting takes considerable distance in soft mud. This may be the most important lesson, since it was observed over and over again.

Danforth HT

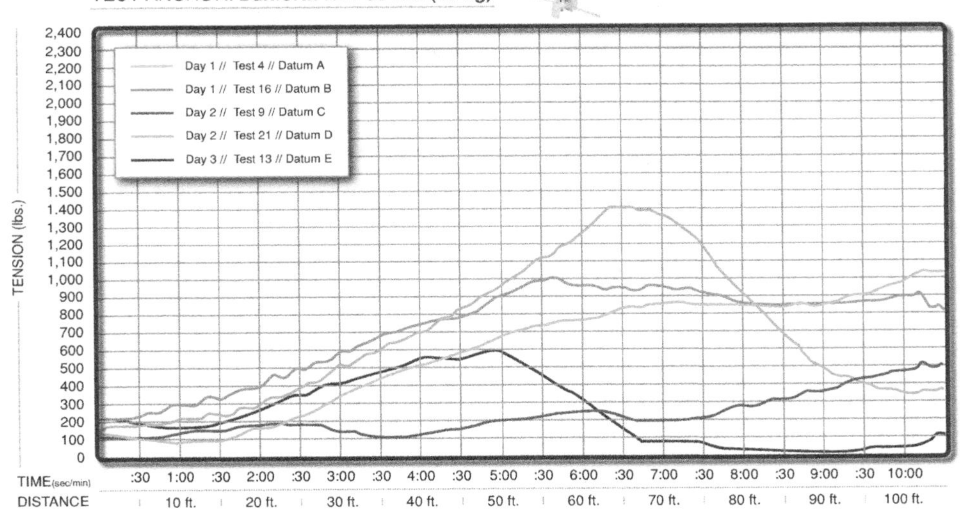

CHESAPEAKE BAY SOFT MUD TESTS

TEST DATES: AUGUST 5-8, 2014

TEST VESSEL: R/V RACHEL CARSON
UNIVERSITY OF MARYLAND CENTER FOR ENVIRONMENTAL SCIENCE
SOLOMONS, MARYLAND, USA
www.umces.edu/cbl/research-discovery/rv-rachel-carson

SPONSOR: FORTRESS MARINE ANCHORS
www.fortressanchors.com

Rocna

TEST ANCHOR: **Rocna / 44 lbs. (20 kg)**

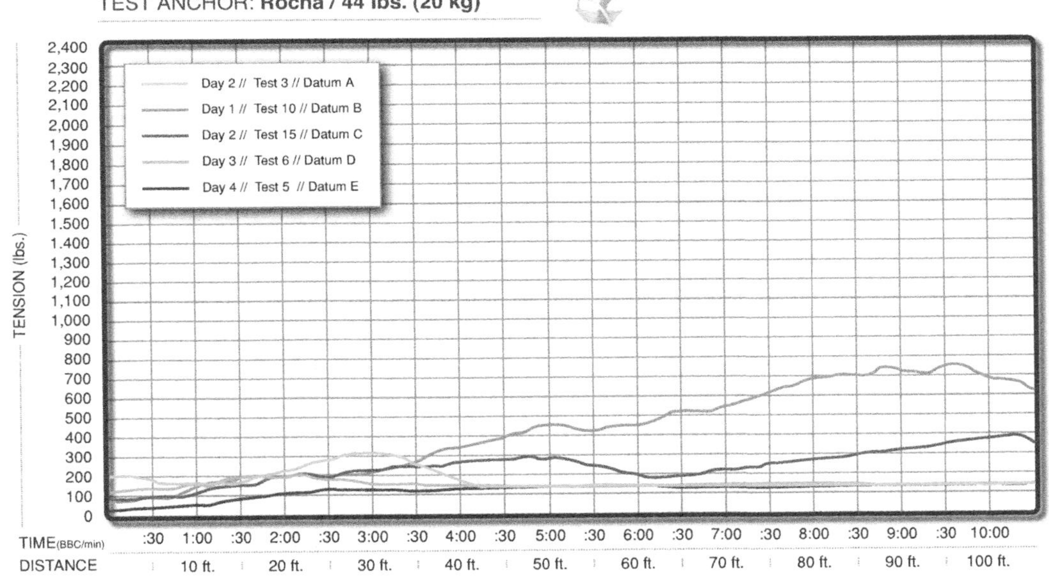

CHESAPEAKE BAY SOFT MUD TESTS

TEST DATES: AUGUST 5-8, 2014

TEST VESSEL: R/V RACHEL CARSON
UNIVERSITY OF MARYLAND CENTER FOR ENVIRONMENTAL SCIENCE
SOLOMONS, MARYLAND, USA
www.umces.edu/cbl/research-discovery/rv-rachel-carson

SPONSOR: FORTRESS MARINE ANCHORS
www.fortressanchors.com

Lewmar Claw

TEST ANCHOR: **Claw / 44 lbs. (20 kg)** 

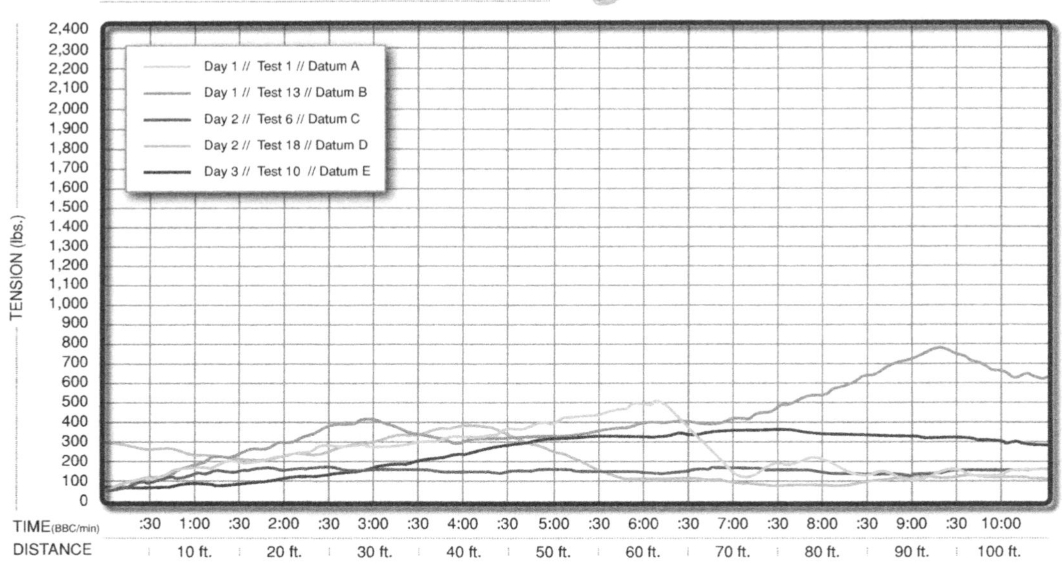

CHESAPEAKE BAY SOFT MUD TESTS

TEST DATES: AUGUST 5-8, 2014
TEST VESSEL: R/V RACHEL CARSON
UNIVERSITY OF MARYLAND CENTER FOR ENVIRONMENTAL SCIENCE
SOLOMONS, MARYLAND, USA
www.umces.edu/cbl/research-discovery/rv-rachel-carson
SPONSOR: FORTRESS MARINE ANCHORS
www.fortressanchors.com

Lewmar Delta

TEST ANCHOR: **Delta / 44 lbs. (20 kg)** 

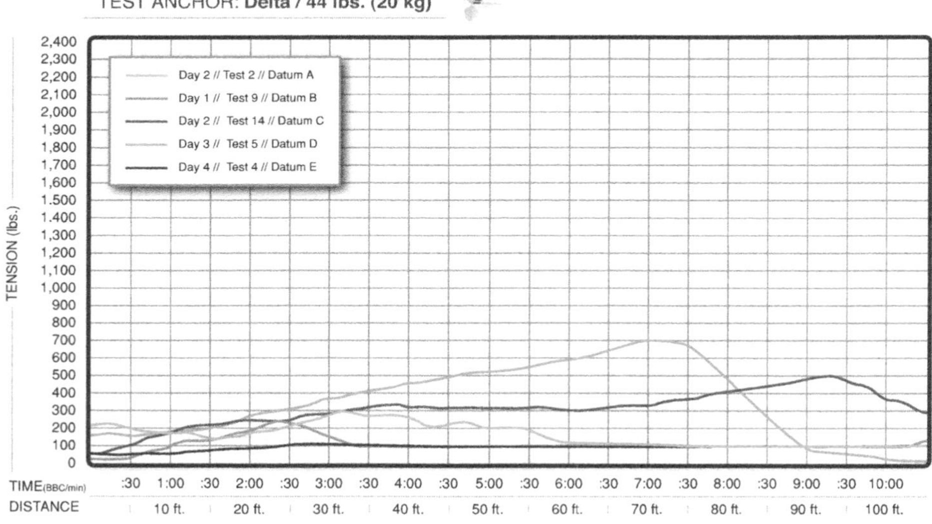

CHESAPEAKE BAY SOFT MUD TESTS

TEST DATES: AUGUST 5-8, 2014
TEST VESSEL: R/V RACHEL CARSON
UNIVERSITY OF MARYLAND CENTER FOR ENVIRONMENTAL SCIENCE
SOLOMONS, MARYLAND, USA
www.umces.edu/cbl/research-discovery/rv-rachel-carson
SPONSOR: FORTRESS MARINE ANCHORS
www.fortressanchors.com

Mantus

The roll bar was bent during test 18. The damage was easily repaired.

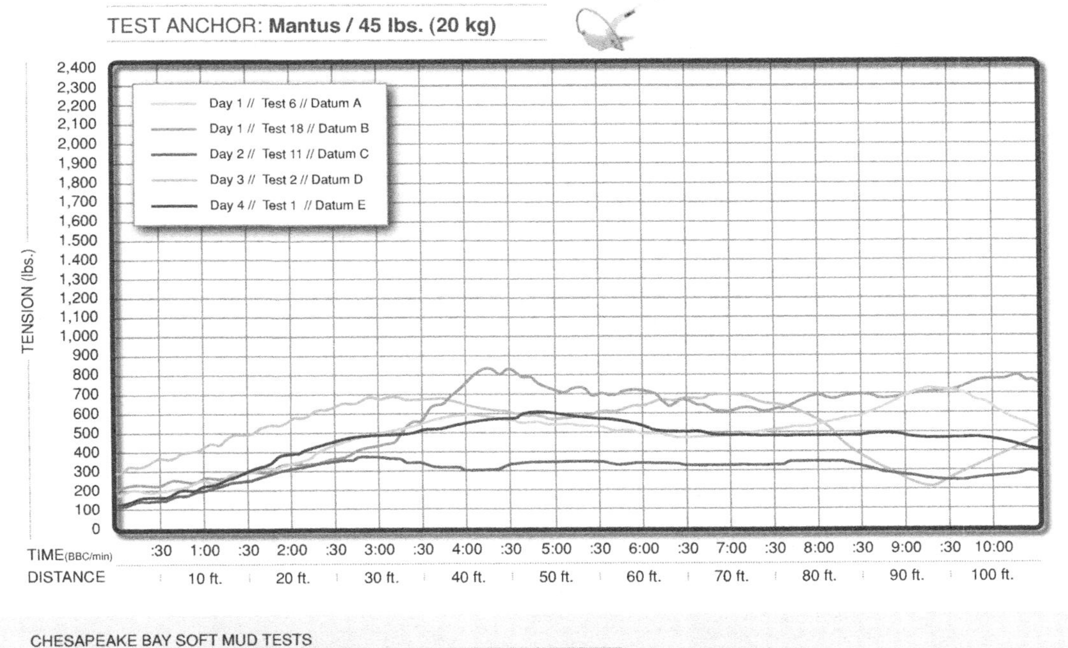

CHESAPEAKE BAY SOFT MUD TESTS

TEST DATES: AUGUST 5-8, 2014
TEST VESSEL: R/V RACHEL CARSON
UNIVERSITY OF MARYLAND CENTER FOR ENVIRONMENTAL SCIENCE
SOLOMONS, MARYLAND, USA
www.umces.edu/cbl/research-discovery/rv-rachel-carson
SPONSOR: FORTRESS MARINE ANCHORS
www.fortressanchors.com

Manson Supreme

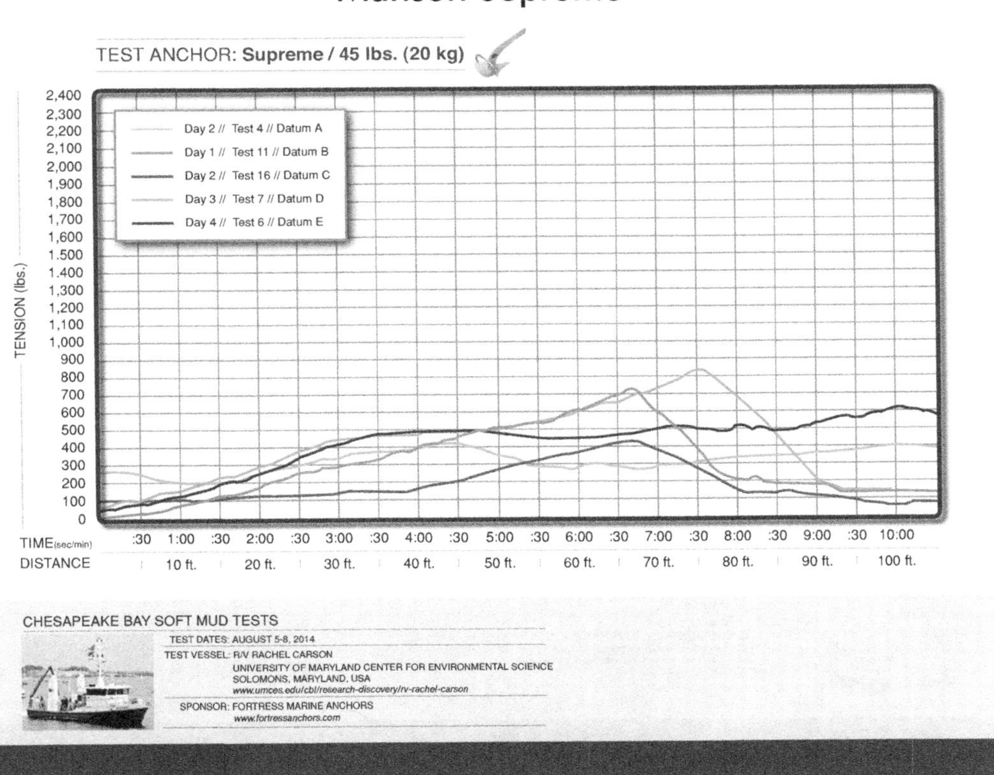

Manson Boss

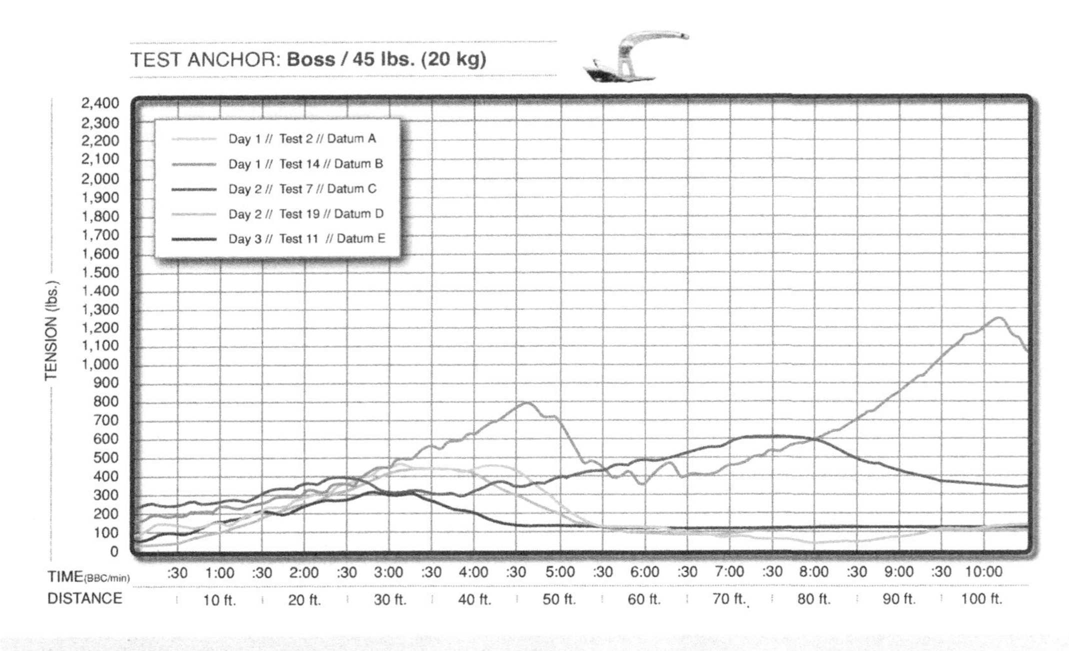

CHESAPEAKE BAY SOFT MUD TESTS

TEST DATES: AUGUST 5-8, 2014

TEST VESSEL: R/V RACHEL CARSON
UNIVERSITY OF MARYLAND CENTER FOR ENVIRONMENTAL SCIENCE
SOLOMONS, MARYLAND, USA
www.umces.edu/cbl/research-discovery/rv-rachel-carson

SPONSOR: FORTRESS MARINE ANCHORS
www.fortressanchors.com

CQR

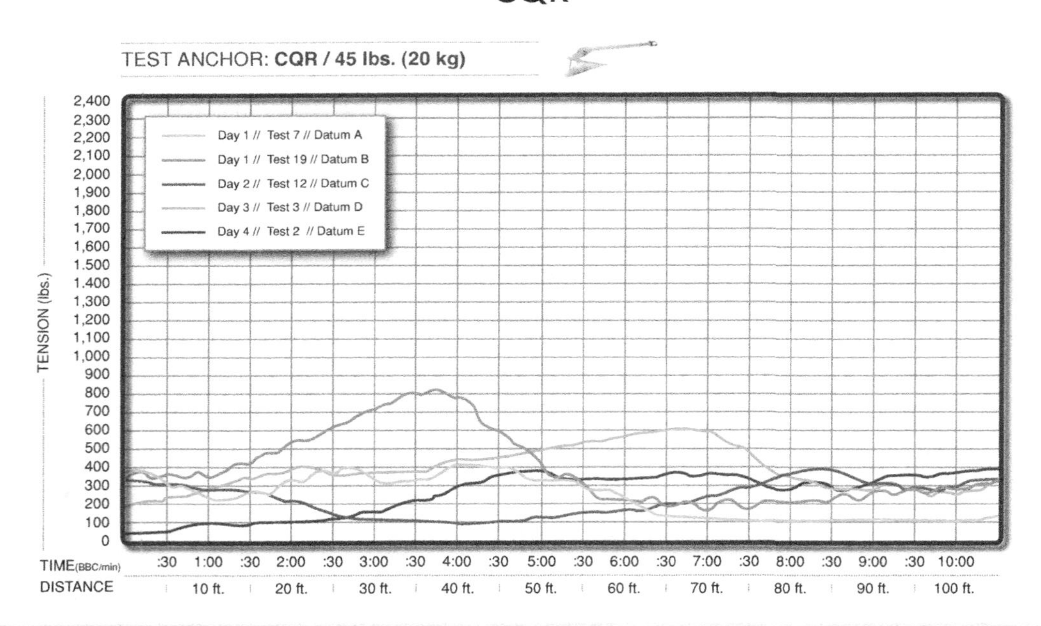

CHESAPEAKE BAY SOFT MUD TESTS

TEST DATES: AUGUST 5-8, 2014

TEST VESSEL: R/V RACHEL CARSON
UNIVERSITY OF MARYLAND CENTER FOR ENVIRONMENTAL SCIENCE
SOLOMONS, MARYLAND, USA
www.umces.edu/cbl/research-discovery/rv-rachel-carson

SPONSOR: FORTRESS MARINE ANCHORS
www.fortressanchors.com

Fortress 32 degree

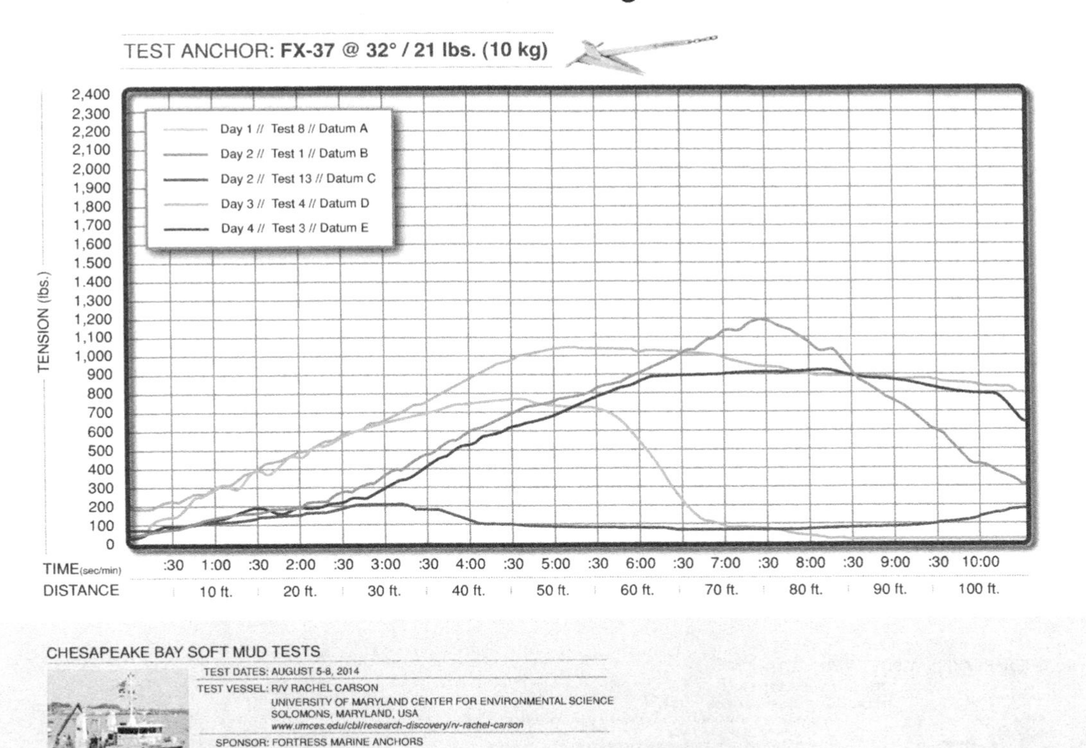

Fortress 45 degree

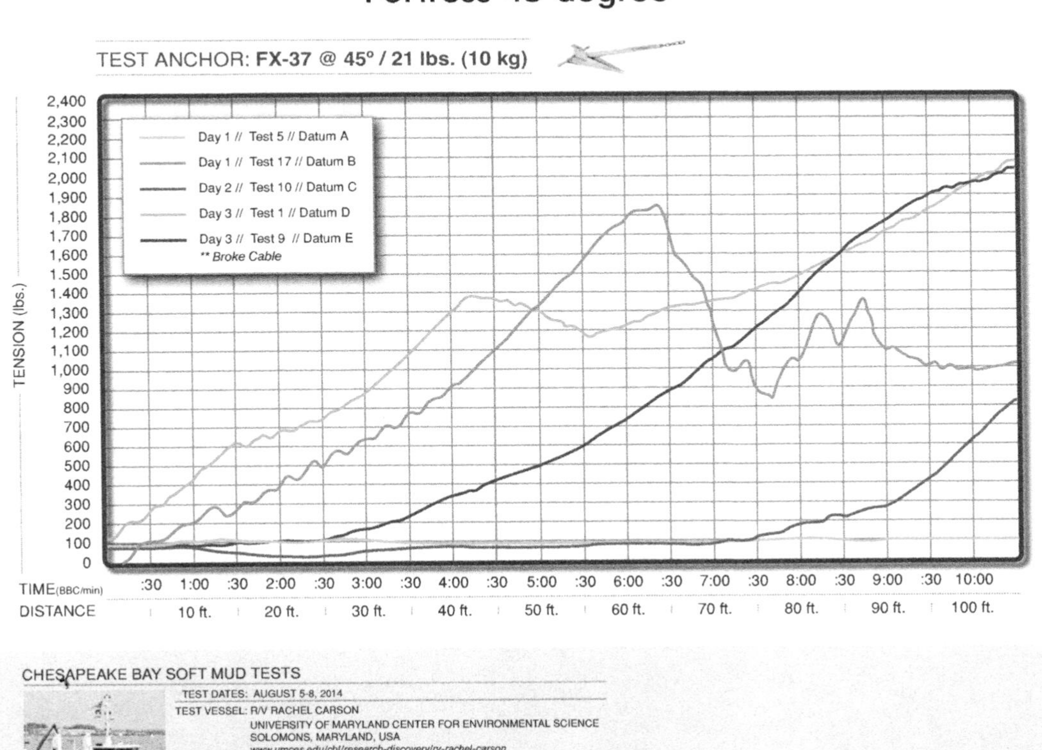

Ultra

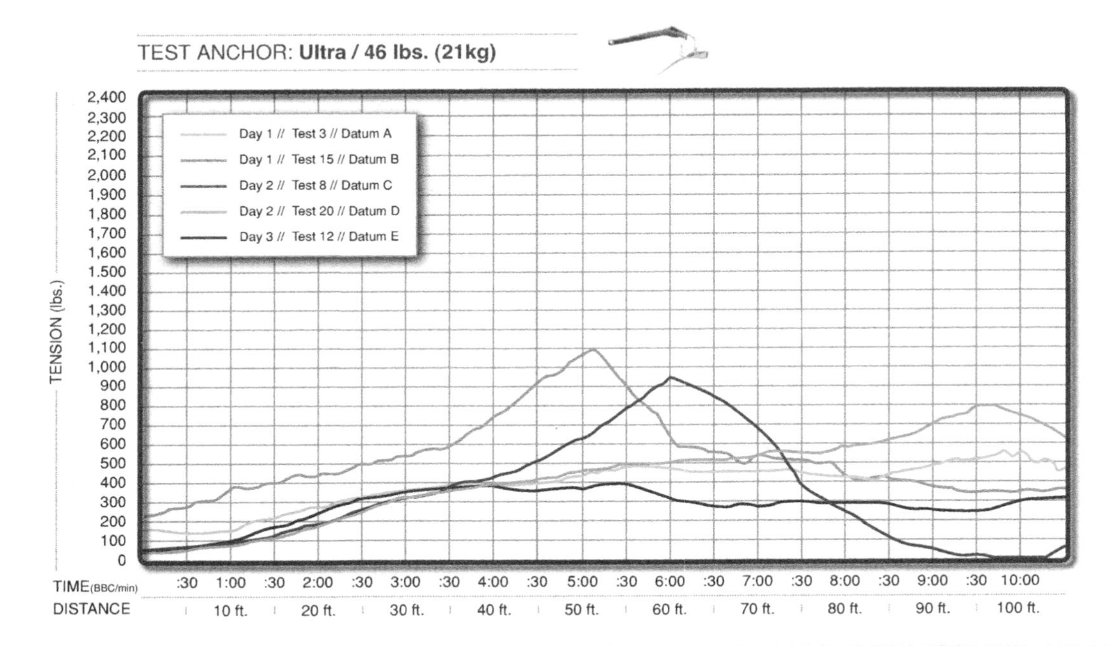

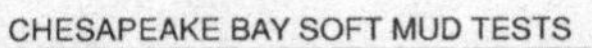

CHESAPEAKE BAY SOFT MUD TESTS

TEST DATES: AUGUST 5-8, 2014

TEST VESSEL: R/V RACHEL CARSON
UNIVERSITY OF MARYLAND CENTER FOR ENVIRONMENTAL SCIENCE
SOLOMONS, MARYLAND, USA
www.umces.edu/cbl/research-discovery/rv-rachel-carson

SPONSOR: FORTRESS MARINE ANCHORS
www.fortressanchors.com

Appendix IV
Bridle Plate and Anchor Turner. Open Source Designs.

These simple designs have been in use for 5-8 years. Initially developed because nothing on the market did everything we wanted, they still outperform and outlast commercial designs. Drawings are provided for only one size, but they can be adjusted to other materials and chain types.

Although galvanized steel is a favorite for anchor materials, aluminum has the advantage of not requiring galvanizing, reducing the one-off cost for the DIY sailor. Anchor shanks are commonly made from high strength aluminum alloys. This is important to the open-source concept; I want these designs to be accessible. Stainless steel is also acceptable.

Anchor Turner

- Alternate Materials. Aluminum or weaker alloys can be substituted by increasing the thickness in proportion. For example, if the Anchor Turner is made from 7075 aluminum, (55,000 psi) it must be 3/8-inch x (80,000/55,000) = 1/2-inch thick.
- Larger Chain. Increase all dimensions in proportion.

Bridle Plate

- Grade 30 Chain. Aluminum alloys can be used by increasing thickness in proportion to the difference in strength. For example, the Bridle Plate can be made of 6061 aluminum (35,000 PSI) instead of 80,000 PSI steel plate for 1/4-inch grade 30 chain by adjusting thickness as follows: Thickness = 3/8-inch x (1900/5400) x (80,000/35,000) = 7/16-inch 6010 aluminum plate. In this case a much weaker material is acceptable because the chain is not as strong. However, this does not work for higher grade chains because of the limited space between the links.
- Grade 43 Chain. Only 7075 aluminum may be used. Plates made from lower strength alloys will be too thick to fit between the links.
- Larger Chain. Increase all dimensions in proportion.

The dimensions allow for coatings (galvanized or paint) and normal manufacturing tolerance. There is no harm in being slightly oversize, but minimum clearances between holes and edges must be observed to maintain strength.

Use with snubber as per Chapter 2 specifications.

Bridle Plate

This simple design has a number of advantages over any commercial product:

- Strong. Designed to be full-strength with the gate open and only one leg attached, it is monstrously strong with 2-legs attached and the gate closed. Can also be used with a single line; the gate reinforces the hook.
- Attachment point for second rode.
- Positive lock, even if the rodes are pulled at odd angles.
- Fast and jam proof.

Instructions:

- Chamfer all edges 1/16-inch radius. Chamfer the entrance of the slot 1/8-inch to allow smooth chain entry. Do NOT chamfer the bottom of the slot where the chain lies; this reduces support.

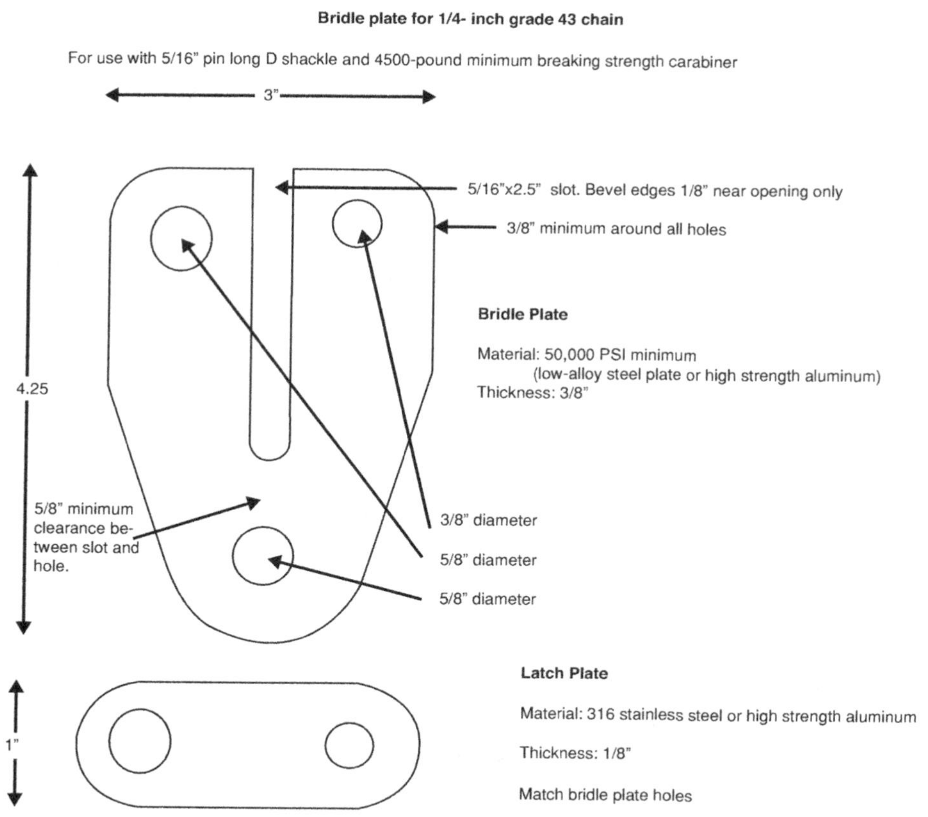

Bridle plate for 1/4- inch grade 43 chain

For use with 5/16" pin long D shackle and 4500-pound minimum breaking strength carabiner

3"

4.25

5/16"x2.5" slot. Bevel edges 1/8" near opening only

3/8" minimum around all holes

Bridle Plate

Material: 50,000 PSI minimum
(low-alloy steel plate or high strength aluminum)
Thickness: 3/8"

5/8" minimum clearance between slot and hole.

3/8" diameter

5/8" diameter

5/8" diameter

Latch Plate

Material: 316 stainless steel or high strength aluminum

Thickness: 1/8"

Match bridle plate holes

1"

- It is helpful if the D shackle is long enough to allow the latch to swing 360 degrees.
- Bridle plate thickness should roughly match the gap between links, so that the chain is well-supported.
- Match slot to chain. Thicker material better supports the chain. The slot must be wider than the nominal chain size because chain is actually slightly oversized and to clear the weld.

Anchor Turner

Products that attach directly to the anchor, without a swivel, are never acceptable. Stainless can be prone to cracking. Although this design looks thick and clunky, it is slender when viewed from the direction the chain is slicing down through the sand and should actually improve setting.

- Bend. The bend must be sufficient to roll the chain. However, it must not be large enough to jam if it comes over the roller sideways. The reason for the asymmetry is to conserve width; if the short end is oriented toward the anchor, the chain has rolled by the time it gets there and additional length is unnecessary.
- Groove. If the roller has a groove the anchor turner material should be either thinner or considerably thicker to prevent jamming.
- Isolation Links. For best action, it should be isolated from the anchor by 5-9 chain links (an odd number insures the correct alignment). This allows the anchor to turn gently. If there is insufficient space, the Anchor Turner may be attached directly with one shackle, but the windlass must be paused at the correct moment.

Anchor Turner (AKA Boomerang)
For Up To 5,400–Pound WLL Chain (3/8" Grade 43)

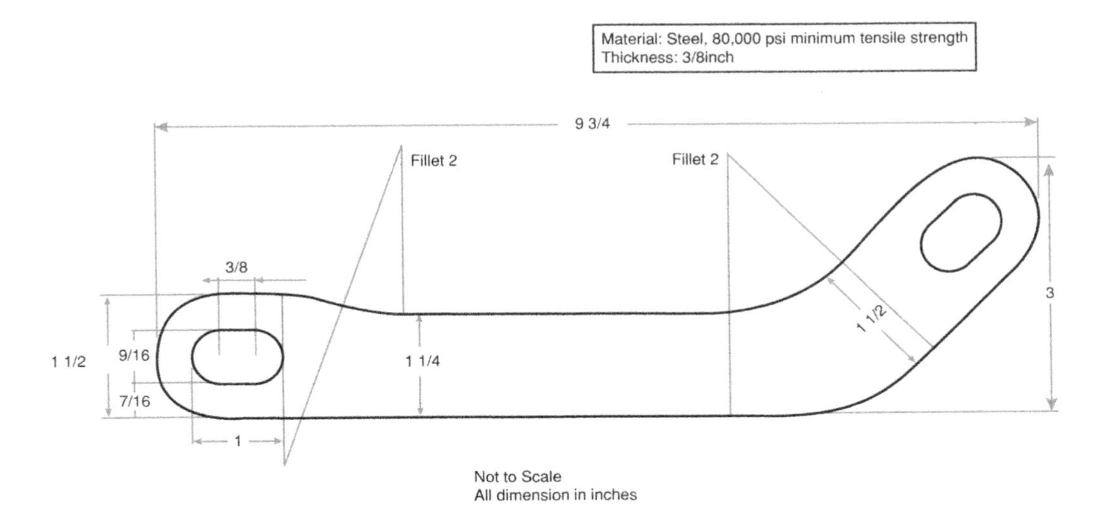

For larger chain, increase all dimensions in direct proportion to the chain diameter. For higher grade chain, increase all dimensions in proportion to the square root of the increase in chain strength. Original design by Rick Neeves, Australian sailor.

Anchor Turner (open source)
For Up To 2,600–Pound WLL Chain (1/4-inch Grade 43

Material: 5460 or 6061 aluminum (33,000 psi tensile strength).
Thickness:7/16–inch

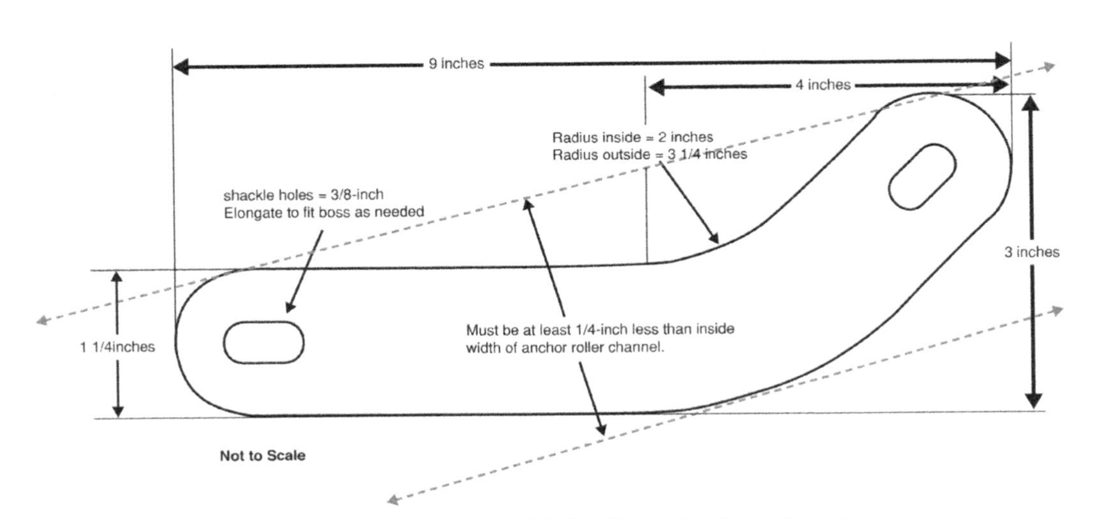

A simplified design, suitable for fabrication in steel or aluminum.

Appendix V
Chain and Rope, Strength and Toughness

From Chapter 1, a reminder of the strength requirements:

From ABYC H-40

Table 1

ABYC Design Loads For Deck Hardware

Horizontal Working Load, Pounds
Boat Length, Feet

Windspeed, Knots	25	30	35	40	50	60
15	125	175	225	300	400	500
(Working Anchor) 30	490	700	900	1,200	1,600	2,000
(Storm Anchor) 42	980	1,400	1,800	2,400	3,200	4,000
(Permanent Mooring) 60	1,470	2,100	2,700	3,600	4,800	6,000

Table 3

Horizontal Working Load at 60 Knots--Assorted Rode Types

Horizontal Working Load, Pounds
Boat Length, Feet

Rode Type	25	30	35	40	50	60
Wind Load Only	266	516	664	885	1,181	1,476
Rope	323	627	807	1,076	1,434	1,793
Long Snubber	337	655	842	1,123	1,498	1,872
Short Snubber	975	1,895	2,437	3,249	4,332	5,415
Chain only	1,238	2,408	3,096	4,128	5,504	6,880

AP. Table 1- Working Load Limits for Anchor Rodes

Working Load, Pounds

	Nylon			Galvinized Chain			
Nominal Diameter, inches	3-Strand and Plait	Double Braid	Fits chain size	BBB	Grade 43	* Grade 70	** Grade B Shackles
1/4	186	208		1300	2600	3150	1000
5/16	287	326		1900	3900	4700	1500
3/8	405	463		2650	5400	6600	2000
7/16	557	624		* 3700	* 7200	8750	3000
1/2	709	816	1/4	4500	9200	11300	4000
9/16	888	1020	5/16	5875			
5/8	1114	1275	5/16	6900	11500	15800	6500
3/4	1598	1813	3/8	10600	16200	24700	9500
7/8	2160	2063	3/8				12000
1	2795	3153	1/2, 5/8				15000
1 1/4	4345	4838	3/4				23000
1 1/2	6075	6875					
2	10575	12363					

* From NACM Standards

ABYC provides the working load limits for chain and nylon rodes. (Adapted from H-40 appendix table 1.) Elongation data in Table 4 is combined from direct measurement, calculation, and extrapolation using the relationship:

Strain ~ P/d^2

Where strain is in %, P=force, and d=diameter.

Basis

- Energy absorption is calculated at the WLL.
- Scope is 7:1 using 100 feet of rode.
- Energy absorption is based on sustained wind at 20 knots and gusts sufficient to reach the WLL.
- No snubbers, only the material under evaluation.

Notes and Observations:

- Yield (permanent stretching of the chain) begins at 60-70% of BS, or about two times the WLL. The windlass will jam when the yield stress is exceeded and the links stretch. The attachment of a snubber with a metal hook may reduce the yield strength 20-50%, depending on the hook design.
- About 80% of chain energy absorption (stress x distance) is from elongation, not catenary.
- Toughness of chain is proportional to the WLL. This includes alloy chains.

Table 4

Chain: Strength and Energy Absorption at WLL

35-foot example
50-foot example boat

Energy Absorption Between 20 Knots and WLL

Grade 30

Chain Size	WLL (pounds)	Min Breaking Strength (pounds)	Elongation at WLL (%)	Weigh per 100 feet (pounds)	Energy Absorbed Below the WLL Energy Absorption Elongation	Energy Absorption Catenary	Total Energy Absorption (per 100 feet, ft-pounds)	Typical Boat Size (feet)
1/4	1300	5200	1.0%	88	636	380	1016	<30
5/16	1900	7600	1.0%	110	929	475	1404	30-35
3/8	2650	10600	1.0%	160	1296	691	1987	35-45
7/16	3700	14800	1.0%	245	1810	1058	2868	45-55
1/2	4500	18000	1.0%	280	2201	1209	3410	55+

Grade 43

Chain Size	WLL (pounds)	Minimum Breaking Strength (pounds)		Weigh per 100 feet (pounds)	Energy Absorbed Below the WLL Energy Absorption Elongation	Energy Absorption Catenary	Total Energy Absorption (per 100 feet, ft-pounds)	Typical Boat Size (feet)
1/4	2600	7800	1.5%	75	1950	324	2274	30-35
5/16	3900	11700	1.5%	110	2925	475	3400	35-45
3/8	5400	16200	1.5%	149	4050	643	4693	45-55
7/16	7200	21600	1.5%	240	5400	1036	6436	55-65
1/2	9200	27600	1.5%	280	6900	1209	8109	70+

Grade 70

Chain Size	WLL (pounds)	Min Breaking Strength (pounds)	Elongation at WLL (%)	Weigh per 100 feet (pounds)	Energy Absorbed Below the WLL Energy Absorption Elongation	Energy Absorption Catenary	Total Energy Absorption (per 100 feet, ft-pounds)	Typical Boat Size (feet)
1/4	3150	12600	1.8%	66	2862	285	3147	35-45
5/16	4700	18800	1.8%	100	4248	432	4680	45-55
3/8	6600	26400	1.8%	145	6050	626	6676	55-65
7/16	8750	35000	1.8%	235	7975	1015	8990	70+
1/2	11300	45200	1.8%	270	10410	1166	11575	

Rope: Strength and Energy Absorption at WLL

Energy Absorption Between 20 Knots and WLL

Nylon Rope, 3-Strand

Rope Size	WLL (pounds)	Min Breaking Strength (pounds)	Elongation at WLL (%)	Weigh per 100 feet (pounds)	Energy Absorbed Below the WLL Energy Absorption Elongation	Energy Absorption Catenary	Total Energy Absorption (per 100 feet, ft-pounds)	Typical Boat Size (feet)
1/2	570	5700	6%	6.5	1710	0	1710	30-35
5/8	1220	12200	6%	10.5	3660	0	3660	35-45
3/4	1670	16700	6%	14.5	5010	0	5010	45-55
1	2940	29400	6%	26.4	8820	0	8820	55-65

Polyester Rope, Double Braid

Rope Size	WLL (pounds)	Min Breaking Strength (pounds)	Elongation at WLL (%)	Weigh per 100 feet (pounds)	Energy Absorbed Below the WLL Energy Absorption Elongation	Energy Absorption Catenary	Total Energy Absorption (per 100 feet, ft-pounds)	Typical Boat Size (feet)
1/2	1000	7000	2%	6.5	1000	0	1000	not recommended
5/8	1571	11000	2%	10.5	1571	0	1571	not recommended
3/4	2357	16500	2%	14.5	2357	0	2357	not recommended

- The toughness (total energy absorption) of fiber rode and chain rode are similar if sized properly. A fiber rode must be monitored for chafe, and a chain rode must be monitored for corrosion.
- Rope can be slightly weaker than chain because the average working load will be much lower. However, in extreme storms, both will operate near their WLL. The chain will subject the anchor and the boat to much higher loads unless the rode is quite long.
- If a snubber is used, the snubber will work harder and the chain will work less. This is acceptable, because the snubber is disposable and should be replaced every few years of hard use.

Minimum Link Thickness

Chains wear during use, the result of corrosion and abrasion. The following tables give NACM (National Association of Chain Manufacturers) minimum specifications for continued use. If a chain is to be re-galvanized, the chain should be no less than the average between the nominal size and the NACM minimum, to allow for future wear. Grade 70 chain may lose some strength when re-galvanized because of the effect of heat on steel temper—re-galvanized grade 70 chain is typically no stronger than new grade 43 chain. Chain stretch should not exceed 3%, of which a maximum of 0.8% can be due to chain wear. No visible deformation is allowed. (Stretch is best determined by measuring a sample of the actual chain before and after, to correct for manufacturing variations).

Connectors

High strength chain is of little benefit if the connectors are weak. Connectors for grade 30 chain are readily available through industrial supply houses and chandleries, but connectors matching the strength of grade 43 and grade 70 chains are scarcer. Match the working load limit (WLL).

Chain: Minimum Link Thickness			
		Grade 30	
Chain Size	WLL	Min Link Thickness	Nominal Link Thickness
(inches)	(pounds)	(inches)	(inches)
1/4	1300	0.239	0.276
5/16	1900	0.286	0.331
3/8	2650	0.342	0.394
7/16	3700	0.405	0.468
1/2	4500	0.443	0.512
		Grade 43 and Grade 70	
Chain Size	WLL	Min Link Thickness	Nominal Link Thickness
(inches)	(pounds)	(pounds)	(inches)
1/4	2600/3150	0.239	0.276/.281
5/16	3900/4700	0.297	0.343
3/8	5400/6600	0.351	0.406
7/16	7200/8750	0.405	0.468
1/2	9200/11300	0.460	0.531

Anchor Shackle. The largest shackle that will fit high tensile chain is normally too small for the anchor shank hole. Fit a larger shackle to the anchor, with the bow through the hole to prevent side loading (side loading weakens the shackle as much as 50%). Thread the smaller chain shackle or connector through that.

An oversize link can be welded to the end of the chain; however, there are limitations. The end of the chain cannot be trimmed for wear or corrosion. Most vertical windlasses cannot pass an oversize link, even manually during installation, in which case only one end can have an oversized link. An oversized link will not feed through a windlass if a combination rode is used.

The nominal size and the pin size are different.

- 1/4-inch chain = 5/16-inch shackle
- 5/16-inch chain = 3/8-inch shackle
- 3/8-inch chain = 7/16-inch shackle
- 1/2-inch chain = 5/8-inch shackle

Shackles for Grade 43 Chain. Grade B shackles generally match grade 43 chain strength; for example, 5/16-inch grade 43 chain has a WLL of 3,900 pounds, and the 3/8-inch grade B shackle (fits 5/16-inch chain) has a WLL of 4,000 pounds. The exception is 1/4-inch grade 43, where available shackles are generally weaker.

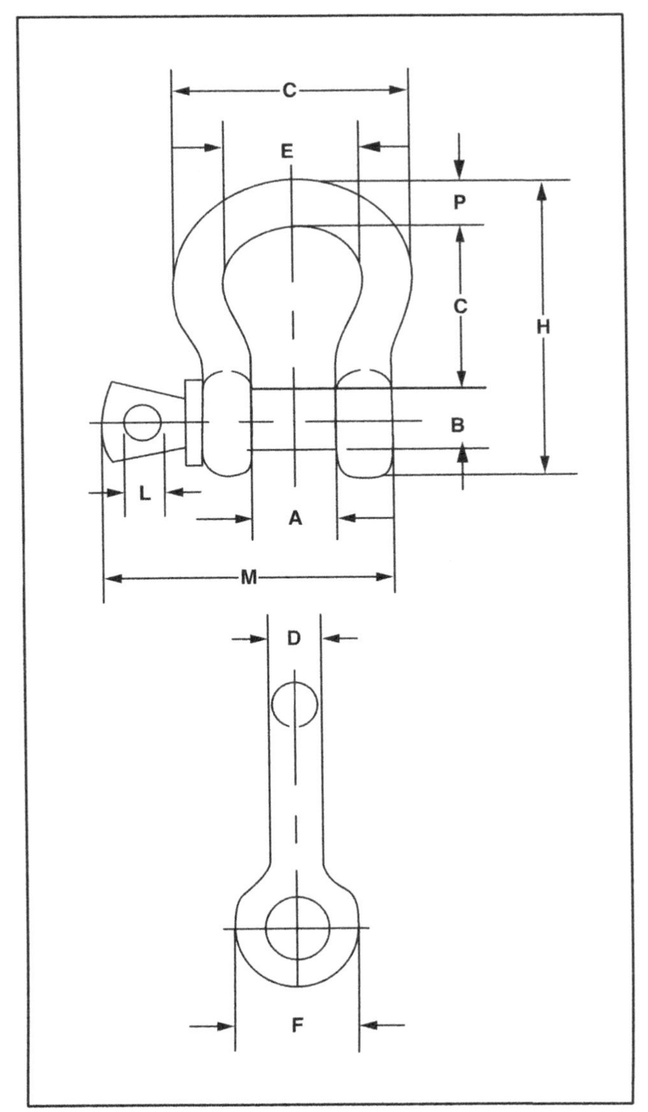

Galvanized Bow Shackle Dimensions

Nominal Size (inches)	Grade A Working Load (tons)	Grade B Working Load (tons)	a	b	c	d	e	f	g	h	l	m	p
5/16	3/4	1	0.53	0.38	1.22	0.31	0.84	0.75	1.47	2.09	0.22	1.66	0.31
3/8	1	2	0.66	0.44	1.44	0.38	1.03	0.91	1.78	2.49	0.25	2.03	0.38
7/16	1 1/2	2 2/3	0.75	0.5	1.69	0.44	1.16	1.06	2.03	2.91	0.31	2.38	0.44
1/2	2	3 1/3	0.81	0.63	1.88	0.5	1.31	1.19	2.31	3.28	0.38	2.69	0.5
5/8	3 1/4	5	1.06	0.75	2.38	0.63	1.69	1.5	2.94	4.19	0.44	3.34	0.69

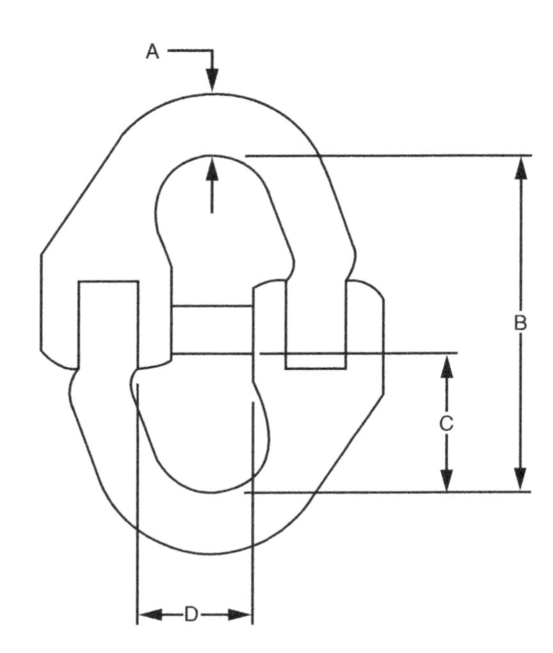

Shackles for Grade 70 chain. An oversize end link is one solution. Mechanical connectors suitable for Grade 70 chain can be found through industrial lifting companies, although availability in galvanized is sporadic. Because dimensions are different from common shackles, take a few links of chain with you to confirm the fit.

Appendix VI
Anchor Size Recommendations—Emphasis on Mud Bottoms

There is considerable variation in how vendors rate their anchors in terms of weather and bottom type. I have commented where testing and cruisers' experience indicates they are underspecified and put my recommendation in GRAY. On the other hand, pivoting fluke and new generation anchors have adopted the admirable habit of being more conservative in their sizing, virtually guaranteeing good performance.

Vendor Anchor Size Recommendations

Minimum recommendation for soft mud is given in Grey.

A "conservative" rating implies vendor sizing is based on very strong weather

Approximate weight in pounds [model in brackets]

Boat Length	Danforth * High Tensile	Fortress *	Lewmar Claw	Lewmar CQR	Lewmar Delta	Manson Supreme	Mantus	Rocna	Spade Aluminum	Spade Steel
25-30	12	7 [FX-11]	16 / 35	25 / 45	22 / 35	25	34 [15]	34 [15]	15 [80]	33 [80]
30-35	20	10 [FX-16]	22 / 44	25 / 60	22 / 44	35	44 [20]	44 [20]	15 [80]	33 [80]
35-40	35	15 [FX-23]	33 / 44	35 / 60	35 / 44	35	55 [25]	55 [25]	22 [100]	33 [80]
40-45	35	21 [FX-37]	44 / 66	44 / 75	35/ 70	45	85 [39]	66 [30]	22 [100]	44 [100]
45-55	60	32 [FX-55]	66 / 85	60 / 105	44 /70	60	105 [48]	88 [40]	41 [140]	55 [120]
	conservative	conservative					conservative	conservative		conservative

* Larger size recommended for winds over 30 knots, although in our experience, this is not needed.

Index

S

T

U

V

W

Y

Made in United States
North Haven, CT
30 August 2023

40891826R00089